CARIBBEAN NATIONAL FOREST

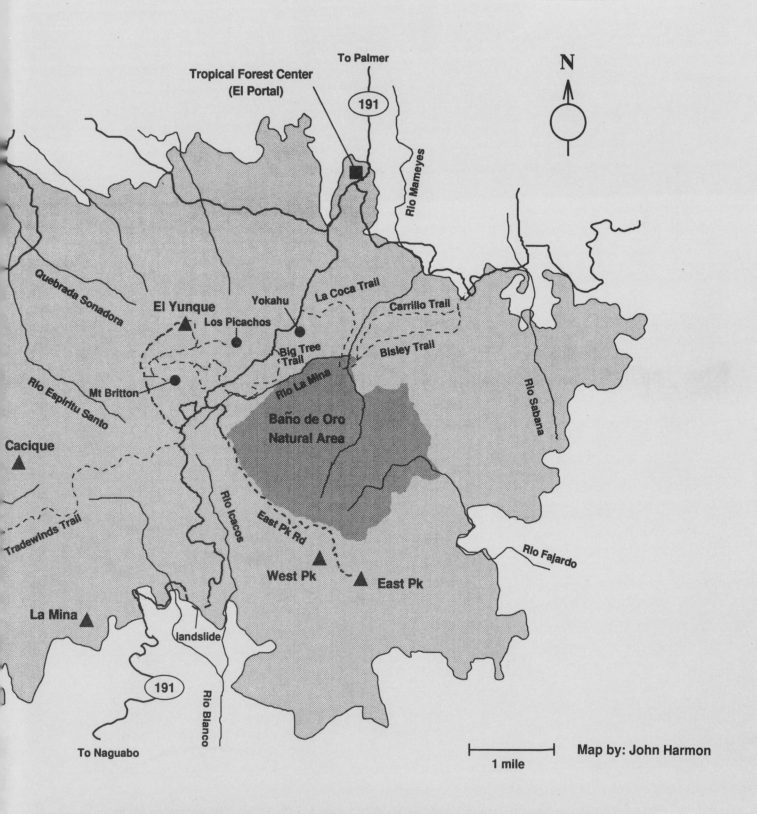

Tropical Forest Center
(El Portal)

To Palmer

191

N

Rio Mameyes

Quebrada Sonadora

El Yunque

Yokahu

La Coca Trail

Carrillo Trail

Los Picachos

Big Tree Trail

Bisley Trail

Rio Espiritu Santo

Mt Britton

Rio La Mina

Baño de Oro
Natural Area

Rio Sabana

Cacique

Rio Icacos

East Pk Rd

Tradewinds Trail

West Pk

East Pk

Rio Fajardo

La Mina

landslide

191

Rio Blanco

To Naguabo

1 mile

Map by: John Harmon

WHERE DWARFS REIGN:
A TROPICAL RAIN FOREST IN PUERTO RICO

KATHRYN ROBINSON

WHERE DWARFS REIGN:
A TROPICAL RAIN FOREST IN PUERTO RICO

Photographs: JERRY BAUER
Drawings: JOSÉ VÁSQUEZ

EDUPR

UNIVERSITY OF PUERTO RICO PRESS
EDITORIAL DE LA UNIVERSIDAD DE PUERTO RICO

First Edition, 1997
©1997 by the University of Puerto Rico

Library of Congress Cataloging-in-Publication Data

Robinson, Kathryn.
    Where dwarfs reign: a tropical rainforest in Puerto Rico / Kathryn Robinson; photographs, Jerry Bauer; drawings, José Vásquez, -- 1st ed.
       p.   cm.
    Includes bibliographical references (p.   ) and index.
    ISBN 0-8477-0255-3 (hardcover: alk. paper)
    1. Caribbean National Forest (P.R.)--History. 2. Caribbean National Forest (P.R.)--Management--History. 3. Natural history--Puerto Rico--Caribbean National Forest. 4. Rain forest ecology--Puerto Rico--Caribbean National Forest. I. Title.
SD428. C24R63 1996
972.95' 1--dc20

96-22091
CIP

Designer and Compositor: Ninón León de Saleme
Printed in Hong Kong

EDITORIAL DE LA UNIVERSIDAD DE PUERTO RICO
PO Box 23322
San Juan, Puerto Rico 00931-3322

Administration: Tel. (787) 250-0550 Fax (787) 753-9116
Sales: Tel. (787) 758-8345 Fax (787) 751-8785

CONTENTS

ACKNOWLEDGMENTS

Originally, forester Jerry Bauer and I planned to write a guide book to trails in the Caribbean National Forest, and I owe much to Jerry for his enthusiasm in getting us out on the trails and into the homes of forest residents. Eventually the book became what it is now, and he went on to work in Guatemala. When the book reached its final stage and I began to despair it ever being completed, Jerry came through once again with his enthusiasm as well as with wonderful photographs. My thanks to him are great.

Virtually every page of this book refers to people who have studied, work in or lived by the forest. One reason El Yunque is so special is that it has been so carefully documented. As I researched the never-completed trail guide, I realized what a comprehensive story I could tell about El Yunque and decided to make this into an in-depth book, covering everything about the forest. Some eight years and 100,000 words later, I realize one can never cover everything, but the fault lies with the lone author, not with the thousands of people who have tales to tell. Some of these people I met personally; others I know only from their articles or books; many I, unfortunately, never got to know. I thank all of them. Special thanks for above-and-beyond help go to Frank Wadsworth, Fred Scatena,

Ariel Lugo, Bob Waide, Pete Weaver, George Proctor, Joe Troester, Gus Pantel, Jalil Sued Badillo, Miguel Canals, Alejo Estrada Pinto, Ramón Alonso, Vicente Quevedo, El Indio, Jim Ackerman, Jeff Walker, Carlos Rivera, Pablo Cruz, Angel Rosa Torres, Lucrecia and Manuel Vázquez, and Manuel Corsino.

I would particularly like to thank the U.S. Forest Service, which manages El Yunque, for opening so many doors to this woman who decided she wanted to write about the forest. Especially helpful have been those mentioned above as well as librarians Joanne Feheley and Giselle Reyes, and Carolyn Krupp.

The process leading from rough manuscript to actual book is a difficult one, and here, too, I have many people to thank. Editor John Bowman did an insightful job of polishing and questioning, José Vásquez drew lovely drawings for the book, and those at the University of Puerto Rico Press have been gracious and positive as they help me mold the manuscript into a book. Others helped in diverse and supportive ways. Among them I would like to thank Joe Stryffeler, Bienva Bauer, Gonzalo Córdova, Maritza Alvarez, Ronnie Kicliter, Sherry Marker, Kay Showker, Mary Anne Hopgood, Loretta Córdova, and Javier Blanco.

Lastly, I would like to thank my family, John, Astrid and Elise Harmon, who put up with this project for so long.

INTRODUCTION
SHEPHERDS OF THE TREES

For millenniums, the forests of Puerto Rico's Luquillo Mountains were left to themselves. Large animals never reached this Caribbean island. Native peoples came late, a mere couple thousand years before Christ, and remained relatively few in number. In the centuries after the arrival of the Spaniards, the island was more outpost than mecca, a place to fortify rather than populate. Because of the steep terrain and wet climate, the rain forests of the Luquillo Mountains remained isolated, even from the rest of the island. They endured, altered only by the occasional hurricanes that swept over them. By the turn of this century, the Luquillo Mountains sheltered Puerto Rico's last remote region and its last major tract of virgin forest – forest that has never been altered by humans.

In the 1870s, when Puerto Rico was still a colony of Spain, the Spanish colonial government set aside some 12,000 acres of these mountains as a forest reserve, making El Yunque, as this forest has come to be known, one of the oldest reserves in the hemisphere. In 1917, two decades after Puerto Rico came under sovereignty of the United States following the Spanish-American War, El Yunque was declared a national forest, then and now the only tropical forest within the U.S. Forest Service system. For over 70 years the Forest Service has maintained El Yunque, officially known as the Caribbean National Forest. During that time, it has developed recreation areas, established research areas, and, perhaps most importantly, reestablished forest on more than 15,000 acres below the original forested area, making El Yunque a model for forest management.

Today, the millenniums of "neglect" to the untouched upper forests combined with the successful reforestation of the lower slopes have turned El Yunque into a place of tremendous importance, a priceless remnant in a world of shrinking forests. The Luquillo Mountains will probably never again be left to themselves, never again be isolated from the rest of the world. If the forests atop these mountains are to endure into the next millenniums, they will need special care.

But what is care to one person might seem like neglect to another or even abuse to a third. How will El Yunque best survive the millenniums? The early covers of a magazine published by the Forest Service in Puerto Rico, titled the *Caribbean Forester*, showed a simply-sketched scene of trees, palms, mountains, baguette-shaped clouds and a meandering river above a humble motto –"It is my pride and joy to be the shepherd of my country's trees". As the island becomes more populated and its manmade constructions more numerous – and Puerto Rico is but a microcosm of the world at large – an ever larger number of people look with ever greater concern at the remaining forests and forested areas. Not content to accept unconditionally the way others care for these areas, they begin to ask questions. Who decides what happens within a forest? Who should be the shepherds of the trees?

A decade ago such questions were asked about the Caribbean National Forest. When the U.S. Forest Service in Puerto Rico announced its long-term plans for the forest, several groups challenged these plans, and El Yunque found itself in the national spotlight.

It all started in the 1970s, when Congress passed two acts calling for the U.S. Forest Service to assess its forests and provide a long-range management program, complete with environmental impact statement, for each one. In order to comply with these acts, in the early 1980s the Forest Service in Puerto Rico began to fashion an environmental impact statement and a 50-year land and resource management plan for the Luquillo forest. Draft statements and proposed plans were published and distributed to a variety of interested parties, comments were made, hearings were scheduled, changes were approved, and, in early 1986, the Forest Service released the final version of its long-range plan.

The plan's hundreds of pages of text, tables, figures, facts, summaries, glossaries, appendices and maps describe the Luquillo forest and zero in on the multiple ways the Forest Service makes use of it. Foresters considered timber, recreational, wildlife, water, wilderness and research resources within the forest and came up with eight different alternatives for managing it well into the next century. One alternative gave preference to wildlife habitats, another emphasized scientific investigation, a third basically left the forest untouched.

The alternative preferred by the foresters favored multiple-use management, that is, balancing the uses of the forest's various resources. There would be selective (in which only mature trees are felled) commercial timber harvesting in some of the reestablished forests on the lower slopes. A wildlife management program would maintain healthy wildlife populations and aid in the recovery of endangered plants and animals. Road construction would be reduced (though not eliminated) from what had been done in the past, and recreational activities would become more dispersed throughout the forest. All this would be done without compromising the optimum production of quality water.

Shortly after the final version was released, a dozen primarily local but also national and international environmental organizations – among them, the Natural History Society of Puerto Rico, Sierra Club, Wilderness Society and National Audubon Society – requested a stay of the plan. Appellants were concerned with what they considered several weak points in the plan – the fact that most of it wasn't published in Spanish, the proposal to construct more roads within the forest, the reduction in size of a recommended wilderness area, a lack of firm protection for the endangered Puerto Rican parrot, inadequate assessment of the environmental impact of certain projects – but their major concern focused on plans to harvest timber commercially within the forest.

Though such a challenge was new to Puerto Rico, it wasn't the first time concerned citizens had challenged the U.S. Forest Service's management plans. From the start of this century, and even earlier, there has been debate over who should be the shepherds of the United States's trees, and just how they should take care of them. Perhaps inevitably, this debate has come to influence the care of forests around the world.

For centuries, United States citizens considered their country's forests and other natural resources limitless, but as the nineteenth century drew to a close, a small but increasing number of people realized that the vast forests were in fact decreasing and needed to be protected from indiscriminate lumbering, mining and grazing. In 1905, the U.S. Forest Service came to life under the Department of Agriculture with the promise that, though the nation could continue to use its forests, it would use them wisely so that the forests would endure for future use. Its creation marked an important milestone in curbing forest exploitation.

However, even then there were those dissatisfied with the Forest Service's objective of using the forests wisely. Why use them at all, they argued, why not set them aside untouched for future generations to enjoy? These people wanted to see the establishment of more national parks (national parks, starting with Yellowstone in 1872, actually pre-dated national forests), for which the primary goals were preservation and recreation rather than management. Two men – preservationist John Muir and the first Forest Service chief, Gifford Pinchot – along with one place – Hetch Hetchy, sister valley to Yosemite in California – loom larger than life in the debate between managing (using wisely) and preserving (leaving untouched) forests. In the early 1900s Muir fought to save Hetch Hetchy while Pinchot favored damming it (Yosemite itself was al-

ready preserved as a national park) in order to provide water for the city of San Francisco. Muir lost the drawn-out battle, but in a way he won the war, for in 1916 Congress created a separate National Park Service, within the Department of the Interior, and imposed tighter regulations on preserving both present and future parks. The United States now found itself with two distinct organizations for caring for its public lands, and the U.S.-originated dichotomy between preservation and management continues to this day, from El Yunque to the Amazon to Alaska.

As the decades passed, the Forest Service found it increasingly complicated to practice wise-use management. Harold Steen, in his book on the history of the U.S. Forest Service, explains: "Mining, timbering, recreation, and other legitimate demands on the national forests required the administrator to achieve a balance of uses. A rising population and expanding economy – but a fixed land base – made the balancing act more and more difficult. By the 1950s it was obvious that the national forests no longer held enough resources to meet burgeoning demands." Out of this dilemma came the Multiple-Use Sustained Yield Act of 1960, in which the five major uses of national forests – timber, wildlife, range, water and outdoor recreation – were officially given equal priority. Foresters hoped this would resolve their administrative headaches, but it didn't. During the 1960s, the public's awareness of ecological issues grew tremendously, and safeguarding the environment became an urgent priority. Muir's views captured the public's affection more than Gifford's. Groups like the Sierra Club and the Wilderness Society acted as watchdogs over national forests, proposing more wilderness areas and criticizing lumbering.

It was against this background and in part for these reasons that the Forest Service's decision to harvest lumber on the lower slopes of Luquillo met with an outpouring of opposition. El Yunque, being the only tropical forest within the Forest Service system and home to hundreds of diverse plant and animal species, many of them rare, became an obvious rallying point for environmental groups.

For several months, a barrage of opinions surfaced in the local papers as to the wisdom of commercial harvesting in El Yunque. Many, such as scientist Daniel Janzen, vehemently opposed the idea: "Since when does the richest nation on earth have to cut even a single tree from its absolutely unique tropical forest? Cut the giant redwoods first." A few, including a coalition of environmental groups writing to the local English-language newspaper, urged caution: "Without doubt Puerto Rico and other tropical countries can benefit from a program of research and wood-cutting practices. But the environmental damage and economic losses are considerably less if this project is done at an experimental level rather than on a commercial level." Several foresters, including then-Regional Forester John Alcock, whose office oversees the Caribbean National Forest, defended the plan: "Virtually every acre of pristine forest now existing would have been modified in some way if the Forest Service had not resisted pressures from potential developers for tramways to the peaks, orchid gardens, hotels, trailer parks, amusement parks, horse corrals, dams on the streams and general public vehicle access to the major peaks. Concern for future generations is no less a part of national forest policies than those of the national parks."

Even within the published final management plan, the dichotomy – to preserve or to use wisely – was apparent. Forty-four letters of response to an earlier draft of the plan were reproduced in an appendix. Three-quarters of those letters originated in Puerto Rico. A handful of the respondents supported the Forest Service's vision; some commended the organization for its efforts but expressed concern about certain aspects of the plan while others took the organization to task for its efforts and expressed concern about many aspects of the plan; a handful wanted the Forest Service to throw in the towel on the whole concept of multiple use and just preserve the forest; and two or three had their own personal agendas, such as returning the Baño Grande and Baño de Oro pools to swimmers. Most of the concerns centered directly or indirectly on lumbering – the steepness of the slopes being considered for lumbering, the roads being built for lumbering, sedimentaion in streams caused by lumbering, reduction of possible future habitat of the Puerto Rican parrot after lumbering, and using a temperate rather than a tropical approach to lumbering in the forest.

Frank Wadsworth, who has worked in the Caribbean National Forest for 50 years, felt prompted to write because of the many negative responses the Forest Service was receiving for its plan. In summing up the benefits of timber production, Wadsworth wrote, "The real 'payoff' is in an arena much greater than the Luquillo Mountains. What is possible there is not even being tried anywhere else in the hemisphere. It could show whether and how well such forests, common throughout tropical America, could be made to produce wood needs for society. ... This type of demonstation/test cannot be carried forward on the basis of small forest plots. It must simulate commercial production. Companion to it should be (and is planned) an intensified research program to monitor and compare results by sites, species, and practices on both environmental and economic grounds."

In another letter, Bob Waide, head of the Terrestrial Ecology Division of the University of Puerto Rico (which conducts much of its research in the Luquillo Mountains), presented his concerns about the effects of lumbering on Luquillo wildlife. "I am of the opinion," he stated, "that all of the proposed alternatives except G [which recommends leaving the forest alone] will have a detrimental effect on wildlife, [and] the lack of information on wildlife in the Forest and the relatively small investment in research proposed under all alternatives will make mitigation difficult." Timber harvesting, he cautioned, would not only reduce the total habitat available for wildlife but would also fragment the existing habitat into smaller parcels, isolating breeding populations. What would be the effect of this on the forest?

In his letter, Wadsworth stressed the importance of the forest as a place to demonstrate commercial timber harvesting; in his, Waide stressed its role as a unique center for tropical research and course work. Other letters stressed its importance as a tourist and recreational destination; still others, as a sacred depository of the island's plants and wildlife. Each side spoke with sin-

VIRGIN TABONUCO FOREST

cerity and concern, each side felt its point of view was best for the forest.

The debate wore on until November of 1986, when the U.S. Forest Service, bowing to public outcry, cancelled plans to harvest commercially on the lower slopes of the Caribbean National Forest. The long-range management plan would be revised and resubmitted to the public.

Afterwards, I spoke with Wadsworth, who made several interesting postmortem comments about the controversy. Part of the conflict, he felt, centered on differences of opinion among forest administrators and researchers. By having the entire Caribbean National Forest serve as both a place to be managed and a center for research (unlike any other U.S. national forest), clashes are bound to occur. "The administrators have gone to school, they have their ideas, and they don't want to display that they don't know what's going on [in a certain situation]. The research people see that as over-confidence. The research people are also more cautious. In a way the forest is like a small puddle with two big fish. When I was over both [as director of administration and research], the disharmony was less obvious." Most of the time, Wadsworth felt, the two groups come together, albeit at times painfully. "Researchers feel that they are right and the administration wrong. Administrators, on the other hand, can't always wait for the research to come in before they do something." As a case in point he mentioned Puente Roto, a popular local swimming hole and gathering place along one of the forest's major rivers. Crowds of people go there every weekend. The administrators try to accommodate them – "they're there, they exist, something must be done" – even though research concerning the effects of people on the site is incomplete. Wadsworth spoke of a fuzzy rubbing point between research and practice. "According to practitioners, researchers write in Greek, can't be understood and don't bother to explain themselves. According to researchers, practitioners are illiterate, don't read, don't do what's clear to do."

Wadsworth also felt that the thinking generated by the controversy has involved new insights. "El Yunque," he mentioned, "is the biggest patch of primary forest on the island. Primary means it hasn't been touched for at least 80 years." He talked about one new way of looking at this land, crediting the idea to the current director of research, Ariel Lugo. "The primary forest was the gift of King Felipe to Puerto Rico. Of the 12,000-odd acres of Crown Land, some 10,000 of it was primary forest. This was the heritage of the Mother Country to Puerto Rico. For a remote country [the U.S.] to ride roughshod over the forest is unfair. So we are locating these original tracts and saying they should be left alone as the heritage of Spain to Puerto Rico, treated in a way that even the most radical independentista [advocate for island independence] couldn't dispute – no new trails, non-manipulative research, just leave it alone."

Wadsworth admitted the firestorm that rose up about the plan probably did more good than harm. "It put a pressure on the forest not to cut, as opposed to out West where the pressure is on the Forest Service to cut." He added: "The difficulty in sustainability [the ability of a forest to maintain itself while at the same time producing marketable timber] is the human pressure. It is time oriented, do things now at the expense of the future. Foresters are taught better, but they have to live with the pressure from the President or a powerful Senate. For example, the [spotted] owl has kept people from harvesting some six million acres [in the northwestern U.S.], so now lawmakers are thinking, 'where can we find another six million?'. The forester is the messenger, not the decision maker, yet he becomes part of the destroyer of resources."

At the heart of the issue is the century-old dichotomy of management versus preservation. Around the time I spoke with Wadsworth, I also spoke with Ariel Lugo. He talked about the dichotomy, and about an alternative, presented by a man named Aldo Leopold. While Gifford Pinchot heralded forest management and John Muir urged preservation, Aldo Leopold was an ecologist/forester who tried to fuse the two philosophies into a practical, workable model. Lugo agrees with Leopold. He feels both extremes, from razing forests for their timber to over-protecting forests against normal natural disasters, are wrong. "There is marvelous technology on a global level," he told me, "and it should be used. As lifestyles rise, there must be a way to balance needs and nature. Thus the increase in such fields as conservation ecology, landscape ecology. There must be a new common sense."

A year after the management plan was scuttled, Lugo presented a paper on the theme of wise use and preservation of forest resources at a symposium on biosphere reserves. Biosphere reserves, established world-wide by the United Nations' Educational, Scientific and Cultural Organization (UNESCO), are nuclei of virgin forests surrounded by reestablished forests; the reserves demonstrate preservation, research, tourism, rehabilitation and traditional uses of the land. Luquillo was named as one of the first biosphere reserves in 1976.

In his paper, Lugo argues that biosphere reserves provide an excellent opportunity to integrate both the wise use and preservation of biotic (living) resources. In making his point, he takes a look at the evolution of the conservation movement in the United States. In the original use of the word, conservation rested on two strategies, that of protecting and manipulating natural systems. Since the two strategies have become polarized in the United States, arguments over the best strategy for the conservation of natural resources are often "resolved by lawyers, economists or engineers who lack sound understanding of natural phenomena." He continues: "The polarization of the ideas of Muir and Pinchot was unnecessary and unfortunate. Today we understand that the goals of resource preservation and wise use are both necessary and can be integrated into most plans of land development." Lugo argues that "tropical countries cannot afford such a dual conservation strategy, because in the tropics human needs are more critical to the survival of people and natural resources, and because tropical countries lack sufficient financial resources to waste in needless duplication of effort."

Now, almost a decade after the Forest Service decided to revise its long-term management plan, the draft of a new recommended plan has been submitted to the public. The public debate and subsequent profes-

sional debate within the Forest Service seem to have had a positive effect on the forest's future. In the new plan, the Forest Service has addressed many of the public's major concerns with the previous one. Information has been written in both English and Spanish; the Forest Service has greatly reduced the construction of new roads, expanded its recommended wilderness area, and been more specific in explaining how the endangered Puerto Rican parrot will be protected. Commercial timber production is not recommended; instead, a considerably smaller number of acres has been set aside for timber demonstration and research purposes only. In the new plan, the Forest Service has made a greater effort to emphasize preservation within its traditional wise-use management.

So, can we now say that management, research, recreation and preservation have come together in complete harmony, and the forest will live entirely happily ever after?

Probably not. The current recommended long-range plan has not yet been approved, and, while some feel it will be, others think it may have to go back to the drawing board yet one more time. Over the years, as people's opinions change and Puerto Rico's needs change, the forest will face continually changing crises within and around its borders.

Within the forest boundaries, another difference of opinion surfaced in 1991, when highway officials announced that Road 191 would be repaired and reopened. Road 191, the main road crossing the Luquillo Mountains, has been closed for decades due to several major landslides that buried some 600 feet of roadway. Towns and resorts on the southern side of the mountains have long wanted the increase in tourism that the reopening of the road would bring. Road repair companies were asked to submit construction bids. Along with the bids, highway officials got unasked-for submissions by a coalition of environmental groups arguing that the road should be left alone.

The coalition argued on several fronts: the environmental impact statement condoning the project was written a decade earlier, prior to the effects of Hurricane Hugo on the forest; historical sites and endangered species, particularly the Puerto Rican parrot, would be adversely affected; repairing the gaps would necessitate the ecologically-damaging retrieval of large quantities of rocks and other materials, use of explosives and subsequent disposal of construction debris. Yet other groups felt the road should be reopened. It is there, it won't go away, and leaving it as it is would only worsen the landslides and related environmental damage in the area.

The bid for the repair of 191 was awarded, but before work started, the coalition was able to get a stay on the project on the grounds that the environmental impact statement was in fact outdated. For almost two years nothing was heard about the controversy, and it seemed 191 would remain a picturesque artifact of civilization winding through the forest. But in 1993 the issue suddenly came back to life when the highway department expressed an interest in preparing the required environmental impact statement. The coalition once again raised its voice in opposition. As of 1996, the issue remains on hold. The updated environmental impact statement has not been completed, and no one seems to know when it will be.

Beyond the borders of the forest loom other threats to the forest community. Poorly maintained for decades, the island's water system cannot currently fill the population's growing demand, and officials are rather desperately looking for new ways to get water. One way is to withdraw increasing amounts of water from intakes (pipes) that already draw water from Luquillo's rivers and streams; another way is to build an impoundment of some sort along the lower Río Mameyes, one of the forest's wildest and most ruggedly beautiful rivers and the only major river on the island, and perhaps in the Caribbean, to travel in a relatively undisturbed fashion from its source in the mountains down to the coast. Scientists fear the effect these plans would have on the forest's plant and animal community. Just how much water can the forest lose before it begins to suffer?

Another threat is the effect of construction projects that are making their way at an alarming rate up the foothills of the Luquillo Mountains. A special land use plan has been established to create a buffer zone around the forest in order to safeguard the forest community, and the island's planning board is coordinating with forest personnel to maintain this zone. Yet many who work with the forest worry that the plan is not sufficiently effective nor sufficiently enforced. Improper and illegal constructions continue to rise. If left unchecked, what effect will these constructions have on the wildlife that feeds outside the forest or on the forest itself when an international array of house and garden plants escape into the existing vegetation?

There is no doubt that the Luquillo Mountains' millenniums of isolation are over. That the Caribbean National Forest will survive in future millenniums is a very good probability. How it will survive is harder to predict. Why it should survive can be found in the pages of this book, in the tale of one tropical forest.

Chapter 1
WHERE DWARFS REIGN

Taino Indians, Puerto Rico's original inhabitants, believed that gods lived in the highest peaks of the Luquillo Mountains. Modern thought belittles such ideas, but at times, when fog shrouds all but the nearest dwarfed, moss-draped and bromeliad-studded trees, the Tainos' beliefs don't seem quite so farfetched. One visitor, exalted by the mountains' tropical beauty, scrawled in Spanish on a lookout wall the start of Psalms 121 – "I will lift up mine eyes unto the hills...". Today the verse is faded, barely legible. The forest has effaced it, as, if left alone, it eventually effaces all manmade efforts, all history, all except nature itself – and the merest hint of the supernatural.

❦ Compared to the billions of acres of tropical forest that exist in the world, the Caribbean National Forest is a mere pinpoint. Its scant 28,000 acres drape the upper slopes of the Luquillo Mountains in the U.S. Commonwealth of Puerto Rico. These mountains play a secondary role in the island's network of ranges, and Puerto Rico itself is small, the smallest of the Caribbean's Greater Antilles, an island roughly the size and shape of Connecticut. But the forest is an important pinpoint. El Yunque, as this forest is commonly known, is a fine example of the tropical forests that blanket much of the Earth between the Tropic of Cancer (just north of Havana,

Cuba) and the Tropic of Capricorn (just south of Rio de Janeiro, Brazil). Most of El Yunque is also rain forest – a warm, wet and ecologically chaotic realm of tall trees and piggyback plants. The Caribbean National Forest is the most visited tropical rain forest in the Caribbean, the most accessible such forest to residents of North America, and the only one found within the U.S. national forest system. (Although Hawaii also has tropical forest, it has no national forests.)

Recipient of monies and expertise from the Forest Service and other U.S. institutions, El Yunque's relatively few acres are undoubtedly among the most pampered in Western Hemisphere tropics. They are also among the most stable: while tropical forests totaling more than three times the size of the Caribbean National Forest topple everyday somewhere in the world, from Malaysia to the Amazon, El Yunque's acreage is relatively fixed and will remain so as far into the future as humans dare to predict.

Established by Spain in the 1870s as one of the first reserves in the New World, the national forest's original core of some 12,000 acres had expanded to its present size by the 1930s. Since then, thousands of acres have been transformed from plantation land to forest; dozens of tropical tree species from both hemispheres have become the subjects of numerous studies; up to 15,000 trees have been tagged and recorded; and long-term growth plots, some almost 50 years old, have been established throughout the mountains. El Yunque has become a researcher's treasure trove, drawing scientists from around the world and hosting a number of prestigious projects, among them the most comprehensive tropical rain forest study ever done. In 1976 the United Nations' Educational, Scientific and Cultural Organization (UNESCO) recognized the forest's importance by naming it one of the original Biosphere Reserves, a world-wide network of ecologically vital forests.

A decade ago, when the Forest Service announced that trees would be commercially harvested from the mountains' lower slopes as part of its long-term plan for managing the forest, many of the letters sent to the Forest Service opposing this plan further underscored the importance of the Caribbean National Forest. Hilda Díaz Soltero and Cindy Gines-Sánchez of Puerto Rico's Natural History Society and Derb Carter of the National Wildlife Federation wrote: "...the Forest has tremendous values based on its utilization for recreation and research and protection of important watersheds and critical wildlife habitats...". Robin Gottfried, assistant professor at the University of the South, pointed out: "This Forest is one of the best known, if not the best known, tropical forests in the world." Frances Spivy-Weber and Whitney Fosburgh of the National Audubon Society, added: "The Caribbean National Forest provides the only habitat for the Puerto Rican parrot, one of the most critically endangered species in the world."

Fourteen professional scientists from such centers as Stanford University, the Smithsonian Institution, Arnold Arboretum, the University of Michigan and the Missouri Botanical Gardens, cautioned: "The Caribbean National Forest is unique among federal lands in containing an irreplaceable example of the forest types which were once widely distributed in the Caribbean region. Centuries of human occupation have resulted in the destruction of much of the Caribbean's original forest cover, making what little is left especially important for the conservation of biological diversity... We know that the Caribbean National Forest harbors a unique assemblage of plants and animals, including many species that are found nowhere else. What we do not know is how many other species remain undiscovered within its borders. From a scientific point of view, the Caribbean National Forest represents a priceless and unexplored reservoir of biological diversity."

Impressive accolades for 28,000 acres of forest.

Eventually, the Forest Service, which most people admit has done a fine job in managing El Yunque, made a decision to eliminate commercial harvesting from its plan. Shortly afterwards, the public was invited to see firsthand what really happens high in the Luquillo Mountains at El Yunque's first official open house. I decided to attend with my daughter Astrid, who was one year old at the time.

❦ October 8, 1988. This is Astrid's first visit to the forest, and the open house seems an appropriate introduction. My own interest in El Yunque began long before the open house, long before I knew about such topics as endangered parrots and biological diversity. When I moved to Puerto Rico more than a decade earlier from the Southwest, where hiking is a regional pastime, I was interested in trails. El Yunque, it turned out, had the best on the island. It was hiking that first got me to the forest, and it was its exotic beauty that drew me back. Curiosity about ecological matters came much later.

We begin the drive from our home in the capital city of San Juan early in the morning. The San Juan metropolitan area, home to a third of the island's three and a half million people, sprawls along the north-central coast. The Luquillo Mountains lie to the east, near the northeast corner of the island. When there is no traffic, the drive along Highway 3 takes less than an hour. However, northeastern Puerto Rico, site of beaches, coastal resorts and marinas, is a very popular destination, and there is seldom no traffic.

While drivers pay attention to the weathered roadway and expanding lanes of traffic, passengers have opportunity to examine the scenery. Urban scenes of pharmaceutical plants, shopping centers and housing developments, cafeterias and auto shops eventually give way to rural scenes of roadside queen-of-flowers trees, large shade trees that put out purple blossoms in the summer, and venders selling everything from barbecued chicken to hammocks. In the distance, the rumpled backbone of the Luquillo range, shadowy green and topped with cumulus clouds reminiscent of a Cecil B. De Mille spectacular, rises above bright green pastures.

When the range runs perpendicular to the highway, dwarfing all other views to the south, the narrow road to El Yunque appears. Like many country roads in Puerto Rico, Road 191, as this road is officially known, draws one into a yesteryear rural world merely glimpsed from the highway. It is a world little known to those who do not live here, just as Puerto Rico itself is little known to many who

have never been to the island. At times residents in the United States startle islanders with questions that require the following sorts of answers: "No, Puerto Rico is not in the Pacific, it is about 1,000 miles southeast of Miami." "Yes, Puerto Ricans are U.S. citizens, using U.S. currency. The island is a U.S. Commonwealth, tied to the United States in a complex fashion since it was ceded to the U.S. following the Spanish-American War." "No, Puerto Rico is neither the asphalt jungle of West Side Story nor the Amazon jungle of thatched huts and barefoot children; it has much greenery and many prosperous residents, and thatch huts are now found only in museums."

Even those who visit the island often stay in large San Juan hotels with their casinos and international restaurants, and they conclude the city is a Miami with dependably warm weather. It is, in a way, but it is also different. Beyond the urban arteries, numerous backroads wind through the countryside. As they wind, they pass such scenes as scarlet-blossomed flamboyant trees framing wooden houses with wraparound verandahs; Spanish-styled town plazas dominated by Catholic churches; small concrete homes where residents have been known to invite strangers in for a cup of home-grown coffee served with soda crackers and bananas. This is the Puerto Rico on which today's San Juan is based, cosmopolitan though it appears, and this is the Puerto Rico of Road 191.

Mameyes is a two-blocks-wide hamlet nestled along Highway 3 and Road 191. Though tiny and seemingly little affected by recent decades, it has the distinction of being known by two names, Palmer as well as Mameyes. Bananas and flowering plants grow between modest concrete homes, old ware-

Dwarf forest
on
East Peak.

*WHERE
DWARFS
REIGN*

*Peaks
within
the Caribbean
National
Forest.*

*Visitors
at a
forest
open
house.*

houses serve as bars, and stores are small and eclectic in the merchandise they offer. The road briefly enters a newer era when it passes a small factory surrounded by a parking lot and chain-link fence, then shifts into more traditional country scenes – families swimming at a bend in a river, cattle grazing on hilly pastures, vines laced around trees, leaves woven into overhead canopies. As the road ascends, the terrain gets steeper, the canopy denser. A second, smaller community crowds against the road. Beyond the community, a sign announces the Caribbean National Forest, and stands of mahogany and kadam trees tower over the landscape. A year after the open house, Hurricane Hugo will storm through the forest, turning the stands into what look like enormous broken pencils. But when my daughter and I drive up, the trees are still in place.

A square concrete building with an orange tile roof occupies the center of a parking lot near the entrance to the forest. Named after a coffee plantation that once thrived in the region, the Catalina Field Office, a.k.a. El Yunque Ranger Station, was constructed several years earlier to provide work space for foresters and other personnel. The lot is full when we arrive, so we park on the road. Ferns and elephant-ear plants proliferate along the shoulder, and I have to place Astrid's back carrier among them. When I hoist her onto my back, mud clings to the bottom of the carrier. We are in the rain forest.

A festive yellow and white tent set up behind the office for the open house protects an exhibition of the forest and its resources. The exhibit includes samples of forestry equipment; old bottles; copies of forest publications and scientific papers; photos of Indian petroglyphs and old mines; specimens of seeds, fruits and woods from a variety of native and introduced trees. Off to one side workers periodically put an old hand saw and a modern chain saw to use in cutting pieces of wood. Visitors mill around the parking lot. When it drizzles, as it does from time to time, we crowd into the muggy confines of the tent.

Certain aspects of the open house seem to be taken from a similar stateside national forest activity. Program pamphlets, available in English and Spanish, feature Woodsy Owl and his forest friends on the cover. A map of Road 191 shows eight stations holding activities every hour during the open house. The field office is Station #1. Visitors are encouraged to visit at least three stations, where we will receive a stamp on our program, and to take part in picking up litter at several often-visited sites grouped together as Clean-up Station #8. We will then be eligible to receive a special certificate of participation. Yet the tropical way of doing things, less bound by structure, overlies the basic format. The welcome ceremony starts late, and program stampers are not obvious after the first station.

Station #2 is a nearby nursery, where mahogany and other saplings are readied for planting within the forest. Additional stations line 191 in its ascent up the mountain. Spindly La Coca Falls is a clean-up station. The medieval-looking Yokahú Observation Tower is Station #3. Pools at Juan Diego Falls mark another clean-up station. The popular Big Tree Trail is Station #4. These sites do not tempt me today. I prefer to pass them by and save my daughter's limited attention span for the visitor centers near the top of the mountain and Station #7, which, for me, is the highlight of the open house. We return to our car and begin the drive.

With the exception of two or three homes and a few roadside snack stands on patches of private land, forest monopolizes the upper Luquillo Mountains. Unlike temperate forests, which tend to stretch out in gentle symmetry, tropical forests wrap their visitors in a tangled cloak of vines and branches and leaves. The sheer bulk of the greenery would be monotonous if it weren't for an intricate intertwining of textures and shapes. The shapes seem markedly oversized. Fifty-foot-high bamboos look like a Brobdingnagian's quills arching over the road. Several species of ferns have reached the size of trees; their spindly trunks shoot up to more than 30 feet and their fronds extend to ten feet, lording over other plants and even a few trees. Yard-long philodendron leaves coil around tree trunks. Roots dangle as much as 100 feet from tree canopies to the ground. Yet of all the objects growing alongside 191, the emotional favorite for most visitors is neither green nor oversized: it is, instead, tiny and pink. Tens of thousands of impatiens border the road, doing for forest visitors what daffodils did for Wordsworth.

I like to think of this forest as jungle, though I hesitate to say so out loud. "Jungle" is one of those words that evoke personal, and often vastly different, pictures in the individual mind. To people who grew up in regions of white winters, as I did, a jungle is a fascinating place – primeval land barely marred by human touch, dense forest shielding exotic vegetation, guardian of lost civilizations. I still remem-

BAMBOO IN FOREST

ber childhood books chronicling the thrilling discoveries of lost cities in dim jungles, and, whenever I hike in tropical forest, some remnant of those cities seems just around the bend, just over the next hill. But what delights some offends others. To people who were born here, "jungle" conjures up an uncivilized place teeming with rank vegetation and savage animals; to suggest they live on the edge of such a primitive state is insulting.

Scientists also disapprove of the word when it is used to refer to tropical forests in general or to tropical rain forests. One evening I thought to look up "jungle" in the Oxford English Dictionary. Oddly enough, the word first meant "desert" or "wasteland", a far cry from its present meaning. The word originated in India, from the Hindi and Marathi jangal, which in turn came from the Sanskrit jangala. "Jungle" as waste or uncultivated ground eventually came to mean such land overgrown with unruly undergrowth: the ground was still basically uninhabitable, although for opposite reasons. ("Forest", a Latin word, had a similar transfer, I found when I also looked it up: originally referring to a waste or unenclosed place, it later described land covered with wild trees.) The OED goes on to define "jungle" as land overgrown with underwood, long grass, or tangled vegetation; the luxuriant and often almost impenetrable growth of vegetation covering such land; or the physical setting of such growth, especially as the dwelling-place of wild beasts. In any case, to scientists the word "jungle" applies to a specific type of forest found in limited areas of the tropical region, such as along river banks or roads in the Amazon. In these places, light is able to filter down to the ground and produce the impenetrable vegetative tangle characteristic of a jungle. Of course, the majority of visitors to the tropics don't go much beyond roads and rivers; even in El Yunque, most visitors stay on or near Road 191, so what they see is in fact a jungly tangle of vegetation flourishing under a high amount of sunlight. But what they see isn't typical tropical rain forest. To scientists, tropical rain forest is another type of forest, a wet forest that exists under certain conditions throughout the tropical region. Though lush, it does not have dense ground growth because such a small amount of light filters through its canopy to the forest floor. It is a shadowy, multi-storied region of trees and plants that grow on trees; being scarce of ground cover, it can be penetrated fairly easily. When I asked one scientist about the word "jungle", he dismissed it in short order: "It's a term used by people from the temperate zone who don't really know the tropics." I still like the word.

Near the top of the mountain in the heart of El Yunque Recreation Area, the Sierra Palm and Palo Colorado visitor centers nestle unassumingly between neighboring parking lots and the forest wall. Both are small and L-shaped, of stone and concrete painted a drab-earth color and finished off with pine paneling and parquet floors. Built some 50 years ago when the local Civilian Conservation Corps transformed the forest's recreational facilities, the buildings have long settled into their damp surroundings. Inside, the exhibits – simple murals and maps, drawings and photographs –have a dated feel. Even the personnel who

operate the centers belong to an earlier age: most have been hired through a senior citizens' program. For technical or in-depth orientation, one must drive back down the mountain to the Catalina Field Office, Station #1 of the open house, which is usually closed on weekends.

Though not without their charm, these visitors centers are no longer adequate for the large numbers and varied interests of forest visitors. The Forest Service recognized this, and in 1996 a new center was opened across from the Catalina Field Office. El Portal Tropical Forest Center, as it is known, is an ambitious project that will include facilities for environmental education programs and tropical forest management training as well as a visitor center. Visitors will find much more detailed information about flora, fauna, programs and points of interest in El Yunque and about the relationships of tropical forests and their global influences.

During the open house, the Sierra Palm and Palo Colorado visitor centers become stations #5 and #6. Slide presentations focusing on forest wildlife take place inside the Palo Colorado Center. Astrid, perched on my back again, and I wander around the parking lot, where scientists and foresters stand dutifully beside displays of wildlife found in the forest. We examine a number of birds, reptiles and insects. Some of the specimens are stuffed, others dried, a few alive. Among the live specimens are two *Anolis cuvieri*. Bright green and a foot long, they represent the only species of giant anole lizards on mainland Puerto Rico. Members of another species on the offshore island of Culebra have not been spotted for decades. A. cuvieri is feared for its tenacious bite. One superstition has it that if the anole bites, it won't let go until thunder strikes or a black cow moos; another superstition swears that the bite is poisonous and the only way to be saved from sure death is by crossing three rivers. These lizards are actually rare, shy, non-poisonous animals, and it was a stroke of luck when a forester happened to spot the two in a tree two days before the open house. When it is over, they will be returned to the forest.

The most spectacular live exhibit features two Puerto Rican parrots, representing almost one-fortieth of their population at the time we visit the forest. They are shown with a Hispaniolan relative in large cages containing cupey branches and sierra palm fruits. This is their first public display since the project to save the parrots began in the late 1960s, and U.S. Fish and Wildlife officials, primary caretakers of the birds, have viewed the exhibition with understandable trepidation. All goes well during the day, a project member tells me later, but that night someone breaks into the visitor center. Fortunately, by then the parrots have been safely removed to their aviary.

I think Astrid might like to take a short hike, so we strike out on a mile-long interpretive loop near the visitor centers. Numbered sticks mark historical and natural landmarks along the way, but brochures explaining the numbers are not available. The first half of the loop follows an old trail that was recently paved with roughened concrete. Though concrete might not seem the material of choice for a nature trail, it makes for safer hiking and easier maintenance in the tropics, and the Forest Service has opted to pave several of the short, popular trails in the recreation area.

Baño de Oro Pool marks the start of the loop. Formed when a stream was dammed to provide bathing in a tropical setting, the pool

has long been closed to bathers. Its water is low and muddied, the current domain of tadpoles and water bugs. Plants encroach on walkways and grow out of cracks on an aging bathhouse. The calls of nearby birds have a lonely sound. The trail continues through palo colorado forest, where the palo colorado tree is dominant but willowy sierra palms are more obvious. Two streams slipping around rocks on their way down the mountain join together near the trail. A narrow channel and round structures resembling large wells lie half buried under soil and plants near one stream. Though they look like vestiges of a lost civilization, they are actually the remains of a quixotic and unsuccessful attempt, decades ago, to stock the mountain streams with trout. From here the paved trail connects with a mostly unpaved trail up the mountain to El Yunque Peak. We follow the trail down the mountain to return to the visitor centers.

After the hike, we drive to the place that is my primary reason for coming to the open house – Station #7, the dwarfed forest of East and West peaks. Normally East Peak Road is closed to public vehicles; though one can usually walk its three-mile length, driving is a lot easier. The road clings to a ridge that strikes out in a southwesterly direction away from the main northeast-to-southwest chain of Luquillo's mountains. Built in the days when ecology was less of an issue, East Peak Road came to exist at the expense of priceless acres of dwarf forest. As partial compensation, the drive provides instant and glorious gratification for scenery buffs as well as easy access to two dramatic patches of dwarf forest along East and West peaks. Of greater importance to those who had it built, the drive ends at a small complex of buildings, antennas and a weathered-white dome, set atop East Peak and surrounded by a fence. The complex is a radio and radar communications center manned by the U.S. Navy. It overlooks the island's easternmost extension of coastline, ragged with bays and points and cays, which is the home of Roosevelt Roads Naval Station, largest U.S. Navy facility in the Caribbean.

Initially the vegetation along the ridge is sparse – grasses, ground ferns, shrubs, an occasional tree fern, a couple of spindly Cecropia trees of the mulberry family. Below the road, forest falls down tiers of symmetrically-spaced hills. Only a few tree species brave the steepest slopes. Most noticeable are the sierra palms, looking like giant green feather-dusters bunched together on the hillsides. As the slopes level out, a larger number of species has put down roots. At lower elevations the forest pulls all stops with over 150 kinds of trees, many of them quite majestic. From where we are, the forest looks like nubby wool in varying shades of green –light green, deep green, chartreuse green, reddish green, silver green, khaki green, virtually any kind of green. Below Luquillo's forests the foothills swirl to the coasts in a mosaic of denuded hills, interconnecting lagoons, palm-shaded beaches and gleaming weblike networks of towns. On a clear day from East Peak Road you can see to the coasts and the nearby islands of Vieques, Culebra, even St. Thomas, 35 miles away. When the fog rolls in, you can barely see to the far side of the pavement.

As the road approaches East and West peaks, the setting changes. The sky clouds up, breezes become winds, the fog dominates. Hills form pockets of shade along the road banks; the vegetation takes on a wet look, and impatiens multiply. Road signs are illegible under a mottled patchwork of growths. On the hillsides short gnarled trees, rarely more than twelve feet high, form gray-blue silhouettes against the sky. Where the trees are exposed to the wind, the canopies are flat and slanted toward the hills, as though someone has pruned them. Above the canopy, occasional dead twigs are all that remain of branches that had dared to grow higher. Groupings of delicate tree ferns huddle on the more protected slopes. This is dwarf forest, so named for the diminutive size of the trees, and this is what I would like Astrid to see.

Vicente Quevedo, a botanist with the Forest Service staff at the time of the open house, leads us into the dwarf forest along a path leading to West Peak. Station #7 is still relatively undiscovered by late morning. Only a half dozen people show up for our tour; when we drive back down East Peak Road afterwards, I spot a group of more than 30 amassing at the start of the road. Quevedo is a young, soft-spoken man who is knowledgeable about the forest and enthusiastic about sharing this knowledge with others. His specialty is sensitive plants, plants one step from becoming endangered. It has begun to drizzle when we arrive. We start our walk by scrambling up a slick, steep embankment, using roots and the muddy impressions left by others to reach the path. Immediately we are surrounded by the twisted trees; they seem to crowd in on us, curious for a look.

Progress is slow. Quevedo encourages us to step on roots in order to protect both our shoes and the selaginella and other plants growing on the ground. Once I miss a root and slip ankle-deep into the mud. After that, he watches protectively as I concentrate on steering two heads around the gnarled branches. Quevedo points out details of the forest. We examine an orchid that is not in bloom and an anthurium that is. We feel the claylike mud. We look, unsuccessfully, for an elfin woods warbler, a bird found almost exclusively in the Luquillo Mountain dwarf forest. We stop and listen: the fog wraps the peak in a pale gray that is as quiet as falling snow. I turn my head toward my daughter's to see if she is taking in this special place. She seems as attentive as a one-year-old can be. We squeeze watery moss that grows on thin trunks. Quevedo shows us a stunted nemocá of the laurel family and a limoncillo of the myrtle family. We study the leaf pattern of a small tree fern found only in Puerto Rico. When the drizzle becomes rain and we start back, the road, we discover, is only a hundred feet away.

Dwarf forest is no place for trees. Wind and rain rule this region, and they impose harsh conditions. The wind is strong and continual, battering against the slopes and sculpting the trees into submission. Rain and fog visit the forest everyday, often several times a day, and humidity is excessive. Branches drip water, and the ground is perpetually soggy. Those who have ever over-watered their plants know what should happen, but it doesn't. The trees live, even flourish, but they aren't "normal". The wind gnarls them, the rainfall stunts them. These are nature's bonsai. Few trees will put up with such abuse. Of the handful of tree species commonly found in El Yunque's dwarf forests, virtually all are tough, runted relatives of trees found in lower, more hospitable terrain. Most are shrub size, with intermingling root

systems and small leaves that reach for air near the canopy.

On the other hand, soggy dwarf forest is an epiphyte's dream. One small patch of dwarf forest can host thousands of specimens and hundreds of species of epiphytes. Epiphytes are also known as air plants; they are plants which grow on other plants or objects, depending on them for mechanical support. Any number of plants, from algae to ferns to orchids, are epiphytic in the dwarf forest, and they cling to just about anything. Epiphytes revel in moisture; many of them literally soak it up and can be wrung like sponges or tipped like tiny buckets.

When the fog moves in – first as thin wisps, then as a pearly white gauze that erases all but the nearest vegetation – the forest is transformed into an eerie other-worldliness, the closest the natural world comes to those enchanted forests of fairy tales. Sit alone in this fog-draped kingdom for awhile, and the trees cease to be trees, becoming instead misshapen dwarfs. Tree ferns turn into parasols, the sort that shaded Egyptian queens. Spanish mosses are now cloaks, bromeliads are ornate rings. Sit alone too long and the dwarfs begin to laugh and dance, flicking their cloaks, tipping their parasols, showing off their rings. They laugh and dance until the sun withers the fog. But beware: it is said –by an old stooped man, I imagine, who slips out of the fog, touching you with his skinny hand and fixing you with his glittering eye – that those who see the dwarfs dance never return to the world below.

CHAPTER 2
BEFORE THE CHRONICLES

On September 23, 1493, Christopher Columbus and 17 caravels left Cádiz, Spain, on his second voyage to the New World. His first trip a year earlier had been a tremendous success. On his return to Spain, he dazzled King Ferdinand and Queen Isabella with a royal court extravaganza featuring amber and gold, parrots, and native people he thought were Indians. The royal couple quickly outfitted a second expedition. This pleased Columbus, for he was eager to return to the settlement he had left on Hispaniola, the large island now shared by Haiti and the Dominican Republic. He needn't have hurried. The Hispaniolan settlers, a bit too lustful after gold and local women, were massacred by the natives shortly after Columbus left.

On November 3 Columbus reached the West Indies at the island of Dominica, his first glimpse of the Lesser Antilles. From there the sailors continued in a northerly direction, on a voyage as incredible as that of Coleridge's ancient mariner — inventing names for dozens of islands that appeared, enlarged, diminished and disappeared on the horizon, and sailing into turquoise bays never before seen by anyone from their world. Puerto Rican historian Salvador Brau writes: "On the afternoon of the sixteenth day a short line stood out on the horizon; growing the following day

as the ships pushed forward, it marked the largest of the islands discovered on that voyage..." The island was Boriquén, the native word for today's Puerto Rico. In a footnote Brau identifies the short line the sailors first saw from the east as "El Yunque Peak, highest point in the Luquillo Mountains [so he thought] that rise 1,520 meters above sea level and can be seen, on calm days, from Saint Thomas". The Old World got its first glimpse of the Luquillo Mountains.

While the Spaniards looked in awe at this new world, the native Indians on shore, hidden behind dense forests, must have felt similar disbelief as they watched the ships sail by. One can imagine the scene — men and women with roughly cut straight black hair, copper skin, wearing loin cloths and parrot feather ornaments, perhaps stepping out of a thatched hut or rising carefully from a hammock, rubbing their eyes as if to erase the vision.

Known as Tainos, these Indians proved to be the final native people to inhabit Puerto Rico. They were not the first. Humans reached the island well before the birth of Christ. Confirmed archaeological finds place them here around 300 B.C., and a new discovery seems to push the date back a dramatic 2,700 years, to 3,000 B.C. These Indians, known as Archaics, were non-sedentary. Unfamiliar with agriculture and pottery making, they lodged in coastal caves or under rocky outcrops, living off shellfish, wild fruits and small animals. Their origins are unknown, though archaeologists suspect they came from Central America.

Around the time of Christ, Arawak Indians began to navigate up the Caribbean archipelago. Originally from the Amazon region of South America, they embarked from the Orinoco river basin in Venezuela, settling on various islands in the Lesser Antilles before reaching Puerto Rico. Unlike the Archaics, Arawaks were both farmers and potters. They cultivated cassava to make bread, and they produced ceramics of outstanding quality, finely polished and beautifully painted in white geometric designs on a red background. Three phases of Arawakan culture evolved in Puerto Rico — the Igneris (Saladoids) until roughly 700 A.D., the Ostiones from 700 to 1,000 A.D., and the Tainos after 1,000 A.D.

The Tainos on Puerto Rico and neighboring Hispaniola developed the most advanced Indian culture found in the Caribbean. They spoke a common universal language, erected villages, practiced farming, hunting and fishing, and participated in a disciplined social organization. Although their pottery was not as fine as that of the early Igneris, they excelled in wood and stone work. Skilled navigators, the Tainos traveled easily between Puerto Rico and Hispaniola and to other islands in the Caribbean. Their vessels were long, simple canoes carved from tree trunks.

The Tainos had never seen the complex hulls and masts of the European ships. They watched as Columbus sailed by, and, as many people do when something can't be explained, they attributed the apparition to the gods.

Later, when Juan Ponce de León began a settlement on the island in 1508, many Tainos looked to the Spaniards and their powerful firearms as saviors from warring Arawak Caribs who were invading along Puerto Rico's east coast. Two years later, several Indians who had become concerned about the encroaching Spanish settlements drowned a young conquistador, one Diego Salcedo, to test his immortality. Spaniards, they discovered, weren't gods after all, but by then the Tainos were heading towards extinction.

An estimated 40,000 people inhabited Puerto Rico when Columbus discovered the island: by the mid-1500s all but a handful of Tainos had died, victims of disease, slavery and military skirmishes. Similar losses occurred throughout the Caribbean. Today, all that remains of Puerto Rico's prehistoric cultures is a scattering of archaeological sites, a sprinkling of Arawakan words, a couple of musical instruments, a genetic remnant of Taino features, and a wish on the part of most Puerto Ricans that there were more.

The Tainos on Boriquén lived in villages presided over by regional chieftains known as caciques. In their villages, circular thatched huts (bohíos) surrounded bateyes, plazas of smoothed earth bordered by rocks. Bateyes formed the setting for ceremonial activities. A ceremonial soccerlike game was played wearing painstakingly carved stone collars and using balls made from tree latex. Areyto dances featured native legends and traditions acted out to the accompaniment of gourd güiros and other percussive instruments. Individually, Tainos worshipped triangular stone cemí idols that they kept in their homes. Chieftains and priests communicated more intimately with the deities by using two-pronged pipes to snuff the ground and toasted hallucinogenic seeds of a native legume tree, mixed with a catalyst of burnt shells.

For the more mundane matter of feeding themselves, Tainos fished in the ocean and nearby rivers, hunted for birds and small forest animals, and farmed on plots scattered through the forests. Farming followed the common slash-and-burn technique, which involved girdling trees (removing a band of bark from their circumference, in order to kill them), clearing a patch of land with digging sticks, growing such crops as tobacco, sweet potatoes and cassava (yuca) for two or three years, moving on when the soil deteriorated. The destructiveness of this technique didn't matter much, since village populations were small and the island was covered with forest.

There were mangrove swamps along the coast, semi-evergreen forests on the low hills, rain forests higher up, and dwarf forests atop the highest peaks and ridges. Biologists estimate more than 500 tree species grew on the island; though most still exist, few reach the imposing size of those pre-Columbian trees. For an idea of what Columbus saw on Puerto Rico you must picture the statuesque rain forests of Guyana today. Such forests have almost entirely disappeared from the island. The largest tract of virgin forest survives in the upper reaches of the Luquillo Mountains, the central core of the Caribbean National Forest.

On a world map, Puerto Rico is a mere speck of land, with scarcely enough room for the dot marking the capital as San Juan. In latitude, it roughly parallels Bombay or Mexico City; in longitude, Caracas or Halifax, Nova Scotia. Puerto Rico marks the northeastern bend in the Caribbean archipelago, smallest (at 110 by 35 miles) and most easterly of the Greater Antilles. Like most mountainous Caribbean islands, it claims to have been described (by Columbus, no less) as a piece of paper crumpled and tossed upon the sea. The cliché is apt: the Cordillera Central rises to 4,390 feet along the length of the island. The northeastern Luquillo Mountains, totaling 48,550 acres, form barely more than two percent of the island; the Caribbean National Forest, with 28,000 acres, barely more than one percent. Within the forest, millions of trees, billions of plants and innumerable boulders conceal several special rocks. It is far easier to find Puerto Rico on a world map than to find these rocks. On them, Tainos carved childlike stick figures.

When I spoke with archaeologist Gus Pantel, he took issue with the description of Taino petroglyphs as childlike. "Though they do seem simple figures..." He stopped, deciding instead to show me something he does with students. In my notebook, he drew a long thin rectangle topped with squiggles, surrounded by a circle and slashed in half by a diagonal line. The meaning is clear: no smoking. "The whole concept of hieroglyphics is becoming common in today's international world." In the same way, he feels, Taino petroglyphs were not drawn as great art but as symbols which had meaning for the Indians, just as the totem poles of the Pacific Northwest carry a meaning. What the petroglyphs meant is not known.

I was trying to get a picture of the Tainos and their pre-Columbian life within the Luquillo Mountains. Years earlier Agamemnon "Gus" Pantel, a Greek-American who has resided in Puerto Rico for decades, spoke to me about the island's indigenous groups for an article I was writing for a local newspaper. With his portly frame and beard, Pantel looks like the archaeologist he is. Equipped with a doctoral degree, he has

*Old-growth
forest along
Juan Diego
stream
and waterfall.*

*Taino
Festival
in Jayuya.*

*Rafael Corcino
examining
petroglyphs
along the
Río Icacos.*

worked extensively in Puerto Rico and the Caribbean as a consultant in cultural resources. Contacting him seemed the logical first step in my current research. As it turned out, it was also the last step: Pantel, his wife mentioned when I called, was at that time the archaeologist for the Caribbean National Forest.

As we spoke, Pantel repeatedly stressed the success of the Tainos, rebutting the general conception that they were a roughly cut group who struggled to survive and proved no match for the superior Spaniard. "The Tainos represent extremely successful adaptation over the centuries to an environment totally distinct from that of the Europeans. Probably much more adaptation has had to go on on the part of the Europeans, some unsuccessful, in order to live in the tropics." He mentioned sugar cane as a case in point. Though it proved lucrative for Spain, its production went against nature, denuding forests and lowering water tables; Puerto Rico now pays the costs. "Archaeological records clearly demonstrate that in Puerto Rico, for about 2,000 years, the Indians not only existed, but existed successfully. For example, there were major ceremonial plazas, immense village sites. These were groups that went way beyond merely coping. They came here first as hunters and gatherers, then successfully exploited the environment."

Pantel also gave his views about Spanish ships versus Arawak canoes. "The dugout canoe was a really efficient vehicle for travel. Why develop a hulled vehicle if you don't need one? Kayaks are efficient, too. Spanish ships were designed for passengers and for cargo. There was not much need for pre-Columbians to carry cargo. The Spaniards had huge vessels, not because they were superior but because there was a historical necessity." He

thought of another angle on the idea of success: "We live in a modern age of tremendous advances, we call ourselves advanced, but how many of us can actually build a radio, make a lightbulb? We take credit, but we're really only adept in surviving by producing income, redistributing goods." Pantel then returned to the concept of necessity being the mother of invention: "The Europeans came to Puerto Rico with armor, and they bogged down. A lot of things in the tropics are not necessary, like clothing, which requires a need for certain skills, making thread, cloth, that sort of thing. A whole gamut of skills evolves out of need, and a lot of skills don't evolve because they aren't needed."

It was easier to get Pantel to talk about the success of the Tainos than about their relation with the Luquillo Mountains, primarily because little is known. For the past several years Forest Service crews have been systematically surveying the forest, looking for archaeological sites while they plant timber seedlings, covering a certain number of acres every year. Yet to date very little archaeological evidence has been found — simple tools, flakes of stones, perhaps used for gathering plants, and other artifacts discovered at a gathering site under an overhang; and several petroglyph-inscribed rocks.

Some time ago I saw one of those rocks near La Mina Peak on the southern slopes of the mountains. Set under a ledge, the rock was in shadow, its two petroglyphs barely visible. One is a figure with double-rimmed eyes and mouth grouped triangularly inside a lollipop head which is placed, without neck, above a straight stick torso and two stick arms bent at the elbow. The other, which has two lines extending from a hump encircling a smaller hump, vaguely resembles a snail. A rock along the Río Icacos, also on the southern Luquillo slopes, showcases a more elaborate petroglyph. Its triangular head encompasses oval eyes, an oval mouth curved into a smile and a Y-shaped mark extending from the mouth to two points at the top of the head. Above the head is a three-pronged ornament, perhaps representing feathers; on either side are heart-shaped ears; below is the outline of a neck and a necklace that resembles a shirt collar. Interestingly, the petroglyphs are all located near streams or rivers; they seem to have some connection with running water.

Pantel mentioned two general explanations for the dearth of archaeological evidence. First, geography. The rugged terrain of the Luquillo Mountains did not encourage settlement, nor even agriculture. In fact, the entire eastern region of Puerto Rico was not as constantly inhabited as other parts of the island, probably because it lies directly in the path of oncoming hurricanes. The second explanation relates to forest activities. Pantel believes there was a lot of activity in the forest, but "the forays were itinerant things, building campsites, not the sort of thing that would leave a mark."

IN THE HEART OF THE FOREST

Any reconstruction of what happened in the mountains comes from inference based on what happened on the rest of the island. "Indians probably used El Yunque for very sophisticated and specific reasons, in the same way the beaches had specific uses. It was probably a fruitful resource base, with a fair amount of specific resources, ones not found commonly in other areas." Resources may have included thatch and vines for shelters, fruits for food, trunks for canoes, leaves and roots for medicine, barks for rope and gourds for bowls. "The rain forest has unique vegetation, niches that would have existed in pre-Columbian times. The Indians were probably much more aware of variegations in El Yunque than we are. They certainly knew of the dwarf forest, it is too unique to have been overlooked." He went on to summarize, "El Yunque probably had enough unique elements to be a special type of place, but our current knowledge isn't enough to know what it was. There is evidence, tangible evidence, to demonstrate it was used for non-ceremonial, daily activities. And I would imagine there were ceremonial activities as well; I would be much more surprised to learn that there weren't."

Ceremonial activities most likely would have been connected to El Yunque Peak. For Tainos, El Yunque was a sacred peak. Some historians believe "luquillo" to be a corruption of the word Yokahú, name of the supreme being in Taino mythology. Down through the centuries Yokahú became known as the god of good, contrasted with Juracán, the god of evil. Yokahú and other gods were said to live in the fog-enshrouded recesses of El Yunque Peak, from where they protected the Indians. Other sources differ: according to a 1582 report by one Johan Melgarejo, the Spaniards had named these mountains Luquillo, spelled Loquillo in the report, for a Taino cacique, a chieftain who had lived in the region and kept up a constant battle with Christian colonizers.

In my varied readings about the forest, I came upon a story in a school primer that rather neatly encompasses the chieftain Luquillo, the forest, and the Taino gods. Written by an early twentieth-century author, Juan Huyke, it is most likely nine parts fiction and one part distant legend, but it does give an idea of the sentimental reverence many Puerto Ricans hold for the pre-Columbian islanders. The story goes something like this:

Luquillo and Canóvanas, cacique of a neighboring settlement, made life miserable for Spaniards who ventured into the northeast corner of the island. Yet for all the attacks they led and deaths they caused, the two men held no illusions. They knew they would soon be killed in battle themselves. Luquillo had a beautiful daughter, Niyu, whose name meant "white water". Canóvanas was in love with her, but she was in love with Yarubo, a young and valiant warrior who also hated the Spaniards. In normal times, Niyu would have become Canóvanas's wife, not Yarubo's. But now there was war. One day Luquillo instructed his daughter to climb the mountain with Yarubo and, when they reached the highest peak, to ask the gods to prepare a peaceful refuge for him. Though he didn't tell her so, Luquillo didn't expect to join them; the journey was actually to keep his daughter safe from an imminent battle. At first Niyu was immensely happy to be with her young love. Leaving a trail of stones to mark the way for the cacique, the couple ascended the mountain. They climbed for days and days and finally reached the summit. (They must have been very slow hikers, I might interject, for the distance is less than eight miles from the coast.) The view from the top was beautiful, a vast panorama of peaks and forest and ocean on all sides, but it wasn't enough. They felt great sadness in having left their land. After several days, they decided to return to the coast. On the way down, Niyu got sick with fever and died. Grief-stricken, Yarubo carried her back to the highest peak, where he buried her and marked her grave with the stones meant to guide Luquillo. Niyu had learned that the most important of all loves is the love felt for one's land.

Jalil Sued Badillo doesn't place much stock in such stories. Sued Badillo, a distinguished white-bearded man wearing a beret and white guayabera shirt, sat with me one morning in the cool inner patio of the University of Puerto Rico Museum while my daughter scattered books and other impromptu toys nearby. Of Lebanese extraction on his father's side, Sued Badillo was born in Puerto Rico. He is a history professor at the university, specializing in the fifteenth and sixteenth centuries in Puerto Rico. Pantel suggested I talk with him to find out if historical documents could shed more light on the relationship between the Tainos and the Luquillo Mountains.

"By the 1600s the population on the island had shrunk dramatically," Sued Badillo explained to me. "Social continuity can't really be traced back to the time of the first settlers, and you can't trace the legends, either." In other words, there simply weren't enough people left on the island in the 1600s to pass on much word-of-mouth history. Some of the compilers of legends, he added, were novelists (Huyke was apparently prodigious, if not well known, in all the literary genres), and they

didn't hesitate to include their own creative touches. Many of the legends one assumes to be based on historical facts may not be so at all. In the Luquillo story, he pointed out, the chieftains themselves are the only bona fide facts. Like many other island caciques — Utuado, Jayuya, Guaynabo, Orocovis — Luquillo and Canóvanas attained a sort of immortality by becoming town names that are still used today.

Glancing occasionally at research file cards he had brought with him, Sued Badillo went on to debunk most of the meager bits and pieces I had managed to collect connecting the Tainos with the Luquillo Mountains. Take, for example, Taino mythology and El Yunque Peak. He agrees with other historians that Yokahú was considered the first man in Taino mythology, the counterpart of Adam in the Christian religion. He feels the word came from "lukuo", the Taino word for man. But he finds no historical backing to say that Yokahú was the good god and Juracán the bad one. "Nineteenth century historians had little information, and they oversimplified. They thought every religion had to have a duality. In the Arawak language "juracán" meant storm and nothing more." In fact, he pointed out, in Taino mythology the god of storms is a goddess, Guabancex, who, when angry, would move wind and water, fling houses and uproot trees.

"Up until recently," he continued, "a lot of people believed El Yunque was the highest mountain in Puerto Rico." Actually, the highest is in the island's central mountains, and even within the Luquillo range El Toro Peak is higher than El Yunque. Yet El Yunque is certainly the best known mountain in Puerto Rico, the sentimental favorite. "These people also believed the Indians looked up in simplistic awe at the mountain," attributing all sorts of magical powers to it. Sued Badillo considers this mere speculation.

The problem, he explained, is that many of the island's historians have used earlier historians who did a lot of speculating. Until recently, there was little delving into the original sources. And even the original sources present problems to historians. Some are second- or third-hand accounts of events. Others, he feels, reflect strong biases, depicting the Indians as primitive savages. One very compelling reason to interpret Indians as savages relates to the question of slavery. The government in Spain permitted enslaving warlike tribes but not peaceful ones. Settlers needed slaves to hunt for gold and farm the land, and Africans were prohibitively expensive. "Like tractors today," he mentioned by way of comparison, "you couldn't afford too many of them." So it was to the settlers' benefit to embellish horror tales of bellicose Tainos.

To illustrate his point, Sued Badillo mentioned the Caribs, Indians based on the Lesser Antilles islands who were reputed for their warlike ways and cannibalistic tastes. A small but growing number of historians and anthropologists theorizes that the Caribs not only were not cannibals but were not even a separate ethnic group from the Tainos. Pantel, whose thoughts about the Indians seem to dovetail with those of Sued Badillo, had introduced this line of thinking earlier when he told me there was no archaeological evidence to suggest a separate Carib culture. All Caribbean Indians were Arawaks, Sued Badillo feels, and any differences were more of a social nature than an ethnic one. There are indications Indians used the terms Carib, Taino and Arawak interchangeably, in the same way

some members of the same family today might consider themselves Puerto Rican while others might prefer to be known as Hispanic. By singling out a group called Caribs and making them sound mean and cruel in their reports to the Spanish government, the settlers could justify taking them as slaves. This sort of bias, in turn, could have distorted many of the early chronicles.

Not everyone agrees. One historian I spoke to said he is still waiting to see the sources used to back up these new claims, and a friend who has great interest in such matters remarked that many intriguing pre- and post-Columbian theories have cropped up as a result of the recent 500th anniversary of Columbus's historic voyage.

When I asked about indigenous life in the Luquillo Mountains, Sued Badillo said he doubts Tainos inhabited its steep terrain. Though they did make forays there, as confirmed by the riverside petroglyphs, he doubts the forays were on a regular basis. Most of what they needed could be found in forests closer to the coast. Tainos were primarily a coastal people, he reminded me; when they settled in the interior regions, it was along plains or wide valleys. As for historical documents which Pantel thought might exist, Sued Badillo was equally discouraging. The few written mentions of Tainos in these mountains refer to later times, to sixteenth-century skirmishes between Spanish settlers and the Taino caciques — Luquillo in the north, Canóvanas to the west, Daguao in the southeast.

A dozen petroglyphs, a couple of stone tools, a remark or two in old documents, an improbable twentieth-century story: any clearer picture of what the Tainos did in the Luquillo Mountains seems to have vanished long, long ago.

CHAPTER 3
WHEN IT RAINS...

Puerto Rico, which is smaller than every state in the Union but Delaware and Rhode Island, has 550 native and 200 introduced tree species, as many as are found in the entire continental United States, including Alaska. In a research paper on trees that grow within the Caribbean National Forest, Elbert Little and Roy Woodbury listed 225 species of native trees — that is, trees that have grown here naturally as far back as anyone can determine — more than in any other area of equal size in the United States. Of these, 91 species are also native to continental tropical America and 64 to other Caribbean islands. Sixty-eight species are endemic to Puerto Rico — they grow here naturally and do not grow anywhere else — and 23 are endemic to the Luquillo Mountain region. Of these 23, seven are also found in a nearby commonwealth forest. The remaining 16 grow within the Luquillo Mountains. Period. They grow nowhere else in the world. In addition, the forest shelters 47 species of introduced trees (trees brought here from other regions), more than 150 types of ferns, 80 orchid species and a host of bromeliads, vines, grasses, mosses, lichens, herbs and sedges.

Climate plays a crucial role in this grand diversity. Frank Wadsworth, forester in the Luquillo Mountains for half a century, defines climate in his doctoral dissertation on

Luquillo's forest resources as a combination of temperature, rainfall, humidity, winds and evaporation. He goes on to pay the elements a compliment: "Most resources are exhaustible and must be used conservatively. Some, such as minerals, are not only exhaustible but are non-renewable. Others, such as soil and forest, may be renewed by wise husbandry. A third type of resource, which may be considered inexhaustible, includes favorable climate."

Fred Scatena, Forest Service hydrologist, agrees with Wadsworth's definition but cautions that, though climate is inexhaustible, it is sensitive to changes. If El Yunque's climate changes, the forest in turn will also begin to change. It is the spring of 1989. Scatena and I bounce along the north-coast Highway 3 in a Forest Service truck that needs work on its shock absorbers. He is driving out to collect data at the Bisley Watershed Project; I tag along to see the project and to pester him about weather in the Luquillo Mountains.

For several years Scatena and other scientists have been meticulously studying 13 acres of land along three streams which flow into the Río Mameyes in the northeastern part of the forest. Climatic conditions have been measured, the quality of the water analyzed and the surrounding forest examined with a thoroughness that would impress Sherlock

Holmes. The goal of the project has two phases: first, to understand the local ecology well; second, to manage it properly. When I visit the project with Scatena, scientists are in the process of completing the first phase. As part of the second phase, they plan to develop a method to harvest a small amount of timber, then reexamine the forest to determine the effects. By evaluating the impact of lumbering on watershed areas, they hope to develop a method that would minimally harm the environment, one that could then be used in other tropical forests. Though we don't know it at the time, the second phase of the project will change greatly in several months when Hurricane Hugo skirts the Luquillo Mountains. The scope and perhaps the longevity of the project was greatly expanded several months before we drive out to the forest. The Institute of Tropical Forestry, research branch of the U.S. Forest Service in Puerto Rico and coordinator for the study, won a prestigious Long Term Ecological Research (LTER) grant from the National Science Foundation. One of a dozen sites designated by the foundation to study long-term changes on the environment, the Bisley Watershed Project is the only one taking place in the tropics. When I ask Scatena what long-term means, he answers, "forever".

Climatic research in El Yunque has come a long way. While we drive, Scatena obliges me by supplying an offhand history of such research. A rain gauge installed in 1897 at Hacienda La Perla in the northeastern Luquillo foothills marked the first known attempt to measure the mountains' weather over a long period of time. Early stations used simple equipment and primarily measured rainfall. In the 1930s the Institute of Tropical Meteorology in Puerto Rico, an impressive group of scientists who developed many of the general theories related to tropical circulation and precipitation, worked extensively in the Luquillo Mountains. World War II apparently put a stop to their efforts. When Wadsworth collected data for his dissertation in the 1940s, he set up several rain stations, using such equipment as mechanical drums with tipping buckets for measuring rainfall extremes, and horsehair humidity gauges. The horsehair was strung, like a violin string, onto the gauge; it would tighten or sag, depending on the amount of humidity in the air.

In the 1960s Charles Briscoe produced one of the most extensive climatic studies within the forest. He set up stations at several elevations, collecting basically the same data that is collected today — rainfall, relative humidity, temperature, solar radiation, wind speed and direction. Briscoe's strength, according to Scatena, was in accruing copious amounts of information; later, other scientists pulled much of the data together and plotted it up. At about the same time, Howard Odum zeroed in on the climate of El Verde, the northwestern region of the forest, as part of a monumental study on the effects of irradiation on tropical ecology. Gone were the horsehair gauges. Odum and his fellow scientists used state-of-the-art electronic equipment: a photograph from that project shows two men, dressed in slacks and short-sleeved shirts, standing proudly beside instrument panels the size of large file cabinets.

A photograph of Scatena and his equipment, taken when we reach the forest, would show something quite different: it would show a tall, well-built man in his thirties, wearing a pink teeshirt, jeans, hiking boots and thick mismatched socks over the jeans, carrying his electronics in a pack on his back. The towering analyzers Odum was so proud of have given way to portable components that can be hooked up to equipment in the forest and to personal computers back at the scientists' offices.

As Scatena speaks and the truck bounces, I attempt to scribble everything down. He is very articulate. Ask him a question, and he takes off in a casual way with an answer that is concise and interesting. I envision him writing scientific articles with little more effort than talking into a tape recorder. Scatena has been involved in the project since its inception. Originally from the San Francisco area, he first lived in the Caribbean as a Peace Corps volunteer, working on ground water hydrology. He later got a doctorate from Johns Hopkins in environmental engineering with a concentration in geomorphology, which, he explains to me, is the study of land forms and the processes that form them. In 1987 he arrived in Puerto Rico to start up the watershed project. Though not without the usual bureaucratic frustrations, the job has been good, even fun for him, and he is pleased with the quality of the people and institutions now connected with the project.

Rain reigns over a rain forest. Being the most dramatic of the elements, it has also been the most studied. There is always a lot of it, averaging from 97 inches a year in the foothills up to 180 inches at higher elevations. The averages don't take into account the great fluctuations in rainfall from one year to the next, fluctuations which make short-term precipitation studies frustrating and unreliable. Take, for example, Wadsworth's La Mina Station, at an elevation of 2,350 feet. Though it only operated for eight years, between 1935 and 1943, the station's location in the heart of the recreation area near the highest peaks has made

its statistics among the most interesting and most often quoted for the Luquillo Mountains. The highest figure ever given for annual rainfall, 254 inches, was recorded at La Mina, yet the same station counted a mere 147 inches another year. (Its annual precipitation averaged 180.) March tends to produce the lowest amount of rain, 7 inches at La Mina, while May is the wettest month with 20 inches. La Mina data gets downright painstaking when it pinpoints an average of 1,625 showers a year, four and a half a day, each averaging .1 inch of rain and 19 minutes in duration. Those who haven't been in a rain forest might imagine the showers to be torrential affairs. Though heavy rains do occur, most showers fall in gentle movements of moderate rain bounded by periods of drizzle. Oddly enough, in spite of the frequent showers, the forest is actually free of rainfall more than 90 percent of the time.

Scientists with the Bisley Watershed Project aren't content merely to know how much rain falls from the sky. They want to know what is happening to that rain, where it is going, which plants and animals are benefiting. One of the distinctions of the project is the detail with which it is measuring runoff, the difference between what gets put into the forest through rainfall and condensation and what evaporates back into the air.

When we reach the entrance to El Yunque, we turn left onto the Sabana road on the southern boundary of the forest and, several miles farther, right onto an old lumber road from the 1930s which is now badly rutted and clogged with weeds. Scatena parks, and we walk along the road to the streams, unimaginatively named Watershed One, Two and Three. We reach Two first. Two metal boxes sit on a concrete wier along the bank of the stream next to the road. An upriver screen

*Hydrologist
Fred Scatena
collecting
data
in the Bisley
watershed
research area.*

*When
it
Rains…*

*Making
use of the water,
Río
Mameyes.*

*Stream
in El Verde
after a
heavy rain.*

catches organic matter, for carbon studies, that normally gets washed away along the stream. One box, painted green, contains electronic equipment to determine the water level of the river while a gray box is an automatic water sampler. Its pump can be set to collect samples of stream water at specific intervals while 24 little bottles hold the samples. Some two hundred feet upriver a large net resembling a sagging square hammock collects leaves and other litter that falls into the stream, for later analysis. Watershed One has the same combination of boxes and net. Watershed Three, the largest of the streams, is a long-term control stream which may not be tinkered with in any way. It has two boxes but no net along its banks.

Though the forest in this rarely-visited region looks primeval, it isn't. During the nineteenth century it was cut, first for its excellent woods, later for trees used to make charcoal. Farmers further cleared it for crops, but the San Ciriaco hurricane of 1899 put an end to major farming efforts. Though extensively cut, the forest was never razed. In the 1930s the U.S. Forest Service acquired the land and replanted it. Though many of the trees are now tall, the canopy thick, and the underbrush sparse, there are still vestiges from the past — tree stumps, charcoal pits, skid trails. Scientists working in Bisley have chosen to focus on replanted forest for two reasons. First and foremost, virgin forest in El Yunque cannot be cut, for research or any other reason. Secondly, most of the tropical land which will benefit from what is learned here will probably be cut-over forest as well.

After we look at Watershed Two, Scatena leads me up a hillside to a 70-foot-high aluminum tower located halfway between Watershed One and Two. The tower, a result of

the LTER grant and Forest Service funding, was put together on the site the way one assembles tinker toys. Primarily built to measure rainfall, it is also being used for canopy studies. Scatena climbs the tower to transfer the most recent data into his portable computer; afraid of heights, I drag myself only halfway up.

The scientists measure more than stream runoff. On our way up the hill, the forest, which looked so primeval at first, begins to display a curious collection of manmade objects. Concrete blocks mark the path, dabs of red paint identify tabonuco trees, baskets catch leaf litter, plastic screen bags hold decomposing leaves. In addition, numerous white plastic gallon jugs sit like giant toadstools on the forest floor. Funnels stick out of the necks; screens cover the funnels. Emptied weekly, these jugs are used to measure throughfall, the amount of rain that actually makes it through the canopy and mid-level leaves to the ground. A more complicated but equally homespun contraption lies flush against the lower trunks of several trees. A plastic cracker box is glued to the trunk; from it, a tube leads to a plastic water jug. This measures stemflow, the amount of water that seeps down the sides of trees. Though usually not much in quantity, stemflow is very important in the quality of the nutrients reaching the ground.

Temperature, another component of the climatic picture, varies much less than rainfall, both from year to year and month to month; consequently, it has attracted little interest in the research community over the decades. According to La Mina data, the average forest temperature of 70.3 degrees Fahrenheit is bounded by a mere 12-degree range (from 64.3 to 76.3). This is some ten degrees cooler than the coastal average. Relative humidity, a third component, is also fairly constant, especially in the upper forest, where it hovers around a saunalike 98 percent. Even at lower elevations, humidity rarely drops below 60 percent.

The island's Cordillera Central to the west has its patches of rain forest, but the Luquillo Mountains get more rain, a total of more than 100 billion gallons every year. The primary rain supplier comes from the east in the form of the Atlantic trade winds, historic winds that nudged sailing vessels west from Europe to the New World, as welcome to sailors as the equatorial calms were dreaded.

The trade winds push more than ships across the Atlantic. One of their most curious and least known cargos is Sahara dust. There are summer days in the Caribbean when the skies turn an anemic yellow and the sun sets as a pale taupe disk, when distant points become barely visible on the horizon and a rust-colored dust etches objects outdoors. The dust causing this haze originates in the vast sand storms of the African Sahara Desert. Hot air and gusty winds raise the dry earth; boxed in by high pressure above and the trade winds on the sides and below, it travels west in a giant stream, up to 1,000 miles wide and 2,000 miles long, a mile deep and more than half a mile above the water, reaching the islands within a week. As the larger particles fall, the base of the dust stream erodes, causing the haze below. Droughts in the Sahara tend to increase the amount of haze in the Caribbean.

In the same way, the westerly movements carry accumulating amounts of rain across the Atlantic. Situated at the easternmost edge of the easternmost island in the Greater Antilles chain, the Luquillo Mountains get a bumper share of this water.

"Climate in the Luquillo Mountains," Scatena comments during our drive, "is clearly trade wind dominated." In this respect, islands differ from mainland regions, which are dominated by continental conditions. "Constant winds bring moisture and cool air on a daily basis. There are also occasional frontal winds on a bigger scale which originate in the Atlantic or the Northern Latitudes, but the trade winds are always present. They bring light showers in the morning and late afternoon. A lot of this moisture never makes it through the canopy to the ground. The ground in the Luquillo Mountains loses [actually, never receives] more water to the canopy than most forests. The region also has a muted dry season. During that time, it still gets rain, though not as consistently as during the wet season. The most accurate indicator of seasonality is the number of dry days per month and the amount of throughfall. February through April are dry months; October through December are wet; August and September are wet if there are hurricanes. Yet seasonality is not strongly marked. That and a high number of short, light showers are the unusual weather features in the Luquillo Mountains. A monsoon area may get the same amount of rain, but it will be condensed into a few months, whereas here we always get rain, light showers and the occasional hurricane."

Some time later Scatena asks if he can clarify his views on climate. Earlier he looked on weather primarily in its local context. Now he and other scientists have identified four different weather systems affecting Luquillo — trade winds, northern fronts, tropical storms and hurricanes — and they are focusing on the global picture, identifying where the systems come from and how important the differences are between systems. The trade winds, for example, bring a very good quality of water across the Atlantic; they also bring a lot of marine deposits from evaporated seawater. Northern fronts, a winter occurrence, usually come from North America and bring higher levels of nitrogen and sulfur; they also have the potential to bring pollution, though little actually reaches here at present. Tropical storms follow the path of the trade winds but they bring greater amounts of rain and heavier winds, so they affect the forest in different ways. Hurricanes follow more erratic paths across the Atlantic and bring awesome levels of water and wind. Scatena wants to detail how these global conditions affect Luquillo's watersheds, to figure out how something like the swirling sands of Africa affects the tall trees of Luquillo. The mountains' position at the crossroads of the Caribbean makes them an ideal subject.

 Regardless of origins and chemical properties, the rains, once they hit the ground, become indistinguishable as they make their way down the mountainsides. Runoff within the forest averages some 281,000 acre feet of water annually; monthly flows fluctuate greatly, from a low of 3,400 to a high of 30,000 acre feet. An acre foot equals the amount of water which would cover one acre to a depth of one foot, or 325,851 gallons: 281,000 acre feet translate into 91.5 billion gallons, some ten billion less than the total rainfall. The extra ten billion has evaporated back into the atmosphere. Runoff is highest, up to 80 percent of the rainfall, on the upper slopes; in the lower forest it drops to some 40 percent. Half of all runoff seeps into the soil; the other half flows between winding river banks down the mountains, either to be diverted into municipal water supplies or to continue across the plains and into the sea.

Eleven watersheds, forming the headwaters of six major rivers, originate in the Luquillo Mountains. Río Espíritu Santo, Río Grande de Loíza, Río Mameyes and Río Sabana flow to the north, Río Fajardo to the east, and Río Blanco to the south. The north-facing rivers start along steep courses that eventually level out while the south-facing rivers begin their journey along gradual slopes that later plunge steeply. The Loíza is the longest (37 miles), the Sabana the shortest (six miles), the Blanco the biggest in terms of runoff (one-quarter of the total) and the Espíritu Santo the largest in terms of drainage area (21.36 square miles). Add on all the tributaries, and you have some 1,125 miles of watercourses within the forest, of which more than 80 percent flow year-round.

Enough of statistics. These rivers are also beautiful. In the current proposed management plan for the forest, two — the Río Icacos and Río de la Mina — have been recommended to Congress for scenic river status and one — the Río Mameyes — for wild and scenic status. When I think of the Luquillo forest, the image that first comes to mind is a particular place near the Río Mameyes. A friend, my husband and I came upon this place one day while we were trying to find the continuation of La Coca Trail. Late in the afternoon someone thought of crossing a nearby stream. Sure enough, on the other side we found a trail, rocky, overgrown and laced with spider webs but a trail nonetheless. It ascended the stream bank and looped around to hug the side of a mountain. We could hear a river below. In the distance the forest opened slightly. The others, walking single file along the trail in front of me, suddenly looked like Lilliputians. Sierra palms arched over them, and mahogany and other straight-trunked trees towered over the sierra palms. Lianas dangling from the trees resembled an artist's impressionistic sketch of a downpour; the artist, one could imagine, worked from the numerous "painter's palettes" along the trail, small plants with splotches of white, pink and red on deep green leaves. Some 200 feet below us the Río Mameyes ricocheted along a narrow valley. Water tumbled over room-sized boulders, slid down smooth chutes, plunged into small pools. The order varied over and over — chutes, boulders, pools, boulders, pools, chutes, boulders, chutes — as the river made its precipitous way down the mountain. The trail curved around the mountainside and out of our sight. This was lost-civilization-just-around-the-bend country, but the shadows were deepening and we had to turn back. Eventually we returned to follow the trail.

These rivers can also be beautiful in a delicate way. I've taken more than two dozen hikes through El Yunque with Jerry Bauer, forester for many years in the Caribbean National Forest, who is currently working in Nicaragua. On our last hike together before he left we reminisced a bit and decided that our favorite outing had been along the Río Icacos. A tributary of the southerly-flowing Río Blanco system, the Icacos originates in one of the highest valleys in the mountains, near the old La Mina weather station. The surrounding terrain is a jumble of boulders connected to each other by spongy webs of roots, soil, dead leaves and living plants. When the source surfaces from

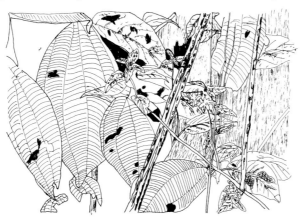

TROPICAL VEGETATION

under these boulders, it forms a wispy stream floating along a looping bed through level forest terrain. The water is shallow, cool and clear, the stream bed as soft and sandy as an ocean beach. Rocks mottled by mosses and lichens catch litter which dams the stream in places, forming small pools. Floral arrangements of ferns, white ginger and red flame plants crop up along the banks. Dead branches straddling the stream support mosses, bromeliads and occasional clusters of tiny orchids. Sierra palms crowd out other trees, and their decaying fronds litter the ground. This part of the Icacos looks like an exotic set that a Disney would spend millions to create. In contrast to a Disney venture, it gets very few visitors.

Farther along, a concrete and metal dam has backed the stream into a 10-foot-wide pool. On the far side, rain gauging equipment —zinc pipe embedded in stone, topped by a turquoise-blue box containing a tube — measures high and low watermarks. Below the dam, the delicate waterway vanishes, lost under huge boulders toppled onto each other in cubistlike arrangements. The terrain begins to tilt. When the boulders give way to modest-sized rocks, the stream re-emerges as a small river. Pools are bigger, up to 25 feet wide. Here the power of the river is more apparent: in heavy rains, the Icacos can increase its normal flow up to 2,500 percent, becoming a torrent that dislodges debris and destroys saplings. At one point a landslide has cut a several-hundred-foot-wide swath through the forest and across the river, opening up a view of ridges in the distance and a small lake below. Some 150 feet in diameter, the lake is actually a reservoir. A thin layer of water flows over its concrete dam and down a 40-foot-high curved wall which terminates at a small guard tower.

A decade earlier, in the mid-1970s, forest had surrounded the lake. I came upon it on one of my first hikes in El Yunque. The lake looked beautiful, a veritable emerald in the jungle, but its algae-green color hinted of all sorts of unknown creatures and organisms. I wouldn't put a toe in the water. In 1979 two back-to-back hurricanes which came near Puerto Rico caused several landslides in the region. Afterwards, I tried to find the lake again but couldn't. If I had, I would have been disappointed, for boulders had tumbled into the reservoir, filling it up. When I returned with Bauer and others (in the mid-1980s), workers had recently finished scooping out the boulders and placing them along the banks. My attitude concerning the water had changed. We had waded through and slipped into the Icacos along its entire length; it seemed far too pristine and swift-moving to produce life-threatening organisms, so we took a swim. Below the dam, the terrain tilts almost vertically, discouraging amateur explorers.

The Luquillo rivers supply an invaluable commodity. With more than 1,000 people per square mile, Puerto Rico is one of the most densely populated regions in the world. A million and a half residents live in the sprawling metropolitan area of San Juan and its neighboring cities of Carolina and Bayamón. In the country, homes hug the shoulders of even the steepest roads, and landscapes that look un-populated beneath the lush vegetation by day become spreading constellations of electrical lights at night. Many people demand much water, and any that is merely coasting down a river toward the sea is considered fair game.

All of the island's mountain lakes are actually reservoirs, built to tap river water for hydroelectric power, agriculture and human consumption. The Icacos dam, the only one in the Luquillo Mountains, forms part of a hydroelectric project along the Río Blanco. The Puerto Rico Aqueduct and Sewer Authority also operates 12 small impoundments within the forest, diverting river water through intakes (pipes) to off-forest filtration plants which serve neighboring townships. A few individual families living along the boundaries directly tap forest streams. In all, more than a quarter million people consume water that originates in the Caribbean National Forest.

The day we visited the Bisley Watershed Project, I asked Scatena to translate a scientific description I had been carrying around with me for some time: riverine waters of Luquillo are cool, neutral to slightly basic, low in conductivity and generally oligotrophic. Cool was obvious, but how cool? "The waters are somewhere in the 20 degree (Celsius, some 68 degrees Fahrenheit) range." What about neutral to slightly basic? "This means they're not acidic, their ph is neutral." So? "Acidic tends to dissolve more, working like vinegar. Basic water is more balanced, its chemistry is balanced." Low in conductivity. "To determine this, scientists put in probes to see how much electricity is there. If it's low it means there's not a lot of junk in the water. Distilled water has no conductivity." Oligotrophic. "Oligotrophic is the opposite of eutrophic." Which means... "Which means the water doesn't have an excess of nutrients [the word derives from the Greek for 'few nutrients'], yet it doesn't lose too many of them, it cycles internally." In summary, "If an area was denuded, the water would be warmer, with higher conductivity and probably more acidic, though this varies a lot. So that definition means the water is good, generally clear in spite of a lot of rain. Though there is potential for losing a lot of nutrients, it doesn't lose too many, the forest has ways to retain them."

Water flowing from the Luquillo Mountains has traditionally not been considered good because of the high level of sediments it contains. Yet there are ways to get rid of sediments in water, and today the Luquillo Mountains are looked to, with urgency, as the last large and relatively untapped water source on the island. In recent years, Lake Carraizo reservoir on Río Loíza east of Luquillo, the primary water source for San Juan residents, has become filled with sediments, able to hold only a fraction of its original capacity, and other reservoirs are suffering similar fates. Spells of dry weather in 1994 and 1995 forced many island residents into periodic and at times severe rationing measures. In addition, resorts, malls and other developments are being constructed at a rapid pace in northeastern Puerto Rico. Increasing amounts of water are being diverted from forest intakes, lowering the water levels of the affected streams and rivers, and the government has plans to tap water along the Río Mamayes just north of the forest.

The pressing need for water for human consumption often overshadows the equally important rights of the forest's original inhabitants, its plants and animals. Water drives the entire forest community. It enables cells to perform the chemical and physical processes

of metabolism that are continually going on in living organisms. Water is essential for plants and animals to grow, to transpire (a scientific word for a process similar to sweating or breathing) and to perform such seasonal activities as propagation. Water provides moisture for gas exchange in amphibians and reptiles, controls the rate of organic matter production and acts as a buffer against temperature changes. It is also a great transporter, carrying seeds downriver and marine life upriver, and a major architect of stream channels and other landscape features.

The balance between the amount of water and a healthy community is a fragile one, and some scientists fear that outside demands for water could hurt the forest uses. "Typically, natural ecosystems are not considered legitimate users of water unless a particularly valuable ecosystem is involved," explains Ariel Lugo, director of the island's International Institute of Tropical Research, in a study of water and the ecosystems in El Yunque. "For example, laws in the state of Florida assure a minimum water supply to the wetlands of Everglades National Park, regardless of water shortages in the city of Miami. The water rights of the ecosystems of the Everglades are recognized as legitimate in that state. In other places, however, water flow to the ocean is viewed as a waste of freshwater." One objective of the current watershed project is to determine just how much water the forest community needs to function properly in order to maintain this level when managing the forest.

When I last spoke with Scatena, in 1995, he felt strongly that El Yunque has given all the water it can without further damage to its ecological and recreational resources. On an average day, he mentioned, about half of the water in Luquillo streams are diverted through intakes for municipal water use. About ten percent of the time stream flow is less than the amount of water that can be withdrawn, and several impounded streams are dry downstream of their intakes for up to 100 days a year.

Scatena is especially concerned about the proposed dam on the Río Mameyes. The Mameyes is the only major river in the forest that does not have a large intake. In addition, he pointed out, "This is the only river on the island, and maybe the Caribbean, that still drains the entire sequence of ecosystems — cloud [forest] to coral — in a relatively natural manner. All the others have large intakes, reservoirs, or urbanizations that impede the travel of species that migrate from the coastal zones to the headwaters. Surveys have shown that the Mameyes, the least disturbed stream, has the highest diversity of all the streams in the forest. And of all the large streams in the Caribbean, it has the best chance of remaining in a natural state."

Ironically, rainfall and the accompanying condensation are not always benefactors to the forest community. Though the few scientists who live on the upper slopes of Luquillo admit sleeping is marvelous in a rain forest, they also have their gripes — mildew, forming virtually overnight, on food, books, electrical items, camera lenses; clothes and shoes that never dry; floors that always carry tracks of mud; rusting cars, corroding equipment. The vegetation could compile its own list of complaints. Rain causes erosion, making land more likely to slide and trees to topple in a storm. It dissolves minerals and organic mat-

ter out of the soil. The excessive saturation level of soils and air, most pronounced in dwarf forests, inhibits growth. When heavy, rain can slash leaves and wash away seedlings.

Paradoxically, in spite of these severe restrictions, tropical rain forests are renowned for their luxuriant and diverse vegetation. Scientists can retard the negative effects of moisture in their offices and laboratories by plugging in dehumidifiers; plants have their own ways to adapt to and even benefit from the less-than-ideal conditions. A Forest Service report summarizing research history within the Caribbean National Forest lists examples of ways the forest responds to water. Trees take advantage of it by synchronizing their germination, growth and fruiting to the slight changes of rainfall. The boat-shaped leaves of bromeliads and other epiphytes store water that is then used by a variety of tiny animals. Trees here have never needed to develop tap roots, growth rings and deciduous leaves — features characteristic of marked wet and dry seasons.

At the same time, the forest minimizes the impacts of too much water. By collecting water, the millions of epiphytic plants tucked onto trees keep the rain from saturating other surfaces; epiphytes also absorb minerals which might otherwise flow out of the forest. Plants develop certain anatomical and morphological characteristics, such as enlarged pores, to increase sweating and reduce water loss. Many trees have developed extensive root networks that work as a mesh to hold minerals.

"Nature," Scatena commented, "uses what it has. Here it has a lot of rain, and it uses it best."

CHAPTER 4
WILD WINDS

In a study completed some time ago, scientists analyzed storms which had affected Puerto Rico between 1899 and 1928. Among other things, they found that over half of the storms — 60 percent —were considered beneficial; thirty percent proved to be a mix of beneficial and harmful, and ten percent were overwhelmingly destructive.

The most infamous of the destructive storms is the hurricane.

☙ A hurricane is the one climatic condition that only the most intrepid plants can turn to an advantage, and then only after the damage has been done. While the storm is in progress, plants, like humans, do little more than hold on and hope for the best. For centuries, Puerto Rican hurricanes were named for the saint on whose day the storm fell, and older people still mention the names of the first three major hurricanes during the past century — San Ciriaco, San Felipe and San Ciprian — with a quiet reverence and a disbelieving shake of the head, the way those to the north speak of the great blizzards. In recent decades the island has adopted the names used by the World Meteorological Organization. Though practical, the new names do not convey the same romance as the saint names. Who gets goosebumps at the mention of Beulah, or David, or Hugo? Hugo became the fourth major hurricane of the past century to hit Puerto Rico, yet I can't imagine the word Ugo, as it is pronounced here, instilling the same reverence in future years.

San Ciriaco. At 8:00 a.m. on August 8, 1899, San Ciriaco hit Puerto Rico. Six hours later it left, having dumped more than two and a half billion tons of water on the island; killed more than 3,350 people, primarily through flooding; erased entire towns, most of whose homes were made of thatch; and destroyed virtually all of the island's coffee and most of its subsistence crops. Like most of Puerto Rico's worst hurricanes, San Ciriaco followed a diagonal path across the island, entering from the southeast and exiting to the northwest. Along the way, it skirted the southwestern edge of the Luquillo Mountains.

San Felipe. On September 13, 1928, San Felipe lumbered in from the southeast as the biggest, most violent and most destructive hurricane ever recorded to have hit Puerto Rico, with record-breaking winds of 160 miles per hour and a record-breaking barometric reading of 27.5 inches. A photograph taken afterwards shows a wood plank that was seized by the wind and sent through a palm tree as if the plank were a well-sharpened knife. More than 300 people lost their lives, and hundreds of thousands lost their homes. Large sugar mills were reduced to rubble; telephone and telegraph communications became little more than a mass of tangled wires. Like San Ciriaco, San Felipe passed southwest of the Luquillo Mountains.

San Ciprian. On September 26, 1932, San Ciprian also crossed the island from southeast to northwest, killing more than 200 people, destroying whatever crops remained after San Felipe, and striking a death knell for the island's agricultural industry. Unlike the others, San Ciprian churned across the Luquillo Mountains. This was only the fourth major recorded hurricane to pass directly over Luquillo. The first three occurred in 1766, 1772, and 1867.

Hugo. In the early morning hours of September 18, 1989, Hugo hit Puerto Rico's eastern offshore islands of Vieques and Culebra. Instead of following the southeast-to-northwest trajectory, it grazed the island's northeast corner, skimming the Luquillo Mountains to the northeast, and swirled out over the Atlantic to the north. Minimal rain, less than ten inches in two days, produced minimal flooding. Hugo caused only two deaths here, both being older mariners who chose to ride out the storm in their boats. Yet property damage and damage to agriculture, poultry, horticulture and the tourism industry were extensive. For months, the windows of many highrise condominiums were replaced with boards, their glass having snapped during the storm, and for years one particular aluminum shed along Highway 3 looked like a piece of crumpled foil.

What a hurricane is has long been understood: it is a circular storm, a vast cyclone of pearly clouds and heavy rains, originating in the warm waters of the tropics, that moves forward slowly while it spins at more than 75 miles an hour around a core of low atmospheric pressure. As early as the seventeenth century a voyager circumnavigating the world discovered — most likely the hard way — that the typhoons of the Pacific and the hurricanes of the Atlantic were the same nightmarish phenomenon.

How a hurricane works, on the other hand, is extremely complicated, and scientists still puzzle over many aspects of its formation. It has been compared to an immense machine churning across the landscape. The heat energy released by a hurricane in one day alone is often equivalent to that released by the fusion of 400 20-megaton hydrogen bombs, or, as an undated but, by the appearance of its illustrations, outdated National Ocean and Atmospheric Administration booklet puts it, enough energy to supply the U.S. electrical needs for six months. Its winds have been known to lift a piece of lead weighing 400 pounds and to carry it 1,680 feet; its waters once dragged a buoy, chain and anchor weighing more than 30,000 pounds for ten miles. Hurricanes have inspired novels, destroyed libraries containing the documented histories of islands, and altered wars. President McKinley remarked during the Spanish American War that more warships had gone to the bottom of the sea in storms than under fire of enemy ships. Of all nature's disasters, only an earthquake or a tsunami equals the destruction of a hurricane.

Ironically, some of the Caribbean's most violent storms begin in the doldrums, a belt of tranquil water which lies off the coast of Africa near the Equator; an especially active region southeast of the Cape Verde Islands has come to be known as the hurricane incubator. From there, the storms travel in a northwesterly direction. Hurricane season in the Caribbean occurs during the summer months, from May to November, when the ocean is at its warmest. Different islands fear different months. In Puerto Rico, for example, the months of August and September have produced the strongest storms, and for centuries the Catholic church has had island priests recite *As repellendat tempestates* in their masses during those months. Priests in Cuba, on the other hand, have recited it during September and October. Compared to other islands, Puerto Rico has suffered a relatively low number of hurricanes: 11 major hurricanes have passed over the island since 1700. There is speculation that the Luquillo Mountains may tend to deflect storms. Perhaps the Tainos' belief that gods protected the island from atop El Yunque Peak had a basis in scientific truth, after all.

Hurricanes inspire intense curiosity among those who have never experienced them and equally intense dread among those who have. I was vacationing off-island with my family when Hugo struck, so I retain a fascination for the phenomenon. Yet none of my neighbors in the oceanside community where I live seem interested in repeating the adventure. Not the least of their discomforts were the days with neither electricity nor water that followed.

Luis Salivia, a medical doctor who compiled a history of hurricanes in Puerto Rico, suffered through San Ciprian at his home in the metropolitan city of Río Piedras back in 1932. He eloquently put the experience into words: "It is impossible to erase the memory of several hours spent in the net of a hurricane. Everything that was suffered during such misfortune will be remembered as long as one lives: the natural vehement worry in the face of a threat of a great danger whose magnitude we cannot foresee; the deafening and painful buzz that torments us as if the

ears were at the point of exploding; the violent noise formed by wind that spins at very high speeds, and the waters beating against the walls of the house in gusts that seem never to end; the creaking of the entire building with frequent jolts, and of the tables that become loose, split and fly off; the shouts and moans of pain; the infernal darkness that increases even more after a flash of lightning; the copious sweating; the state of nerves that paralyzes us when it seems that the end of existence has arrived... He who has passed through that agony, even without having to lament the loss of a loved one, could he ever forget it?"

The small community of Sabana abuts the northeastern edge of El Yunque. Several of its older residents remember San Ciprian. I first met three of them — Manuel and Lucrecia Vázquez and Angel Rosa — with forester Jerry Bauer, when he and I were interested in knowing more about the history of the forest for a guide book that never materialized. Later, I returned to talk to them about the hurricane. The Vázquezes, who were children at the time, lived with their families on the southern side of the mountains near the town of Naguabo. Angel Rosa worked on a coffee and citrus farm just up the mountain from Sabana, near the current Bisley project. Sabana didn't exist back then. Homes were scattered throughout the region, connected to each other and to the coastal towns by a network of paths. Virtually all homes were made of wood with zinc roofs or of thatch; thatch homes differed little from those used by the Indians. Concrete was expensive, and too heavy to carry up the paths. Each family built a tormentera, or hurricane shelter. The shelters were usually triangular structures made of thatch, some ten feet square and eight feet high. A log in the center of the shelter was set

*Bisley
watershed area
shortly after
Hurricane Hugo
hit.*

WILD WINDS

Forest near Los Picachos Peak shortly after Hurricane Hugo hit.

Same place, five years later.

deep into the soil, and lianas were used to lash the roof to nearby trees. In those days there was little warning of approaching hurricanes — a hazy sun, a light drizzle, an upswing of wind and, most notably, the erratic inland flight of the rabijunco (*Fregata magnificens*), the magnificent frigatebird, also known on some islands as the hurricane bird.

When the drizzle began that September day in 1932, Sra. Vázquez remembers her father saying, "all right, get ready, a bad storm is coming." They covered most of the floor of the tormentera with sierra palm planks, leaving an open space where they set down rocks and a cooking pot. They took in an ample supply of firewood, potatolike tubers and coffee. Almost immediately, Sra. Vázquez's mother began to cook. The storm was, indeed, bad. Nature, usually a tranquil backdrop, had gone mad. Leaves were flapping wildly, young trees were bending to the ground, rain was traveling in nearly horizontal sheets, and winds were prying the roofs off homes. In San Juan, scientists clocked winds at 90 miles per hour and measured rainfall at some 25 inches. More rain fell on the Luquillo Mountains during the time San Ciprian passed overhead — Sra. Vázquez remembers it as seven hours, Rosa as a couple of hours — than falls on southern California in an average year. The Río Icacos rose 12 feet in two hours.

Inside the tormentera, Sra. Vázquez remembers the atmosphere as cozy. It was cool and they had a lot of firewood for cooking, so they didn't go hungry. Less fortunate neighbors who entered the shelter dripping from head to foot would be handed a coconut shell cup filled with hot coffee and a gourd or palm branch dish loaded with boiled tubers. The neighbors kept coming. When the winds were especially bad, the men pressed an oxen yoke against the windward wall to support it. Halfway through the storm came the virazón, when the eye passed overhead and the wind changed directions. The men then braced the opposite wall. Rosa joked that when the hurricane first blew through, it bent all the trees; when it came through the second time in the opposite direction, it straightened them all up. Though the tormenteras were relatively safe, the Vázquezes and Rosa remember neighbors who died, primarily by being caught in the swollen streams or being hit by a careering branch or a piece of zinc roof.

In its wake, San Ciprian left disaster in the Luquillo Mountains. Branches had been ripped from trees, and many trunks had been pulled up by their roots. What the hurricane couldn't pull up, it tore off. With its copious rainfall, El Yunque is the only national forest to boast of virtually no fire worries. Yet after San Ciprian, according to all three witnesses, the Luquillo range looked as if it had been the victim of a great conflagration. Not a leaf was left on any of the trees. Rosa pointed to a gray, twisted, lifeless tree in his neighbor's yard: "They were all like that," he told me. Sra. Vázquez motioned to a spot high in the mountains: "If someone was walking there, you would see him immediately. There was no vegetation to hide him."

All homes were destroyed. Lucky residents recovered the remains of their zinc roofs; everything else had to be rebuilt from scratch. Lydia remembers living in the tormentera until her father could construct a makeshift house, with dirt floors and sugar cane sacks for beds. Fruits were collected off the ground and eaten for several days before they began to rot. Then there was little until the bananas and tubers grew back, which took about a year, Rosa estimated. He doesn't remember anyone starving to death, but the year was very rough. In Naguabo, the Vázquezes told me, the government sent up such staples as corn and flour, but Rosa remembers no government help. Every bush of coffee on the farm where he worked was destroyed; the owner of the land, Mr. Saldondo, who lived in the coastal town of Fajardo, had neither the spirit nor the resources to plant again. The forest proved more resilient than Mr. Saldondo. Within three months, buds began to appear in the trees; within five months, new leaves.

A year and a half passed after Hugo hit in 1989 before I was able to get back to Sabana and have Rosa and the Vázquezes compare it with San Ciprian. By then, the community looked little affected by the hurricane: awnings and zinc roofs had been replaced, and leaves and plants had grown back. I had been concerned about Rosa's wooden house, built on stilts on a triangular lot in the center of the community, but it was still there. Shacks behind the house were missing. Though the upstairs door was open, the house had an abandoned look, and Rosa was nowhere to be found. I crossed the street to the Vázquez home, a sprawling concrete and wood structure which appeared unchanged. The Vázquezes were sitting at a table in a covered patio encroached on by potted plants; Sra. Vázquez, wearing a dress and a baseball cap, was preparing tubers to be boiled over a wood-burning stove. She confessed she prefers cooking on the patio, which is lighter, cooler and more pleasant than the kitchen. I asked them about Hugo. As before, Sra. Vázquez did most of the talking.

For her, Hugo was not as bad as San Ciprian. San Ciprian left absolutely no leaves while Hugo left merely patches of forest with no leaves. She showed me the view from her front yard: a tall Australian pine in the distance was still up, a palm across the street was still up, several other trees nearby were still up. A neighboring concrete house lost only its awning. It was a short hurricane. She and her husband stayed at home, armed with a stored-up supply of water, a large gas lamp, a gas stove, firewood. She made coffee and periodically opened one of the louvered windows a crack to watch the plants flying by outside. Of course, Hugo was destructive, but the damage was spotty. Her son lost some 50 fighting cocks that were in cages in the woods behind the house; all the chickens died; a breeding area for land crabs was destroyed; their tubers, sweet peppers and other crop plants were gone. They were now growing back the crops and replacing the breeding area.

The front door, a window and a zinc roof covering part of the house had to be replaced, and she led me on a tour of her sparsely furnished, very clean house to show me Hugo-caused cracks in the walls. Zinc roofs seemed to be the greatest manmade casualty of the hurricane. A piece of flying zinc struck their truck, and another piece left a scalloped scar on the wall of the house. She offered me coffee, sweetened but without milk, from a thermos before I left. I asked if she had been afraid during the hurricane. She said, "I lived through San Felipe and San Ciprian. This one didn't frighten me." Laughing, she told me about young people in Sabana who were excited when they learned the hurricane would pass over; now they swear they never want to go through another.

As I was leaving, I saw Rosa walking up the street. Sra. Vázquez told me he had gone to a doctor's appointment. Though he was almost 90 years old, Sr. Rosa's memory was sharp: He hadn't seen me for a couple of years, yet he remembered me immediately and led me into his home. It was 11:15 in the morning. Rosa had already been to the doctor in Fajardo, some 10 miles away, and eaten lunch at his brother's. He repeated what Sra. Vázquez had told me about the damage Hugo had done to his home. His roof had come off, his balcony was partially destroyed, and the three shacks were blown away. A couple of zinc panels propped against the house are all that is left of the shacks; he plans to rebuild one. The rain, he added, ruined his bed and his clothes.

Though Rosa agreed that Hugo was a short storm, passing through in an hour and a half, he felt it was stronger than Ciprian. The river didn't rise as much as it had with Ciprian, true, but the wind was strong. Statistics prove him correct: sustained winds in the forest were clocked at over 135 miles per hour, making Hugo a category four hurricane, but only some 13.6 inches of rain fell in the mountains over three days. Leaves had been ripped from trees, he told me, trunks and branches were broken, much of the planted mahogany was damaged. He touched his hands together in an upside-down v-shape to show what the mahogany looked like after the storm. The winds left his banana plants "ironed" flat to the ground, and his rose apple tree "bald". Not a tiny plant was left. There was no electricity nor water for a month; water was trucked in from the center of the island. He was still amazed that the western half of Puerto Rico had barely suffered from Hugo. As we spoke, he jumped up from time to time to spread seed for a bird or to throw bread to a pair of small iguanas.

Sra. Vázquez mentioned and Rosa elaborated on how he had survived the hurricane. He stubbornly refused his brothers' invitations to stay in either of their concrete homes in Sabana, choosing instead to remain in a small concrete bathroom that had been built between the stilts below his house. He dragged an armchair into the room and locked the door. Sitting in the chair, he waited out the hurricane in the dark. Noises swirled around him outside, and the water came up to his knees, but he just sat and chuckled to himself from time to time.

❧ The Bisley Watershed Project, near Sabana in the northeastern part of the forest, faced the eye of Hurricane Hugo. A half year before Hugo hit, project coordinator Fred Scatena had shown me the Bisley site. A year and a half after it hit, he brought me up to date on what happened. During the hurricane, the tower, with its rain gauges and other climatic-collecting equipment, was knocked to the ground. Of six rain gauges connected to the project, only one was functioning by the end of the storm. The boxes and concrete weirs along the streams survived, as did most of the contraptions that were on ground level. The road, strewn with mud and debris, had to be reopened. This was not the only road to suffer from Hugo. Some of more than 200 forest landslides caused by the hurricane tore up parts of the main road through the mountains; that and damage to buildings and picnic areas kept the national forest shut to the public for almost half a year. In addition, study plots had to be relocated and remeasured. All plots survived, but they were drastically changed. Some lost all their vegetation to the landslides. Fortuitously, several months before Hugo two small plotted areas had been clear-cut (all the trees felled). Now scientists can compare their regrowth with that of the hurricane-leveled plots. Congress awarded the Institute of Tropical Forestry $1.7 million, not only to rebuild structures but also to conduct a major survey

*The recovering
forest:
red hibiscus.*

Fungi.

of the hurricane-damaged forest, to look at species, including endangered bats, and to compile a history of the site's flood plain. The original basis of the Long Term Ecological Research component of the Bisley project was to look at disturbances, both natural and manmade. Before Hugo struck, researchers were using the clear-cut plots to study the effects of a manmade disturbance. Hugo gave them an incredible natural disturbance to study, and the LTER project has been altered and expanded to focus primarily on the effects of a hurricane on the forest community.

As for environmental changes, Hugo ripped off all the leaves in the Bisley area, knocked down many trees and cleared the undercanopy. One and a half years' worth of leaf litter fell in a day, and the fresh material began to decompose. The sun was able to reach the forest floor, and the floor became much like the upper canopy in its solar exposure. Temperatures rose and humidity fell. These climatic changes would in turn affect the types of vegetation that could tolerate the new conditions.

The forest then started to rebuild, a process that will go on for some time. The big surprise to scientists is just how quickly the forest responded. After Hugo everything was brown; a year and a half later it was green again. "It's amazing the amount of herbaceous material out there," Scatena told me. Herbs — plants to the layperson — usually play a minor role in the shadowy world of tropical rain forests. But the increased sunlight after Hugo has produced a great increase in light-hungry plants, and they are being studied intensely. Since Hugo, the composition of the herbal community has changed several times. In addition, pioneering tree species like Cecropia, locally known as yagrumo, have

become common, and the number of certain animals such as coquís, local tree frogs, has actually increased. Decomposers like fungi and ants have embarked on an ambitious new cycle of work. Life goes on.

One sunny December day, when tropical storms were the last thing on people's minds, I interviewed research forester Peter Weaver at his office in the two-story Forest Service building, located in a botanical garden in San Juan's Río Piedras area.

Set on a hill, the building is surrounded by several splendid large trees that help keep the hallways cool even on the hottest summer days. Its red tile roof and ornamentation give it a Spanish colonial look, and it has a spacious quality characteristic of older constructions. Weaver and I sat on opposite sides of a large wooden desk in a corner room on the second floor. Part of the institute staff for 20 years, Weaver studied the effects of hurricanes on the Luquillo forest as part of his doctoral dissertation, and Scatena thought he would be a good person to talk to about the local storms.

During our conversations, Weaver mentioned his Uncle George, a part-time junk collector a.k.a. antique dealer. Uncle George is apparently skeptical of Weaver's long-term, in-depth interest in hurricanes. In Uncle George's opinion, "most anyone knows what a hurricane does, it knocks over trees." Weaver doesn't seem to mind his uncle's irreverence, but, he pointed out, the damage is in fact a bit more complicated. First, not all hurricanes are alike. The intensity of a storm, its duration, and the frequency with which hurricanes strike a region affect the final outcome on the forest community. For example, two major storms in short order, as happened to Luquillo in 1766 and 1772, would have much greater cumulative effects on the forest than two hurricanes a century apart.

"Then the forests themselves differ. On the bottom slopes, trees are bigger in the valleys, their crowns are bigger, they get better nutrients. They resist winds, so more trees fall." The soggy soils of valleys also play a part in the likelihood of their falling. "On the ridges, tabonuco trees have intertwined roots and can tolerate the winds better, so they might suffer breakage instead." Tabonucos, the dominant trees in the original forests along the lower slopes, seem to have adapted to hurricanes over the millenniums. In addition to their intertwined roots, Weaver mentioned a study by Howard Odum showing that these trees have developed smaller crowns — the tropical average of units of crown to units of trunk is 22 to 1; in tabonucos it is 17 to 1 — which may help prevent major damage. "As you go up higher, in the palo colorado forest," Weaver continued, "more breakage is done in the valleys, where trees like palms are of a lighter wood. Ridge species have a denser wood," so they are more likely to fall. "On the summits, dwarf forests have developed hardened woods and small crowns which seem to resist hurricanes." This is fortunate, for dwarf forest regenerates very slowly, remaining in the ferns and grasses stage long after other parts of a damaged forest are growing pioneer trees.

When Frank Wadsworth set up study plots in the forest in 1946, he was actually measuring the composition of the forest more than a decade after a major hurricane, San Ciprian, hit in 1932. Fifty years after San Ciprian, Weaver studied the changes on the same plots established by Wadsworth. He found that once-numerous pioneer species like the ubiquitous Cecropia are now almost gone, and there is a dominance of primary trees, the species common to full-grown natural forests. All the changes in the tree community — the shifts in distribution of diameter, height, crown and specific gravity classes — are consistent with the steady trend of a recovering forest. With Hugo, scientists are now able to complete the cycle Wadsworth began in 1946 by studying the first decade of hurricane recovery.

After he completes several other projects, Weaver will turn to the effects of Hugo. "What I'd really like to do," he mentioned at a second interview, "is to sit with a map of the forest, an elevated map," he crumpled a piece of paper to give me the idea, "and look at what happened to every bit of the forest after Hugo, noting the major damage with regards to slope, windward and leeward side, size and species of trees." He felt the damage to the forest had been spotty, with the most noticeable damage occurring in the northeast section, but

HURRICANE HUGO

cautioned that he had no systematic data to back up what he was saying. One cause for spotty damage could be tornadolike gusts of wind which occur during a hurricane.

Several aspects of the hurricane intriqued him. In the hardest-hit places in the dwarf forest, the trees had been cleaned of their leaves and epiphytes. "Hugo was like a vacumn cleaner", sucking off all manner of bromeliads, mosses and liverworts. He visited his dwarf forest study sites a year and four months after Hugo. The epiphytes were back but not as abundant as prior to Hugo. The leaves had also returned, though many of the highest twigs remained bare. He planned to return again three years and four months after Hugo to identify those epiphytes which have come back and to note those which haven't. He mentioned that *Clusia clusioides*, a strangler fig common to the dwarf forest, suffered greatly, while he imagined — again, he cautioned he had no data — the common sierra palms and Cecropia probably survived better. This, he guessed, was because the palm and Cecropia shed their leaves easily, greatly decreasing their resistance to the wind, while the leathery Clusia leaves hung on for dear life, increasing the chances that the tree would topple.

Yet Weaver bet that many of the uprooted trees, in particular the roble of the dwarf forest, would survive. "The lower part will die, but the aerial roots will anchor in soil, and the trunk will curve upward." He bent his arm to show me. Weaver called these "walking trees", and he envisioned them moving ever so slowly from one microsite to another in the forest — toppling, sending down aerial roots and gaining another five feet every sixty years or so when a hurricane hit. It is a nice image of a forest surviving a disaster. Weaver doubted

any forest species became extinct after Hugo, though he admitted all were affected.

El Yunque will probably become the most studied hurricane-ravaged forest, certainly within the tropics. A day after Hugo hit, scientists and foresters began to stalk the forest, searching for endangered Puerto Rican parrots, coquí frogs, rare plants, endemic trees. Scientific articles not yet published were taken back and revised to include data on the hurricane. Students studying in Luquillo at the time suddenly found themselves with greatly expanded projects; one student, from Nepal, worked out some of the ways tabonuco trees in Bisley react to hurricanes. A biometrician began remeasuring forest plots to assess Hugo's damage. The December 1991 issue of the magazine *Biotropica* was devoted to Carribean hurricanes, and of the 30 articles involved, more than half described Hugo and the Luquillo forest. Published by the Association for Tropical Biology, *Biotropica*, a scientific quarterly, is considered among the best of the tropical biology journals; the hurricane issue, institute director Ariel Lugo told me later, became a bestseller, especially after Hurricane Andrew hit Florida. Its Luquillo articles focused on ecosystems (such as light systems, nutrient cycling, root mortality and the modeling of hurricane effects on soil to predict for future hurricanes), on plants (the damage and recovery of trees and seedlings) and on animals (the damage and recovery of invertebrates, frogs, birds and stream animals).

One of the most striking entries in the magazine is a series of photographs taken at exactly the same place in the Bisley watershed, at zero, eight and 17 months after the hurricane. The first photograph shows a tangle of gray trunks and branches, completely devoid

*Visitors
returning to
the forest,
Palo Colorado
Picnic Area.*

of leaves. In the second photograph, new leaves have covered all but the largest trunks. In the third, the addition of ferns and paddle-shaped heliconia leaves and young Cecropia trees give the site a convincingly primeval look. No one looking at the third photograph would imagine the devastation had been so recent and so great.

Laurence Walker, guest editor for the *Biotropica* hurricane issue, was working at the University of Puerto Rico at the time. He concurred when I asked him if this would be the largest collection of articles related to the effects of a specific hurricane on a specific site. What is so special about Luquillo, he added, is that there is so much detailed information about the forest, before and after Hugo, with which scientists can work.

On my first visit with Weaver, I asked about the benefits, the silver lining, of hurricanes on a forest. Most notably, Weaver explained, storms make niches, through land-slides or fallen trees, for light-hungry secondary or pioneer tree species to persist, resulting in greater tree diversity within the forest. When I asked about the most damaging aspect, he thought for a bit, then said, "I guess I have trouble with the question." He could name problems for humans — landslides across roads, soil erosion, clogged reservoirs — and he could imagine the effect on the animal community, especially animals living in rivers, though he hadn't studied that aspect. He reviewed what can happen during a hurricane —defoliation; breakage; uprooting; land-slides; flooding of trees. Most people who visited the forest shortly after Hugo were emotionally saddened by the damage, grieving as one grieves a lost friend. But for Weaver and other scientists I spoke with, these occurrences weren't damages as much as a series of factors trees grow up with and adjust to, a 60-year cycle, a part of life in the tropical rain forest.

CHAPTER 5
GOLD IN THE HILLS

The year 1515 marked the first recorded mention of a hurricane on the settlement at Caparra, Spain's original colony in Puerto Rico, established on the north coast in 1508. The hurricane caused the death of many Indians and undoubtedly didn't improve the Spanish settlers' feelings for the site. Though set on potentially good farmland on the western side of a large bay, Caparra could only be reached by way of a mile-long path inland through mosquito-infested mangrove swamp. Less than a decade later, the settlers overrode the objections of their first leader, Juan Ponce de León, and moved to a breezy narrow islet north of the bay. They called the new settlement Puerto Rico for its rich port and the island San Juan de Bautista in honor of St. John the Baptist; in writings centuries later, the names had strangely and irrevocably become switched. When the settlers weren't involved in skirmishes with Indians or enemy Europeans or in the basic farming necessary to survive, they devoted much of their time to their primary endeavor, that of hunting for gold. And some of the most lucrative gold mining was being done in the Luquillo Mountains.

We can imagine the sort who would sail to the New World in search of gold — a man lured by promises of a better life, by tales of great riches, by thoughts of adventures in a strange land. If he reached Puerto Rico in 1515, our miner might have headed for the settlement of Santiago de Daguao between the southeastern slopes of the Luquillo Mountains and the coast. Daguao was the name of an Indian chieftain who lived in the region. Diego Colón, legitimate son of Columbus, founded Daguao with some 50 colonists from his settlement in Hispaniola (today's Dominican Republic). Colón wanted to take advantage of the fertile soil and rich mineral deposits in the region, to establish a port on the eastern side of the island, and, less nobly, to wrest control of Puerto Rico from Ponce de León. Our miner wouldn't have enjoyed Daguao for very long. The location of this settlement at the edge of rebellious Taino Indian strongholds and in the path of Carib Indian war canoes was precarious at best. Before the settlers could build much more than a fort or even start mining the gold, Indians attacked Daguao, killing or capturing those unable to escape, reducing its few buildings to ashes, destroying livestock and leveling the fledgling farms. We will assume our miner escaped.

Rumors began to circulate that gold was more prevalent on the northern side of the mountains, and our miner may have joined a new settlement on the farm of one Crístobal Guzmán along today's Río Mameyes, in the general area of the Bisley Watershed Project.

Guzmán was a member of the island's small, wealthy upper class, University of Puerto Rico history professor Jalil Sued Badillo informed me. Guzmán had a home in the capital, where he was active in local politics, and his farm in the Luquillo Mountains. He received numerous Tainos as part of the first "repartimiento" (apportionment), in which the natives were distributed among the well-to-do to help with farming and mining. A few of the island's enslaved Indians rose up, but many more just seemed to give up and die. In 1513 African slaves became legal in Puerto Rico, and they were also conscripted into the hunt for gold. One of the early names for El Yunque Peak, Furidi, came from the Africans. It meant "place that is always covered with clouds". The current name, which means "anvil" in Spanish, probably refers to the peak's shape but may also suggest the early residents' preoccupation with metals.

Sued Badillo researched mining in sixteenth-century Puerto Rico for his doctoral dissertation. I originally spoke to him about Taino Indians in the Luquillo Mountains, but as we spoke, we took several interesting detours into the mining period. Sued Badillo likens early island mining to that of the forty-niners. "There were all sorts of miners in the Luquillo Mountains. Some were in highly organized groups, others were independent, similar to the various types you found in the California gold rush. The difference was that in Puerto Rico there were encomiendas [royal grants which gave entire native villages, inhabitants included, to Spanish colonists], which used slaves as a labor force." He visualized a typical placer site. Authorities would come in and divide up the site, designating who got what. Then the miners, or slaves, would build crude huts as well as sheds for

animals, especially hogs, and shacks to store cassava bread. Small outlying farms supplied food, which was often in short supply. Most Spanish settlers borrowed heavily from the Taino culture. Cassava bread, a Taino staple, came from tubers known locally as yuca, and the crude huts were patterned after the Indians' thatched bohíos. Settlers slept in hammocks, ate out of gourds, and, when pork was low, used Taino methods to catch fish and small forest animals. If the mining proved worthwhile, the miners would improve the facilities, but neither the settlement at Guzmán, as Cristóbal Guzmán's farm came to be known, nor any other Luquillo settlement ever reached the dimensions of a town.

Most activity in the settlements revolved around finding gold. In the morning our miner would work his way up the mountain streams. There was no mother lode, no gargantuan nuggets; the largest piece of gold ever recorded in the Luquillo Mountains, along the Río Fajardo, weighed in at four ounces. Instead, very thin veins produced flakes or dustings. Early washings along the upper Mameyes yielded four grams of gold, a measly seventh of an ounce, per ton of material. Yet that was enough for the miners, who sifted through layers of sandy clay on hillsides or panned the sediments in the river beds, where most gold was found. Pieces of the sinuous buttress roots of Pterocarpus trees growing in mountain swamps made serviceable pans. The best time for panning was during or after a shower, when the rain agitated the soil. Gold near the mouth of a river tended to be fine while larger pieces were found near the headwaters; consequently, miners continually headed upriver, hewing out many of the mountains' first paths as they went. In the evening, when darkness hid any glinting flecks, our miner would return to camp. After a bath in the local stream and a spartan dinner, he might settle down to a few swigs of roughly distilled rum, if there was any, and a game of cards using leathery cupey (*Clusia rosea*) leaves that had been marked with a pin. Other miners were too tired to do more than sleep, trying to tune out the cacophony of crickets, frogs and sundry wildlife. The truly obsessed would examine and reexamine their day's findings.

The Guzmán settlement met the same fate as Daguao. In 1530 some 500 Caribs traveling in 11 long canoes landed near Daguao and made their way over to Guzmán. The Caribs were, like the Tainos, of Arawakan descent. An aggressive people, they had come to dominate the Lesser Antilles islands to the south and were making forays into the Greater Antilles when the Spaniards first reached the New World. Agustín Iñigo Abbad, a spunky Benedictine friar who traveled throughout the island in the 1770s and wrote Puerto Rico's first comprehensive history, would tell what happened when the Caribs reached Guzmán. Under orders from the chieftain Jaureyvo, the Caribs destroyed the farm, burned huts, confiscated livestock, slaughtered hunting dogs, attacked the miners and killed or captured some 30 Spaniards, including Guzmán himself, and any Indian or Negro slaves they could round up. The island was frantic. Local leaders asked the settlement at Hispaniola for help, but none came. Guzmán's wife, who, according to Iñigo Abbad, had money and loved her husband, took matters into her own hands. She outfitted an expedition of five ships to sail to the island of Dominica, Jaureyvo's stronghold, and punish the Caribs. The Spaniards stole onto Dominica in the dead of night, attacking the Caribs with such rage that many were killed. Others were captured and re-

turned to Puerto Rico along with the survivors of the Guzmán attack. (Undoubtedly, our miner was one of the survivors.) Guzmán himself, as it turned out, had been killed the same day of the attack, on the island of Virgin Gorda, "where Jaureyvo," Iñigo Abbad wrote, "seeing that he [Guzmán] was badly wounded from the arrows he had received in the fray and that he wouldn't be suitable for the dining table since he was poisoned, cut short his life with a few blows from his macana [wooden swordlike weapon] and left him on the beach, where, even though Guzmán's slaves wanted to give him a proper burial, the chief wouldn't permit it, mistreating any who tried."

Sued Badillo, ever the debunker, doubts the slaves truly wanted to bury their master, attributing the statement to a chronicler's "flowering" pen (Iñigo Abbad had gotten the information from one Juan Castellanos). He also feels it was the upper class in San Juan who organized the expedition, not Guzmán's wife, and he believes the primary reason for the trip was to round up and bring back a new batch of slaves.

Guzmán wasn't the only settler in the Luquillo Mountains to fall victim to poison arrows: around the same time, a young farmer, Sebastián Alonso, went to the aid of a neighbor being held captive by Caribs. Though he apparently freed the neighbor and his slaves and killed a fair share of Caribs, Alonso was mortally wounded, leaving — here history seems to suffer again from a flowering pen — everything he had to the poor.

At the end of the 1530s, our miner had to do some soul searching about his future. Things weren't going so well. Seven hurricanes had devastated the island during the decade, two in 1530 alone; one of them had apparently prompted the hungry Caribs to attack

*Author
witth
Ramón Alonso
at the Río
de la Mina
gold mine.*

Author
and Bienva Bauer
crossing
Rio de La Mina.

Bienva
modeling
in front of
the gold mine.

Guzmán. Each time the storm came, settlements were destroyed, crops were razed and mining sites were flooded by the swollen streams and rivers. Though there was gold in the hills — 1,200,000 ounces had been mined in Puerto Rico during the first 30 years of Spanish occupation, which would fetch some $420 million at today's prices — the easiest pickings had by then been taken. Any rich deposits that were left were now found only in rougher terrain, and they demanded more effort, or more hands, to produce any kind of profit. Gold entrepreneurs couldn't get enough hands to help them: Taino slaves were dying or fleeing, and most Africans were being used in farming, which the government decided held more potential. Bases in the Luquillo Mountains were in constant danger of attack. The Caribs continued their assaults from the east, and escaped slaves hiding in the mountains made periodic strikes. French pirates attacked the nearby coast. Disease further reduced numbers. To add insult to already extensive injury, miners heard fantastic rumors of vast gold and silver deposits being found in Mexico and Peru. Those who left Puerto Rico, though, did so at risk. Spain needed to keep the island populated in order to safeguard it against enemy powers, so the colonial government adopted a number of strict measures, such as lopping off the feet of captured would-be emigrants, to discourage mass exodus.

Mining in the Luquillo Mountains had peaked by 1539, and gold panners began to turn their attention to other occupations. Jhoan Melgarejo reported in 1582 that attacking Caribs had left the mountains virtually uninhabited, with the exception of one brave family (headed by our miner, I would like to think) in the Mameyes valley. Their house had been burned two or three times, but they apparently stayed. Eventually, though, all that remained from the early mining period were several place names, such as Guzmán, which to this day refer to local neighborhoods.

It is 10:20 a.m. on a March day. Forester Jerry Bauer, geologist Ramón Alonso and his two sons, a young woman named Bienva who is visiting from the Dominican Republic and I stand in the heart of the old gold-mining country. We have reached the fork of a small stream, Quebrada Juan Diego, and a small river, Río de la Mina. The route that got us here is somewhat optimistically termed a path but differs little from any number of leaf-cluttered rivulets snaking through the forest. We slipped and slid downhill through forest of slender trees and sierra palms and occasional jagua fruits rotting on the ground. Ramón Alonso, who works with the island's Department of Natural Resources and is leading this part of the expedition, is surprised we didn't come out farther upriver along La Mina.

Above the fork, the waters of both Juan Diego and La Mina are shallow and some eight feet wide, cluttered with moss-green rocks, bordered by clusters of pink impatiens, and walled in by 60-foot-high tapestries of forest. At the fork, Juan Diego merges into La Mina, which immediately widens to 15 feet. Slightly less than half a mile downriver La Mina pours into the larger Río Mameyes. We cross to the far side of La Mina, unceremoniously sloshing through water up to our lower calves. Hikers from the keep-boots-dry-at-all-costs school would not approve, but with the dripping plants, water-saturated soil, periodic downpours and greaselike growths on rocks, boots are not likely to remain dry in a rain forest, no matter what one does. Hikers from that same school might also be perplexed to see us wear long pants and long-sleeved shirts in such hot and muggy weather, but they protect against insects and poisonous plants that take cover in the vegetative stew.

Alonso scoops a handful of dirt out of the river. "It's not dirt," he admonishes when I use the word. "Dirt is a dirty word. Not even farmers like to hear it called dirt, and no geologist will use that word. Use gravel." The gravel glitters, but the specks are fool's gold. Alonso and his two teenage sons head off to find a century-old mining tunnel we have come to inspect. Jerry Bauer sets up a tripod. An avid photographer as well as a forester, he has taken thousands of photographs of the forest. Bienva acts as a model. "You gotta have people in the picture," he explains. He is right, of course. The green of a rain forest can make for monotonous photographs. Yet there is something more to this, for eventually he and Bienva marry.

Following a path that is at best sensed, we soon join the others at the tunnel. A jagged, blackened arch softened by hanging ferns marks the entrance. Mud deposits raise the floor at the entrance to five feet below the roof. Beyond, the manmade cave is 12 feet high and eight feet wide. Shaped roughly like a wind sock, it angles to the right for about 60 feet, then narrows and rises another 15 feet, again to the right, before it terminates. When we step in, bats that were clinging to the unevenly cut ceiling wiggle nervously under the glare of a flashlight. Some swoop out; a few, apparently deciding sunlight is the greater of two evils, swoop back in.

While having lunch at the tunnel entrance, we pump Alonso for his theory on how the tunnel was formed. He imagines that nineteenth-century miners — this was three centuries after the early mining ventures — were making their way up the river in search of quartz veins, which tend to contain gold. Quartz and other mineral formations are most easily found in the exposed rocks along riverbeds. So the miners would study the banks, looking for pale quartz against the gray granite and dark volcanic rock common to the area. When the creators of the tunnel spotted the quartz vein behind us, they began to dig. Most likely they facilitated their work with the use of nitrate, the black powder that was stuffed into muskets and rifles before bullets were invented. The miners would put the powder into a canister, light the fuse and run as fast as they could in the opposite direction. In that way they hollowed the cave, following the vein until it didn't seem worth going any farther.

While Alonso talks, his sons, Ricardo and Ramón, Jr., stand in the shallow pool, panning for gold. They use equipment ordered by mail from a stateside company — one black plastic frisbee-shaped plate, about 14 inches in diameter, with an indented center, semi-circular grooves on one side and two grooves forming a "Y" shape on the other; a metal shovel, similar to those found in sandboxes; an octagonal sieve with one-quarter-inch squares of mesh. With the shovel, they dig up gravel from the river bed and pour it into the sieve. The heavier pieces are quickly checked and discarded. Then they toss the remainder into the plate, swirling it in circular motions until all the water and some of the sand is gone, when they add more water and repeat the process. The lighter particles, including pyrite (fool's gold), will fall out, and the gold, which is heavier, will stay in the grooves or the central cavity. Magnetite, a heavy mineral, will also remain in the pan, but its dark color is easily distinguished from the blond gold. The teenagers work sheepishly, torn between vestiges of boyish enthusiasm and the stirrings of adult cynicism. This is the second time they are trying their luck, but they have yet to find anything. Alonso reminds us that we won't find nuggets; the gold will be fine dust or flakes in the soil. After repeated siftings, the remaining material should be analyzed in a lab; he admits he still has material from the last venture that hasn't been analyzed.

It is 1:20 p.m., and drizzling. We fold up our yard-square official Caribbean National Forest map. According to the map, a little-known trail, which we have dubbed Lower La Mina Trail, parallels La Mina upstream from the Bisley Trail. Bisley is an old mining and lumber route that connects the heart of mining country at the fork of La Mina and the Mameyes rivers with the northern edge of the forest; we have come in from the southwest. The map shows Lower La Mina Trail bordering the eastern side of Río de la Mina and the western edge of a natural area called Baño de Oro up to La Mina Falls; at that point a popular paved walkway follows the upper La Mina to the forest's main picnic area. Our plan is to locate the trail and take it up to the falls, making a large loop as we return to Road 191. Bauer tried to find the trail once before, without success. Alonso and his sons decline our invitation to come along. He's been that route, Alonso says, and won't do it again, not for all the gold in El Yunque, or words to that effect.

Greenery is draped everywhere here. Bauer, Bienva and I see magnificent banana plants along a ravine near the mine, but no sign of a trail. Sawtooth-shaped hills angle to the river on the side where the trail is supposed to be. We climb one hill while paralleling the river. The terrain is not hospitable. Slick, steep ground necessitates the use of roots and saplings as handholds, but the most

commonly available handhold is a pretty tree fern equipped with sharp spines on its trunk. Sandflylike majes, partial to damp close environments, make the most of the arrival of human flesh. Nettlelike ortiga leaves, resembling spiked armor shields, discharge an unpleasant poison onto the unsuspecting hand that touches them. Vines trip us, and, in patches of sunlight, dense clusters of ferns hug at our thighs. So much for the romance of panning for gold.

The hill we have climbed soon overhangs the river, and we crawl onto a square rain-slick rock piled on top of others, forming what looks like a 30-foot-high set of building blocks. At the far end of the blocks, the river plunges down a narrow chute; above the blocks, a squat fall tumbles over horizontal slabs of rock into an almost perfectly rectangular pool, ten by 20 feet in size. Ferns grow from cracks in the slabs, vines dangle from trees, and the trees form a 60-foot-high amphitheater behind the pool. Rays of cloudy tropical light warm the rocks; the water is refreshingly cool. This scene, resembling a *House and Garden* art deco nook, would overwhelm someone who usually hikes in regions of desert or cold; for us, it is merely one of dozens of pools and waterfalls we see along the way and a clear example of why we can't use the river to reach our destination.

The drizzle turns to rain, and the landscape takes on a blurred quality. Dark glistening trunks and tawny-colored mud replace much of the earlier green. For the next couple of hours we take no notice of our exotic surroundings, putting all our efforts into getting to La Mina Falls. We hoist ourselves up and down sawtooth hills until we rebel against such a roller coaster route. We try our luck on a yard-wide ridge, which soon takes us too far from the river. We decide to throw ourselves onto the mercy of the river itself, but our scramble towards it dead-ends at the edge of a 30-foot precipice, forcing us to return to the ridge up an almost vertical slope, with flimsy ferns as our only handholds. The ground feels like carpet being pulled out from under us. (Later, when we view our route from Yokahú Observation Tower, it will become apparent we stepped onto an old landslide.) We go back to hoisting ourselves up and down hills. Rain continually drips from fingers, chins, ponchos. Glimpses of the river appear 50 feet below us, 100 feet below, 35, 70. The umpteenth hill leads to a basin next to the river, and we slide down to a good-sized pool and a 50-foot bi-level waterfall. Upriver, a narrow path approaches the pool, and Bauer realizes we are only ten minutes from La Mina Falls. Downriver, the umpteenth hill overhangs the river. Good-sized trees top it, proof that the hill formed long ago. We have absolutely no idea where Lower La Mina Trail is, and at this point, some four hours after we left Alonso and his sons to travel approximately one-half mile, we don't much care.

Later, on one of those hot tropical nights when one doesn't have the energy to do more than vacantly peruse old magazines or the already-read morning paper, I will solve the mystery of Lower La Mina Trail, or so I think at the time. On the forest map, evenly spaced slashes show trails and unevenly spaced slashes show boundaries. The map maker, spotting the short trail downriver from La Mina Falls, the boundary for the Baño de Oro Natural Area, and the short trail leading upriver from Bisley Trail, undoubtedly got things confused, putting a trail mark where there should have been a boundary line, and incurring the wrath of hikers ever since. I con-gratulate myself on my deduction. However, much later, when talking with former forest supervisor Frank Wadsworth about various aspects of the national forest, I will learn there actually was a trail along the lower La Mina. The Forest Service is currently working on opening it up again, as a primitive trail; however, I, for one, will wait until officials cut the ribbon before I strike out on it.

In its century-long lifetime, the tunnel we visited along Río de la Mina has seen its name change from the specific to the general: originally called Monserrate, it became known as the Old Spanish Mine some time after the United States took over the island; now it is merely referred to as La Mina, along with one river, one peak and at least one other tunnel in the forest. Though the mine was apparently first shaped and worked in the early 1800s, the Quevedo and Hess Company registered a claim for the site in 1891. The claim asked for 12 hectares (one hectare equals 2.5 acres) in a 650-by-2,000 foot rectangular zone to recover alluvial gold. The tunnel was apparently never worked, and the site was abandoned in less than two years. After our expedition, Alonso showed me a 1941 Bureau of Mines report that had this to say about the mine: "It follows a seam of white gouge [a thin layer of puttylike rock next to a vein] containing sulfides of iron, and near the portal it cuts diagonally across a ledge of bluish quartz, which, as near as could be judged without extensive cleaning of the walls, is ten or 12 feet wide. This ledge is liberally sprinkled with fine grains of iron sulphide. A sample was taken from the gouge seam where it was three inches thick and contained considerable sulphide and was assayed. The assay failed to show any gold." Most likely, the original miners came to the same disappointing conclusions.

The Quevado and Hess operation was just one of a flurry of nineteenth and early twentieth century mining ventures. During the previous two centuries, the Luquillo Mountains had been abandoned by all but an occasional lone miner or runaway slave. A similar state of neglect had extended over the entire island: during one particularly bad period in the seventeenth century, not one official Spanish ship stopped in Puerto Rico for 11 years. Inhabitants were few and poor for the most part. Only the military fortresses in San Juan, essential for maintaining the island as a strategic military outpost, were receiving much attention. "The enchanted island", as Puerto Rico is now nicknamed, was passing through a centuries-long slumber.

By the early 1800s Spain had lost most of its New World empire and the wealth that had gone along with it. The government looked to Puerto Rico, one of its few remaining possessions, for new ways to refill its coffers. For a start, the island needed to be developed. In 1815, a royal decree, titled the Real Cédula de Gracias, took steps to promote commerce, industry and agriculture and to encourage the immigration of Roman Catholic subjects from friendly nations. Drawn by the decree's promise of free land, settlers came from such politically unstable regions as Haiti, the Canary Islands, Corsica and Venezuela. Large tracts of forest were cleared for agriculture, primarily for the "after-dinner" crops of sugar, coffee and tobacco. Many other enterprising ventures sprang up around the island, and, perhaps inevitably, miners took another look at the Luquillo Mountains.

In 1832, Manuel Martínez discovered ore on his property, north of one of the forks of the Río Mameyes at the base of the mountains. He had the ore assayed in Spain; it was found

to contain lead and silver as well as gold. In 1837, he began the first large-scale mining operation in the Luquillo region since the early 1500s and the first serious attempt to mine metals other than gold. By 1841, when ill health forced him to stop his operations, he had extracted some 3,000 tons of ore. According to local reports, the mine had the potential to retrieve up to 2,000 pounds of lead, 16 pounds of silver and one pound, three ounces of gold in one day. With the help of a business associate, Martínez set up subscription centers in Puerto Rico, St. Thomas and Cuba to raise funds for slaves and for a mining engineer from Europe so that he could continue his work. By 1843, the funds were raised, but the records do not say whether or not operations began again.

Geologist Walter Cardona searched through local historical documents for records of colonial mining operations in the Luquillo Mountains, unearthing the Martínez claim, the Quevedo and Hess claim for the tunnel we visited, and 21 others taken out between 1832 and 1903. Many claimants dubbed their sites with the names of Catholic saints — San Narciso, Santa Amalia, Santa Teresa and Monserrate. A few of the choicer sites had several names and several claimants: Santa Amalia Mine, for example, started out as Abundancia, but pessimism soon replaced optimism and the site was renamed Perseverancia. In a similar vein, one of the claims bordered a stream which someone unsportingly named Engaño (deception). After the Spanish American War in 1898, several sites — America Mine, Union Mine — alluded to the island's new allegiance.

Most gold mining ventures of the 1800s occurred along the Río Mameyes. One of the most lucrative, run by Betamón and Company, tapped alluvial deposits along the lower section of the river. For several decades in the second half of the century, local workers, slaves and prisoners from San Juan, totaling up to 100 men at any one time, were said to have extracted from one to two pounds of gold a day. In 1879, Puerto Rico's chief mining engineer, a man by the name of A. Vasconi, described this operation: "The soils destined to be washed were conducted by an inclined rail to the opposite edge of the Mameyes, where the washing apparatuses were established, fed by the water of this river, and derived by means of a channel."

Unfortunately, few claims met with such success. Only five of the claims which Cardona described are known to have been worked. Several were revoked because the required fee was never paid. Most claimants seem to have gained little more for themselves than an entry in the general archives, and today we can only ponder the people behind the names — Luis Miner, Lino Ynstander, Carlos Bernstein, Rachel Sayre.

The name Rachel Sayre intrigued me, as she seems to have been the only woman from off the island who, heeding the call of adventure, came and filed a claim in Luquillo. Cardona wrote that she put in a request to search for gold and other metals at the Reina Cristina mine in 1902, four years after Puerto Rico was ceded to the U.S. The site was surveyed and apparently worked. Curious to know

more about her, I went to Puerto Rico's General Archives and requested a box containing a number of mining claims that are now brittle with age. Most of the the papers were of a "to whom it may concern" legal nature, replete with boundary lines and the like, but I was able to find out a few details about this Rachel Sayre. She was a resident of New York City. Her paperwork was done by an attorney, Henry D. Sayre, whom I imagine was her father. He was apparently one of those who came down from the United States to see what could be done on this newly acquired island in the sun, keeping residences on West 87th Street in New York as well as in Corozal, a mountain town west of San Juan, and processing mining claims for several people. Sayre also filed a claim to mine in Corozal, another gold-rich region, around the same time she was supposed to be mining in Luquillo. Oddly enough, there was nothing in the claims personally written by Sayre herself. I suddenly had a disappointing intuition: the intriguing Rachel Sayre may never have left her Upper West Side environs; she may merely have let her father use her name on a business deal. When I was discussing this with Jeff Walker, current forest archaeologist, he suggested with somewhat less cynicism that perhaps the father gave his daughter the mine as a gift. We will probably never know.

A handful of the claimants are recognizable as figures in Puerto Rico's turn-of-the-century

RIO ICACOS GOLD PANNING

history. Santiago R. Palmer was a local farmer and the presumed co-namesake of a small community known as both Palmer and Mameyes. Palmer dug a trench during what was probably an adventurous mood in 1890 but never worked it and abandoned his claim a decade later. Catalina R. de Palmer, whom I assume to be his wife, took out a claim in 1902 but never even paid the required fee. R.A. Macfie was an American farmer in the Sabana area who repeated Mrs. Palmer's efforts, or lack of them. Miguel Porrata Doria, who took out a claim in 1891 to mine copper near the headwaters of the Río Blanco on the southside of the mountains, is better known, to me at least, for his guano operation on Mona Island. Located halfway between Puerto Rico and the Dominican Republic, Mona has a number of caves which, in the late 1800s, were rich in guano (phosphate-rich bat manure, used as fertilizer). Though successful, the Mona operation was marred by workers who ran away, a manager who drowned at sea during a storm, and a farmer who was poisoned by liquor intended for a ship captain. The results of Porrata's copper mining venture in Luquillo are unknown.

Porrata was one of several people to take out claims for copper mining in the region of the Río Blanco headwaters. While gold dominated the mining on the northern slopes, the southern slopes yielded the finest grade of copper ore in Puerto Rico, found primarily in small veins of chalcopyrite. Samples of copper carbonates (averaging no less than 23 percent copper) and copper sulfate (averaging 38 percent) from Río Blanco were displayed at the 1882 Ponce Exposition Fair on the south coast. Three years earlier, 170 tons of copper ore were shipped to Marseilles, France, from the east-coast Naguabo port. Two mines, Santa Amalia and Santa Teresa, were heavily exploited. Vasconi described some of the difficulties the workers experienced at those mines: "In spite of the short distance from the mine to the port of Naguabo (some 14 kilometers), the transportation of the minerals is expensive (eight pesos ton) due to the lack of a regular means of conduction. From the mine to the plain, the mineral was conducted on the shoulders of the workers, in baskets containing a quintal [100 pounds] and later transported through the plain in carts to the port of Naguabo..."

Vasconi's description doesn't go far enough in explaining the workers' hardships. I visited one of those mines. Now called La Mina de Cobre (copper mine), it is either the Santa Teresa Mine, worked for a time after 1877, or an unnamed mine worked a decade earlier. The mine actually consists of three small tunnels, the largest almost 40 feet deep, hewn out of the mountain near the summit of La Mina Peak. Reddish orange flakes of oxidized iron and green streaks of copper resemble dabs of paint on the cave entrance, which is trimmed with ferns. The route leading to the tunnels, through tangled vegetation abounding in stinging ortiga, is at best steep and, at worst, a slippery, almost vertical trek most easily ascended on all fours. Clinging to the slope, one is awed by what people once did, and undoubtedly still do, in order to make a less-than-modest living.

Other minerals found in the Luquillo Mountains are found in small quantities. They have never been mined to any noticeable degree and probably never will be. Included among these minerals are silver, kaolin, prophyry, malachite, white marble, native sulfur, and quartz.

❧ I know someone who mines an infinitesimal quantity of quartz in the Luquillo

Mountains. His name is Indio. Long before I met him, I had heard of his self-taught interest in geology and his knowledge of out-of-the-way forest landmarks, from old mines to Taino petroglyphs. He seemed an elusive person. At least twice Jerry Bauer had contacted him to go hiking with us and, for one reason or another, he didn't show up at the appointed time. I had also heard he was a "character". Acquaintances weren't sure how he made a living, and one person thought he lived on a flour and water diet. These details along with his nickname made me think of him as an old-style hippie. A few of them remain in Puerto Rico. Gravitating from the States to the warmth of the Caribbean in the 1960s and 1970s, they seem to have gotten stuck in a time warp, still living the hippie lifestyle in remote rural locations.

As it turned out, Indio is not a hippie. Born and raised in the Luquillo area, he is neat in appearance, articulate in speech, and normal in his eating habits, although his current work, collecting quartz to make into crafts, has a bohemian sort of appeal. In spite of his name, Indio is not of Taino descent — no one in Puerto Rico can claim direct links to the Tainos — but he does resemble an Indian, with smooth tanned skin, fine straight black hair and a Taino-inspired pendant dangling from a leather cord around his neck. I would imagine him to be close to 50 years old. When hiking, he wears a forest-green shirt, jeans or camouflage fatigues, boots reinforced with strips of tire for better tread and a well-worn green duck Army-style pack. He has been exploring the forest for decades, and his knowledge of it is so extensive that he has been guide to seasoned foresters on more than one occasion.

We took two hikes together. On one of them he was guide for a party of five to reach the copper mine near La Mina Peak. In his travels, Indio is careful to respect others' property. As we approached the base of La Mina, we had to rock-hop along a stream bordering the yard of a farmer because Indio didn't see the farmer, Don Santos, to ask his permission to use the yard. The path up the mountain, through some of the most rugged terrain in the forest, was a path that only Indio could see, or better, sense. He was a patient guide, pointing out different types of rocks and plants, hoisting us up one large boulder with a rope, stopping often to let the stragglers catch up. After we came down the mountain, Indio politely stopped to talk with Don Santos, an elderly man who has been a widower for many years. He lives in a wood house, painted pink, with a silver zinc roof and a new porch. While the two men talked, the rest of us sat on the porch, gazing with tired eye at corn hanging from the ceiling and at goats, calves and chickens wandering about the yard. The yard sloped down to the stream; beyond, the forest swooped up to the conical outline of La Mina, blurred from early evening fog.

On the second expedition, we hiked along the Río Fajardo on the eastern side of the Luquillo range. Jerry Bauer was part of this party, and he was eager to reach the river's source, from where he had begun to descend on a previous hike. Indio came along to show us two of his mining sites and to help us find the way. Once again, the forest thwarted our well-laid plans. Intermittant rain, unruly vegetation and steep banks made the going slow. Bauer coaxed us onward, confident the path he had seen from the top of the mountain was just around the corner. Indio politely dissented, telling Bauer we were far from both a path and the source. He did not share our need to reach a destination. Before long the rain fell harder, making the banks far too slick for hiking, and we had to turn back. When we returned to our cars, we met a middle-aged couple who own property bordering the Caribbean National Forest. They agreed with Indio that we had been far from the source, adding that Bauer's path was actually on the other side of the river.

Indio's mining sites lay part way up the Río Fajardo, on land owned by the couple we met, just east of the national forest boundary. Some time earlier they had given him permission for his small-scale quarrying and loaned him a key to a gate that keeps the public from a rocky, rain-gutted dirt road. The road ends in a valley bisected by the river. A second gate marks the start of a footpath that leads through dense forest to the river. Some 30 years ago coffee was planted well into the forest here, and a bakery farther upriver supplied bread for the barrio (neighborhood), but the old people who maintained the coffee shrubs and the bakery died off, and the young are not interested in such a hard way to make a living. This information came from the couple, who had driven up to check on their property when we met them. They also told us that the barrio is called La Tinaja, tinaja being an earthenware jug once used to store water.

Both of Indio's mining sites lay near the path we were following in search of the river's source. Indio was collecting pyrite-filled quartz that he had found in diagonal ledges along the banks. His quarrying efforts produced small ragged holes that were barely noticeable. Using a large sledge hammer and chisel, he would break off some 70 pounds of quartz at a time, loading it into his backpack and lugging it home. This gave him about 30 pounds of usable material. In order to lighten the considerable load, he had buried his tools near the site. The day we went his tools were gone. We deduced that recent rains had unearthed them and someone, perhaps in search of river shrimp, had profited from their appearance. Ramón Alonso, who had also joined us on this hike along with his sons, offered to loan Indio his own small pick and hammer so that he could do some work, but Indio declined. He took the loss stoically.

Back at his apartment, we learned why Indio collects quartz. His apartment is part of a low-income complex in Luquillo called, coincidentally, Caserío El Cemí. Cemí is the triangular-shaped representation of a deity worshipped by the Tainos. Drab-yellow buildings one and two stories high sit on tidy grounds of well-trodden grass. In his apartment, a narrow living room leads to a small kitchen which opens onto a tiny yard. A pan of dark soil, its use unknown to me, and another containing prehistoric ceramic shards were being stored in the kitchen. The living room had been totally taken over by his work. A metal detector, on loan but not working, lay propped against one wall, a vinyl-covered bench faced another. A long table held his minerals, which were spread out in piles of unpolished rocks in different stages of breakdown, from inch-wide chunks to pepper-fine grains. The rocks, he explained to us, were his livelihood, the main ingredient in his artisan projects. Currently, he was making decorative maps of Puerto Rico using quartz and pyrite to mark the island's outline and its major mountains. Three of them hung on the walls, which were liberally papered with newspaper clippings related to Puerto Rican artisans, places in Puerto Rico, and success stories of Puerto Ricans like tennis star Gigi Fernández. Halfway through our visit, I noticed he peeled the prices off the

*Along the
Río
Fajardo.*

*Old house
near
the river.*

maps; as we left, he gave them to the two women in the group and to Alonso.

While we were resting along the banks of the Río Fajardo earlier, Indio spoke, in Spanish, about himself. He talked in a soft, unpretentious manner yet enjoyed being the focus of attention. "When I was a young boy," he began, "I liked to play Indians, and my mother nicknamed me Indio. The name stuck. It has a much sweeter sound than my real name, Federico Rodríguez Fernández. No one calls me Federico. I began to explore the forest when I was young. Once I rented a shack up there with some friends. It wasn't part of the Boy Scouts or anything. Later I got interested in the rocks and got some books to teach myself. Ramón Alonso showed me some things, too. Then I started collecting and began to mount the rocks and sell them." Though he was working full time on his crafts, he admitted he wasn't making much money. He was trying to become part of the Institute of Puerto Rican Culture's artisan union so he could sell at the larger craft fairs, and he had some sort of patent on a design for the coquí, the popular island tree frog. In addition, he wanted to produce a book about minerals in the Luquillo Mountains. To do that, though, he would have to write everything out since he couldn't type and he would have to find someone to publish it since he had no money for such a project. Large obstacles, yet his work had its compensations. As we sat in his apartment, a young boy from a neighboring building rushed in full of excitement, waving a copy of a newspaper in which there was to be an article about Indio. We leafed through the paper; the article wasn't in that day, which meant it would appear the following week. The boy was caught up in the fame of his colorful neighbor.

With the exception of a handful of enthusiasts like Indio, mining in the Luquillo Mountains declined in the twentieth century. As a boy, around 1915, mountain resident Angel Rosa knew of people who went down to the Río Sabana on their days off to search for gold. His parents talked about the mines, and his uncles would wash once or twice a week, using a pan with a hole in it. They usually got something, several dollars for a few hours work, which they would sell in Fajardo. Although archaeologist Jeff Walker has learned of people who actually did make a living off mining during the early decades of this century, for most local residents mining was little more than a pastime when there was no other work. In the middle of the century a corporation or two had visions of exploiting alluvial deposits along the base of the Luquillo Mountains, below the national forest, but the enterprises were neither successful nor enduring. When asked if anyone washes for gold today, Rosa laughed and shook his head.

CHAPTER 6
AFTER PANGAEA

The tabonuco, once the most common of the tall trees growing in Puerto Rico's mountain rain forests, forms part of a far-flung genus. Called Dacryodes, this group of stately trees also grows in the Lesser Antilles down to Grenada, along the South American coast north of the Amazon, and, according to most botonists, across the Atlantic in western Africa. Today, many genera of trees grow in both the Old and New Worlds, but Dacryodes is native to both places.

The word "native" gives the last sentence a paradoxical quality. All but a handful of trees common to both East and West were transported by man from one side to the other. Many of the introduced trees became naturalized (able to regenerate on their own) into their new settings. Take for example, the coconut palm. It is hard to imagine these trees not swaying over Caribbean beaches, yet they were actually brought to the New World in the early 1500s. Native trees, on the other hand, existed in a particular region long before sailors learned to cross the Atlantic. They form part of the primeval vegetation. A few trees native to both hemispheres undoubtedly made their way across the ocean in the beak of a bird or as a piece of debris, but there is another, more fascinating, explanation to these dual origins. It has to do with geology.

The year 1492, when Columbus discovered the Caribbean, has long marked the start of popular histories of the Americas. For archaeologists, anthropologists and native groups, however, chapter one started tens of thousands of years earlier, when *Homo sapiens* first crossed into this hemisphere. And geologists go back hundreds of millions of years, when the "old" and "new" worlds began to inch away from each other.

To unlock the Dacryodes paradox, let's go back to the beginning, the very beginning, more than four and a half billion years ago. As the Earth took shape, it began to distinguish itself from the other planets that had formed from the leftovers of a newly created Sun. Molten iron sank to its center, and lighter matter floated up to form the outer layers that eventually became continents and oceans. The continents and oceans sat on a rigid outer shell known as the lithosphere, which in turn rested on a partially molten inner layer known as the asthenosphere. The lithosphere was divided into 12 or so independent plates, and the plates slid, and continue to slide, ever so slowly over the asthenosphere. At times they collide with each other, forcing one plate to "dive" under the other; at times they separate from each other; but they are always moving in an infinitesimally slow journey that never ends. And where the plates go, the continents, embedded on top of them, also go. The recent understanding of this process, known as plate tectonics, has completely revolutionized the way geologists look at our planet, and it helps explain the dual origins of Dacryodes.

More than 200 million years ago, when coal deposits were forming and trees and reptiles were in their early stages of evolution, the continents collided in spectacular fashion, fitting together like pieces of a puzzle in one supercontinent that has been dubbed Pangaea, Greek for "all lands". The oceans formed one super-ocean, Panthalassa, meaning "all seas". To the north, the sub-supercontinent of Laurasia encompassed North America, Europe and Asia. To the south, Gondwanaland encompassed South America, Africa, India, Australia and Antarctica. Plants and animals could travel freely over this supercontinent, unobstructed by large bodies of water. The continents of North America, South America and Africa were neatly wedged together. The Caribbean Sea was nonexistent. To get an idea of the distances the continents have moved since then, the point where the three continents connected, where one day the Caribbean would lie, was at that time located halfway between today's South America and Africa, around Ascension Island, 4,000 miles southeast of its present location.

One hundred eighty million years ago birds and mammals made their debut on Earth, and the sub-supercontinents of Laurasia and Gondwanaland began to drift apart. Newly formed ocean completely severed North and South America, while South America and Africa remained joined. This ocean, the origin of today's Gulf of Mexico and Caribbean Sea, was blocked to the east, by Africa, rather than to the west as it is today. Forty five million years later, at the time of

the first flowering plants, North and South America spread yet farther apart, and the southern half of South America and Africa began to split.

By 65 million years ago, when dinosaurs were succumbing to mass extinction, North America, South America and Africa had become almost equally separated by roughly a thousand miles, and Central America was a lengthening bulge extending southward from North America. Plant species that had shared the continents of South America and Africa now evolved separately on their new, smaller continents; most evolved in distinct ways, eventually producing distinct families, genera and species. But a few trees, including the tabonuco's Dacryodes genus, remained basically unchanged through the geological periods and today are considered native to both the Old and New Worlds.

🌿 Historical geology, when sheared of words like schistosity, diastrophism and Turonian, which conjure up little more than incomprehension in the minds of most people, makes a fascinating story. Unfortunately, most books about geology are rife with such words. To add to the difficulties, the study of the Earth's geology underwent major changes in the 1960s, when the theory of plate tectonics became almost universally accepted among geologists. Unfortunately again for me, virtually all books that I found about Puerto Rican geology were written prior to the new theories. Armed with new books about geology in general, old books about geology in Puerto Rico, a geological map of the Luquillo Mountains, a detailed glossary, notes from a conversation with geologist/hydrologist Joe Troester, and a dogged determination to make sense of all this, I began to piece together the major events in a vast and virtually timeless saga.

Within the saga, the Luquillo Mountains have their own interesting subplot. Howard Augustus Meyerhoff, author of a 1933 book about the geology of Puerto Rico, found it difficult to explain the rise of the Luquillo Mountains from the northeast plain. There they sit, separated from the sea on three sides by foothills and coastal plains, isolated from the island's other mountains by a divide only 330 feet in elevation, and etched by a number of rivers which should have worn them down to the sort of eroded plain found around much of the island.

Let's go back to the beginning again, this time to the beginning of the Caribbean basin. The Caribbean got off to a relatively late start in the scheme of things, with some 95 percent of the earth's geologic history having passed before the supercontinents began to separate and the region stirred almost 200 million years ago. Rocks tell the geologic tale: since geologists have found no rocks in the region older than the Mesozoic era (which lasted from 245 to 66 million years ago), they prefer to leave pre-Mesozoic history in the Caribbean a blank. One geologist did attempt to trace the region back to Precambrian time (3,800 to 700 million years ago), but another geologist dismissed his theories as the fertile contemplations of an arm-chair geologist.

As the Americas began to separate, permitting ocean to move in, a large plate known as the Pacific lithosphere started drifting in an easterly direction into a relatively shallow sea basin between the two continents. Eventually it separated from the Pacific plate and became known as the Caribbean plate. In its wake, the land mass which would become Central America began to descend toward South America. A long, flat platform hovered around sea level in the basin. Referred to as

the Antillean Island, it was a sort of super-island, comprised of sedimentary and volcanic materials and stretching roughly from Cuba to the Virgin Islands. In its early period, it alternately rose above and fell below the ocean.

Though one of the smallest of the dozen or so plates that make up the Earth's lithosphere, the Caribbean plate has always been an active one. Its eastern boundary forms a subduction zone, where two plates (the second in this case being the Americas plate) collide, and one rides over the other. The other plate "dives" downward, eventually returning to that partially molten inner core, the asthenosphere. Puerto Rico itself lies at the western edge of this subduction zone and at the eastern end of a transform fault, where two plates slide past each other.

Because of this, Puerto Rico and the rest of the Caribbean have the dubious distinction of being in a cauldron of geological activity, which has resulted in the formation of all sorts of trenches and mountains, volcanoes and earthquakes. The Cretaceous period (144 to 66 million years ago) proved to be an especially rambunctious time. Volcanoes erupted both above and beneath the water into fireworks of lava and debris that settled on the ocean floor. Edges of plates collided with each other, resulting in one colossal slab jacked up on top of another. Fragments and molten matter piled up on top of existing fragments; in time, the accumulating debris formed a series of volcanic cones.

One of these ancient volcanoes, dubbed Hato Puerco by Meyerhoff, lay in the general area of the Luquillo Mountains. Meyerhoff considered Hato Puerco one of the region's largest and most active volcanic centers during the Cretaceous period. Large accumula-

Jerry Bauer
alongside ancient
tabonuco trees
in the
Baño de Oro
Research
Natural Area.

*Young
impatiens
and old rocks
next to a
mountain
stream.*

---

*The sun
working
its timeless
magic on planet
Earth.*

tions of lava flows and pyroclastics — rocks that have been ejected from volcanoes — suggest Hato Puerco's location. One lava flow on the eastern side of the mountains, the Figueroa formation, is 500 feet deep. Yet the amount of lava in the region is less than the amount of pyroclastics. Pyroclastics explode out of a volcano while lava oozes out: this preponderance of pyroclastics suggests Hato Puerco led a violent life. Most likely, it was located over a subduction zone, where two plates collide. Meyerhoff reconstructed its existence, and I have rewritten and simplified the tale:

Imagine a fiery cone exploding through the ocean floor. Quickly cooled by the Caribbean waters, the volcanic debris accumulates in ever-larger piles on the floor. Eventually the cone pokes above the sea, and its occasional eruptions spangle the nighttime sky. A massive collection of materials — an inner lava core, long dikes of volcanic rock, and outer surface flows — continues to pile up on top of the original cone, and Hato Puerco rises a mile above the sea. During the eruptions, rains wash sediments that have collected on the volcano's flanks into the sea. In between eruptions, when the sea is calmer and clearer, coral builds up layers. Apparently unperturbed by the volatile processes going on around them (until the next eruption), ancient plants and trees blanket the island, and marine life — clams, mollusks, gastropods as well as corals —settles into the surrounding waters. Eruptions eventually grow less frequent. When they occur, the cone grows in size; when they don't, the cone erodes. Some 40 million years after it first breaks through the ocean floor, Hato Puerco becomes a mere mound covered by ash, mud and vegetation. Its time as a mighty volcano has ended.

Picturing how volcanic cones like Hato Puerco rise and erode is relatively easy; fathoming the amount of time the process took — 40 million years, depositing an average of less than half an inch of debris per century — is virtually impossible. Meyerhoff speculated that the rate of eruptions in the region, which we tend to compress into an ongoing spectacle of fire and flowing lava, was no greater than that found along Alaska's Aleutian Islands today. Though volcanic activity would continue sporadically for some time, by the end of the Cretaceous period the Antillean Island's most intense vulcanism had ended.

The rest of the region's geologic history is a complex tale of rising, eroding and shifting land. Volcanic activity tends to be followed by movements along the region's fault zones, that is, zones where there are breaks in the Earth's crust. Around 65 million years ago, large areas of the Earth were subject to very dramatic movements which produced or further shaped many of the world's great mountain ranges. In the Caribbean, a mountain range thrust up along the entire length of the Antillean Island.

Following this mountain-building movement, the Greater Antilles entered one of its quieter periods of geologic activity. What the movements had raised up, newly formed rivers eroded down. Sags developed, seas moved into low-lying areas, and marine deposits mixed with land sedimentation. The super-island of Antilles began to disintegrate: Cuba separated first, followed by Hispaniola, some 15 million years ago. Long periods of erosion were interspersed with additional tilting and uplifting movements, eventually producing the asymmetrical look of Puerto Rico, with its Cordillera Central closer to the south coast than to the north.

Now we get to recent geological history — events that began a mere million and a half years ago. The Pleistocene Ice Age was actually not one incredibly long ice age but a series of waxings and wanings on the part of the Earth's major glaciers. During cooler periods, when glaciers were more extensive, much of the world's supply of water was stored in the ice sheets. Oceans became lower, and dryer climatic conditions could no longer produce lush forests. Puerto Rico became a relatively dry island as a result, with savannahs and dry grasslands predominating. Plant species on the island have changed completely since then. When the ice sheets melted for the final time, around 10,000 years ago, the seas rose, separating Puerto Rico and the Virgin Islands by a shallow bed of water. Puerto Rico as we know it was completed.

For the last 10,000 years or so, erosion has played the largest role in the island's changes. However, from time to time an occasional earthquake centered in the Mona Passage west of Puerto Rico (one of the most damaging of which destroyed much of the city of Mayagüez in 1918) reminds islanders that the Caribbean plate still has a lot of pep.

In spite of Hato Puerco and other ancient volcanoes, Puerto Rico is not considered a volcanic island. The Caribbean has three basic island types: flat coral islands like Barbados; jagged volcanic islands like Martinique; and once-volcanic but long-quiescent islands like Puerto Rico. Puerto Rico's volcanic activity has been dead for so long that geologists find it hard even to locate the old vents. In addition, unmodified eruptive materials such as volcanic flows and plutons, which come from the roots of a volcano below the eruptions, have played a secondary role in the island's formation, while modified volcanic materials in the form of heaped-up debris have been much more important.

To return to the Luquillo Mountains, Meyerhoff offered a rather romantic explanation for their continued existence. The early volcanic activity, followed by a period of colossal bending, produced the mountains. Their stubborn resistance to erosion, giving "silent testimony to the ancient majesty of the ranges from which they had been carved", enabled them to endure. To Meyerhoff, Luquillo is a true monadnock, an isolated mountain remaining from ancient topography that rises above the more level, eroded land around it.

Luquillo's endurance is all the more impressive because it lies between the two largest river systems of northeast Puerto Rico. One of them, the Río Grande de Loíza, originates in the mountains of central Puerto Rico and flows north into the Atlantic to the east of San Juan; a reservoir along the river provides the metropolitan area with much of its drinking water. The second system is comprised of several smaller rivers flowing east into the Vieques Passage. Meyerhoff detailed a case in which the mountains' resistance to erosion thwarted a Loíza tributary in its journey to the sea.

When the island was tilting and shifting during its dramatic mountain-building period, the Río Loíza had two main tributaries, one being the present river with its start in the Cayey Mountains, the other being the Río Canóvanillas-Valencianos originating in the Luquillo Mountains. After the shifting, the Loíza branch easily eroded a relatively direct path to the north coast, but the second branch — named Canóvanillas to the north and Valencianos to the south — was unable to carve its way through the hard Luquillo rocks.

Meanwhile, a small feeder stream today known as the Río Gurabo formed along more malleable land south of the mountains. Eventually, it scooped up the water from the Valencianos section of the tributary, severing it from Río Canóvanillas and drawing it directly west into the Loíza. Today, Río Gurabo, erstwhile Valencianos, originates just south of El Toro Peak within the national forest and works its way to the southwest toward the Río Loíza. Río Canóvanillas originates in an eastern chunk of national forest land known as La Condesa and works its way to the north toward the larger Río Canóvanas and the sea. In between stands a saddle of land, the severed stretch of the Canóvanillas-Valencianos, a testimony to the tenacity of the Luquillo Mountains.

On the other hand, Raoul Mitchell, author of a 1954 survey of the geology of Puerto Rico, felt the Luquillo Mountains were no more resistant to erosion than were other island formations. He noted that fewer sediments are found in eastern Puerto Rico than in the western half of the island, indicating that the east merely remained above land more and therefore suffered less from the erosive processes. Mitchell agrees with several other contemporary geologists that the mountains are a product of complex bending and breaking. Those processes resulted in a tilted mountain block that shows the effects of erosion, and not in the resistant remains of a former land surface as Meyerhoff believed. The tilt is quite pronounced. To the north, the Luquillo terrain falls steeply at first, then levels off gradually, while to the south, it falls gradually at first, then drops steeply.

Victor Seiders, who compiled a geologic map of the Yunque quadrangle in 1971, lists three basic groupings of present-day geological formations. The first, stratified rocks, makes up the oldest, most widespread and deepest of the formations. Up to 24,500 feet thick, these rocks date as far back as the early Cretaceous period, more than 100 million years ago. Many of the oldest stratified rocks are found in the southeastern part of the forest. Luquillo's stratified rocks — primarily sandstones, mudstones and breccia — are volcanic in origin. They are the materials that spewed out of the volcanoes and landed on the ocean floor, where they mixed with limestone from coral reefs. Underwater landslides, ash flows and sediment-laden currents transported them into deeper water before mountain-building movements thrust them up to their present position. Visitors driving along the main road into the mountains pass through a stretch of stratified rocks, but the vegetation obscures all but an occasional outcrop.

These are not especially pretty rocks. As the name suggests, sandstone, a gray-green sedimentary stone, resembles its former marine environment; mudstone is little more than petrified mud; and breccia is composed of gravelly, angular fragments. Their biggest claim to fame is their age. Fossils — ammonites, planktons and rudistids — found imprinted on these rocks have helped to date them. One species of the order Foraminifera (unicellular microorganisms wrapped in a shell) is known as *Hedbergella delrioensis* to paleontologists and geologists and is virtually unknown to anyone else. The fossil of this tiny creature is common in many of Luquillo's oldest stratified rocks. Since H. delrioensis lived during the early Cretaceous period (144 to perhaps 100 million years ago), geologists deduce that rocks yielding it were deposited during that time as well.

The second formation, intrusive rocks, are primarily plutons, that is, rocks which originally lay in a molten state a mile or two beneath volcanoes. When a volcano died, the underlying magma cooled, forming plutons. As time passed, these rocks were eventually exposed by the erosion of the volcanoes and overlying rock. Granite-textured quartz diorite rocks, the most common of the intrusives in the Luquillo Mountains, are mainly found in the southern section of the forest, in a ten-square-mile body known as the Río Blanco Stock. Geologist Ramón Alonso once showed me the interior of a piece of quartz diorite by smashing a pale rock on top of a harder volcanic rock. The pale rock broke in two, exposing a beige color speckled with dark spots. This salt and pepper coloring is characteristic of Río Blanco quartz diorite.

Unconsolidated deposits comprise the third and most recent formation. These deposits are sediments which have no sort of cement to bind their grains together. In El Yunque unconsolidated deposits consist primarily of layers of sand, gravel, silt and clay. Products of weathering and the erosive forces of water, the deposits are swept along by rivers and streams during floods and deposited along floodplains and upper river or stream banks. Gravel, the coarsest of these alluvial sediments, is composed of rock fragments or pebbles. It is followed in descending order of coarseness by sand, silt and clay. Clay is very fine-grained, primarily a result of the disintegration of silicate minerals. Such minerals form the basis of common glass and bricks.

Of all the geological features within the Luquillo Mountains, the peaks (none of which ever spewed fire and lava) hold the greatest attraction to visitors. The Luquillo range has three main groupings of mountains — a cen-

tral east-west chain which runs for some five and a half miles from El Toro to East Peak; several peaks slightly to the south, which are irregular but generally parallel to the central chain; and El Yunque Peak to the north, four miles, as the crow flies, from El Toro. The major peaks are El Toro (3,524 feet, 866 feet lower than the island's highest), El Yunque (3,496), East Peak (3,446), West Peak and El Cacique (both 3,346), Los Picachos (3,175), Mt. Britton (3,075) and La Mina (3,035). El Toro (the bull), El Yunque (the anvil), El Cacique (the chieftain) and Los Picachos (the pinnacles) were apparently named for their shapes; East and West peaks were named for their location; and La Mina (the mine) for the mining activity once carried out along its flanks.

El Yunque, the most popular peak in the mountains, is also the most cluttered. Along its ridge a dozen or so media towers resemble garish territorial claim markers; the largest tower could pass for the skeleton of a space ship. Stone lookouts top El Yunque, Mount Britton and Los Picachos. A Navy communications center crowns East Peak. Paths loop across El Toro and West Peak. El Cacique and La Mina remain untouched.

❧ When rocks break apart, they form soil. This happens either through the mechanical weathering of frosts and extreme temperature changes — neither of which occurs in the Luquillo Mountains — or through chemical weathering such as oxidation, leaching, or the decay of vegetation. Soils make up the top layer of the earth's surface, the only layer where plants grow. Though plants grow with lush abandon on the slopes of El Yunque, its soil looks nothing like the loose black mixture one associates with optimum growing conditions. Most of what is found in the forest is taupe or henna in color and claylike in texture, an unpleasant concoction that leaves permanent stains on clothes and, when wet, becomes as slick and compact as oft-trodden snow. This fact has not escaped local children, who equip themselves with boat-shaped sierra palm sheaths to "sled" down the hills.

Such clay-rich soils are common when rainfall exceeds evaporation and when leaching (the condition in which soluble materials are dissolved by flowing water) is continuous. Base materials are washed out, silica is partly removed, oxides of iron and aluminum accumulate as residue, and a clayey texture results. The red or yellow color comes from the iron. Humus, the black decayed matter that provides nutrients for plants and increases the ability of soil to retain water, is in short supply, in part because most trees in the forest are evergreen. Though a few do shed their leaves, fungi and insects often get to the leaves before they can convert into humus. Due to the soil's dense texture, water can't penetrate easily, runoff is high, and droughtlike conditions result. Studies have found that, with the poor drainage and continual runoff, 30 inches of rain in the Luquillo Mountains benefit vegetation to the same degree that 15 inches of summer rain do in a temperate climate. On the other hand, the soil does remain continually wet, and roots must grow on or near the surface in order to get a proper supply of oxygen.

In short, Luquillo Mountain soil seems to be in a sorry state: it lacks nutrients, suffers from too much rain, restricts root zones and hinders plant growth. The bad situation worsens with increases in elevation and inclination, resulting in few species, short trees, shallow roots and many dead upper limbs on the highest slopes. In the 1940s Frank Wadsworth took a layer-by-layer look at a patch of Río Blanco Stock soil on a gradual slope in the area of the upper Río Icacos. The top layer was a foot-deep slab of black, greasy material, impervious to water; in places, it was little more than slimy algae. Not the sort of soil to warm anyone's heart, yet Wadsworth considered it similar in consistency to the peat found on the immortalized heathered moors of Scotland.

Fred Scatena, coordinator of the Bisley Watershed Project within the national forest, offers a modest defense of the forest's soil, pointing out that it is not quite so poor as that underlying most tropical forests of Africa and the Amazon. "It's fairly nutrient rich," he argues, "perhaps because of the volcanic rock which underlies it."

In the same way that plants and animals are grouped into orders, families and genera, soils are classified, based on such physical properties as the arrangement and thickness of soil layers and such chemical properties as the amount of organic matter and the degree of acidity. The most common soil type in the Caribbean National Forest is known as Los Guineos clay, clay being a finely grained, firm natural material that is made up of water combined with silicates (a compound found in most rocks) of aluminum and is the preferred medium of potters, tile and brick makers. It develops in steeply sloped higher elevations, where the weather is generally cool, wet and windy. In a 1942 soil survey of Puerto Rico, R.C. Roberts described Los Guineos clay. On the surface, down to three inches, the clay is grayish-brown, slightly granular, gooey and strongly acidic. The subsurface clay, down to six inches, is more brownish-yellow in color. Then the clay abruptly becomes red, still gooey and strongly acidic but more permeable. At a depth of three to four feet, it becomes lighter in color and more brittle. Rocks are found on the surface and throughout the soil layers.

Roberts wrote his survey for the U.S. Department of Agriculture. Agriculturally, he considered this soil of low value except for forestry. Since Roberts wrote his book, a more detailed classification system has been developed. Half of the soil in the Luquillo Mountains has now been placed in the order Ultisols, primarily a clayey, highly leached (dissolved) and well weathered soil.

Though not very exciting to most visitors in El Yunque, this clayey concoction may unlock secrets to the forest of the past. Through samplings of pollens and Carbon-14 substances found in soil cores, paleoecologists like Grace Brush of the University of Florida are beginning to piece together the forest community of centuries ago. These studies are in their early stages. Only one core, from East Peak dwarf forest, has Carbon-14 old enough to date (going back to around 300 A.D.), and only a small sampling of local pollen, necessary for comparison with the core pollen, has been collected. Accurate identifications of the forest's centuries-old species will have to wait.

Soils also have much to do with shaping — literally — the forest of the future. Every time a chunk of soil and rock slides down the mountainside, the forest's topography changes.

"Landslides are one of the most important processes in forming the forest's

RIO ICACOS

landscapes," Matt Larson told me. Larson, a U.S. Geological Survey geologist, has been analyzing landslides found in the upper reaches of the Luquillo Mountains for several years. He has focused on slides within the Río Blanco Stock, a geologically interesting body formed by once-molten rock that thrust itself into the area of the Río Blanco river basin. Joe Troester suggested I might be interested in his work, and Larson and I spoke by phone.

"Walk around and look at the forest," Larson suggested. "After [Hurricane] Hugo knocked down all the leaves out there, we could see a lot of ancient small- and large-scale landslides." Within the Río Blanco Stock, landslides occur more often and on a grander scale than in other parts of the forest. The predominant diorite rock, being less dense than volcanic rock, permits water to permeate it more quickly, resulting in more rapid weathering.

"A lot of the rock you see out there is actually rotten rock, what we call saprolite," Larson continued. "Jab your finger into it and it disintegrates, yet it still retains the crystalline structure of rock."

The Río Blanco Stock contains some of the deepest soil in the forest. In one place, men drilled more than 70 feet before hitting rock. That is a lot of soil poised to loosen and tumble down the mountain during a heavy rain, thus, the large number of landslides. As part of his study, Larson has collected rain data — how much rain falls, how fast it falls, how fast it moves, how high the pressure of the water is within the soil (landslides occur if the pressure exceeds the cohesive force of the soil). He has also measured the angles of the slopes. Road 191 within the Río Blanco Stock, for example, is subject to being hit by landslides, and part of the reason undoubtedly has to do with the steep slopes in this area.

Before Hurricane Hugo, Larson had mapped some 200 landslides of up to 80 years in age. He stopped at 80 because the forest canopy covers those which are older, making them hard to spot. The slides range from 15 to 3,000 feet in length. The 3,000-foot slide, one of the largest on the island, started in 1970, when a storm dumped 38 inches of rain on the forest in five days. Road 191 suddenly found itself in two disconnected sections. Before the road was repaired, back-to-back hurricanes in 1979 caused a 1,800-foot slide next to the 1970 one. It dumped close to a million tons of rock and soil down the mountain and turned an emerald-green reservoir into a lake of boulders. At the time I was speaking with Matt Larson, the Federal Department of Transportation was attempting to put Road 191 back together again in an effort as complex as repairing Humpty Dumpty himself. Many scientists, appreciating the remote, untouched state of the back side of the mountains, were keeping their fingers crossed that the effort would fail. As of now it has, for reasons related to the environment, not to engineering. The road remains closed to traffic shortly past kilometer 13, and it is severed by the landslide some three and a half miles beyond.

Since Hugo in 1989, Larson has counted approximately 200 additional landslides. Hugo was an unusually dry hurricane; as a result, most of the slides formed by it are relatively small and shallow. A severe hurricane with lots of rainfall would cause great changes in the forest landscape.

❦ Trees common to the Americas and Africa; soils resembling the high moors of Scotland; outcrops dating back a hundred million years; volcanic materials from the origins of the Earth mixing with later-blooming corals on the ocean floor, then being thrust up to form today's mountain peaks — geology has certainly made a jumble of time and place in the Luquillo Mountains.

CHAPTER 7
FOUR FOREST TYPES

Luquillo research forester Peter Weaver's Uncle George, who dismissed the complexity of hurricanes with the opinion "most anyone knows what a hurricane does, it knocks over trees", would probably make similar short work of forests. I can hear him say, with an impatient flick of a hand, "most anyone knows what a forest is, it's ground covered with trees." And so it is. Millions, possibly billions of trees cover the slopes of the Luquillo Mountains. These trees have trunks, branches and leaves, trillions of leaves. When viewed from a distance, the leaves blend together into a uniform green, and the forest seems a simple place. Up close, the apparent uniformity turns to chaos. Unlike forests in, let's say, the Rocky Mountains, where three or four fir species and a couple of deciduous trees encompass hundreds of thousands of acres, tiny El Yunque shelters 240 distinct tree species. There are trees that grow more than 120 feet tall and trees that barely reach two feet; trunks two grown men joined together couldn't embrace and trunks a young child could encircle with his hands; straight branches and crooked branches, satiny leaves and scratchy leaves. Scientists who have spent a lifetime looking at the Luquillo forest have attempted to make some sort of order out of this chaos. In the process they have developed a scheme of forest types.

Up until the early decades of this century there was no generally accepted classification system for the New World tropics; in fact, there weren't enough studies even to describe the forests, much less classify them. In 1942 former Luquillo forest supervisor William Barbour pioneered a list of forest types common to the neotropics. He developed his list using an American concept. According to Barbour, U.S. foresters tended to define forest types as "group stands of similar character" while their European counterparts classified according to climatic and soil conditions, not actual tree species. Americans seem to focus on results, Europeans prefer to look at causes. Barbour found four basic forest types common to the tropics — dry forests, deciduous (leaf-shedding) forests, rain forests, and cloud forests.

Around the same time, botanist J.S. Beard was working with the British Colonial Forest Service in Trinidad and Tobago when he published an article on climax (mature natural) vegetation in tropical America. Beard developed a more detailed classification system than Barbour, basing his system on associations of vegetation which are then placed together according to their habitats.

Later in the decade, U.S. Forest Service researcher Frank Wadsworth adapted Beard's system to establish forest types in the

Luquillo Mountains. He grouped the region into four major vegetative communities — tabonuco, palo colorado, sierra palm and dwarf. Since that time, other classification systems have been developed. Best known is the ecological life zone system, which was created by Leslie Holdridge, a scientist at the research branch of the Luquillo forest in the 1930s. In the Holdridge system, foresters plot simple climatic data — primarily temperature and precipitation — to determine the region's vegetative type, more in the European tradition of classification. Today most Western Hemisphere tropical regions have been mapped according to their life zones, and scientists refer to Holdridge's zones when writing about El Yunque for an international audience, but Wadsworth's classification system remains the one most commonly used.

TABONUCO

For years I was nagged by a simple statement in forest brochures that pronounces the tabonuco type as the true rain forest. What then were the other types? Shrewd impostors? Eventually I learned that tabonuco forest most closely resembles the vegetation of tropical rain forests found throughout the Caribbean, Central and South America. According to Beard, rain forest refers to "the tallest, most luxuriant and most complex type of vegetation in the American tropics, the vegetal optimum". He cautions, "rain forest is by no means so common in the tropics as is popularly supposed, for these ideal growth conditions [well-drained land, deep and permeable soil, sufficient year-round moisture, shelter from winds] are rare." He breaks away from his scientific descriptions to give a poetic rule-of-thumb for newcomers to the tropics: "True

rain forest always gives the impression of the vault of cathedral aisles."

The name tabonuco comes from the name for the most common of the tall trees that traditionally grow within this forest type in Luquillo. Known as *Dacryodes excelsa* to scientists, tabonuco's crown (the upper leafy section of the tree) makes up one-third of the mature forest canopy. With an upright trunk that can grow more than five feet in diameter, an imposing height of 100 feet or more, smooth bark and an elongated puff of dark-green leaves, this was considered the most majestic tree in Puerto Rico by several early botanists. The wood resembles mahogany, though it is not as resistant to termites, and it was once used extensively for furniture. Member of a genus found in both the old and new worlds, this tree is also common to the rain forests of the Lesser Antilles, where it is known as gommier. On the Lesser Antilles island of Dominica, it dominates the large virgin forests, considered models for the way Puerto Rico's original forests looked. There, Carib Indians still hollow out the trunks to make canoes, as Indians did centuries ago on Puerto Rico and other islands. Caribs gave the tree its name; tabonuco means "white-barked". The bark of the tree has a whitish resin, used for centuries in candles and torches, as incense in religious ceremonies, and for medicinal purposes.

The tabonuco forest community, making up some 70 percent of the Luquillo Mountains, thrives on foothills and lower slopes below 2,000 feet, where yearly rainfall averages between 90 and 140 inches, temperatures hover around 73 degrees, and soils are moderately to well drained. It is considered the most spectacular of Luquillo's forest types: it claims the most tree species, more than 150, and the tallest, most stately trees.

But don't expect to see a preponderance of tabonuco in most of today's lower Luquillo forests. It and several other species have nicely grained woods, and the eighteenth-century traveler Friar Abbad wasn't the only one to realize their potential for lumber. The combination of good woods and relatively accessible slopes proved unfortunate for the original forest. Over the centuries most of the timber trees were removed, and crops were planted on the partially cleared land. Hurricanes and other factors eventually discouraged local farmers, and in the 1930s the Forest Service bought up numerous abandoned plantations to replant in trees. Though today the forests in the lower elevations of El Yunque look as if they have always been there, most are what is known as secondary forest. Tabonuco does poorly in reestablishing itself in secondary forest; foresters who have tried to coax it along have fared little better. Consequently, though it remains common on the untouched slopes, there are patches of secondary tabonuco forest that boast nary a tabonuco tree.

On the other hand, those trees that exist are likely to be around for some time. When scientists surveyed the damage to the Bisley Watershed Project after Hurricane Hugo hit in 1989, they discovered tabonuco was the tree which had best resisted the hurricane. Almost half of those in the study area suffered little more than defoliation. This was in striking contrast to other trees, virtually all of which suffered serious damage. Tabonucos prefer to grow on slopes and ridges, where drainage is good. By joining their roots with other roots and attaching them to rocks lying under the soil, they seem better able to withstand the forces of a hurricane.

A vertical profile of original tabonuco forest, in which the crowns are drawn as free-form lollipops, shows three levels of trees — the highest, from 100 to 120 feet; the middle, from 60 to 70 feet; and the lowest, from 10 to 30 feet. This tri-level canopy permits little light to reach the floor, and the ground collects more dead than living matter. A mere scattering of shrubs and plants fringe the large, straight trunks. Trees run the show here. In one study, Wadsworth measured off an acre of tabonuco forest and counted its trees. He found 63, belonging to 33 different species, that were greater than 12 inches in diameter (measured at a person's breast height). Coexisting with tabonuco are other canopy trees — motillo (*Sloanea berteriana*), a statuesque tree with distinctive split seed capsules resembling wooden tulips and prominent roots that act as buttresses to support the large tree in the forest's saturated soil; ausubo (*Manilkara bidentata*), known in English as bulletwood for the hardness of the wood, once the most important timber tree in Puerto Rico because of its mahoganylike color, its resistance to dry-wood termites and decay, and its great durability (many centuries-old ausubo beams still hold up the ceilings of historic homes in Old San Juan); and laurel sabino (*Magnolia splendens*), native only to the Luquillo Mountains, a magnolia with large branches and large white flowers, whose wood when first cut is an unusual olive-green color.

Medium-sized trees include yagrumo macho or matchwood (*Schefflera morototoni*), of the ginseng family, traditionally used in Trinidad and Guyana for matches and match boxes; and the ubiquitous *Cecropia schreberiana*, known as yagrumo hembra in Puerto Rico and as trumpet tree (the hollow branches make primitive musical instruments), pop-a-gun, bois trompette and wild papaw in other places. Throughout the Car-

View of
Cecropia
leaves
reaching for
the sun.

ibbean, Central and northern South America Cecropia is a sun lover and pioneer species, one of the first trees to grow back on newly cut or damaged forest. It bears large fan-shaped leaves with white undersides which, when seen, indicate wind and bad weather and give the tree yet another name, the weather vane tree. Among the shortest trees is camasey (*Miconia prasini*), whose long narrow leaves are etched with symmetrical veins. In addition, tabonuco

forest has four species of the curious tropical strangler trees. One of them, jagüey blanco or shortleaf fig (*Ficus citrifolia*), sometimes originates as an air plant high on the fork of an older tree, where birds have deposited its seeds. The plant sends vinelike aerial roots to the ground and grows rapidly. Its roots usually unite to form a trunk, and, in an inhospitable gesture, the trunk often strangles the older tree, thus the nickname.

Big Tree Trail is, as its name suggests, the best place from which to view Luquillo's original tabonuco forest. Found in the untouched upper reaches of the mountains, the trail begins at La Mina Falls, reached by taking a short walk along a path from the Palo Colorado Picnic Area. Though La Mina Falls takes a back seat in popularity to La Coca Falls along Road 191, it is a much more robust cascade. Framed by cliffs and forest,

the water from Río de la Mina drops 35 feet into a circular pool. On weekends, families sit on boulders and a moss-covered trunk around the pool; some bathe in the chilly water, and the adventurous climb the cliff behind the falls.

Big Tree Trail crosses the river below the falls and winds through tabonuco forest back out to 191. This is one of the forest's most popular trails, and it is well maintained. Part

Top left:
Old-growth tabonuco forest in Baño de Oro Research Natural Area.
Botton left:
Old palo colorado tree in forest of the same name.

Top right:
Sierra palm forest type along a rocky ravine.
Botton right:
East Peak dwarf forest, covered in clouds.

of the path is paved and bordered with markers interpreting the forest, and several wood and zinc shelters protect hikers from the intermittent rains. Even so, hiking requires a bit of a balancing act — straining the neck upward to get the full effect of the forest's height while at the same time keeping the eyes lowered on the wet rock- and root-strewn path along the unpaved stretches. Visitors pass below several large tabonucos as well as ausubo, motillo and other venerable species of the Caribbean rain forests. Much of the forest is in deep shade, the ground is relatively free of clutter, plants and vines keep their piggyback antics to a minimum, and massive trunks resemble spires reaching for the distant canopy. This is the cathedral country that Beard described.

PALO COLORADO

If a tree is curious in some form or another, it will attract more attention than its more normal neighbors. The strangler fig, for example — the tree that grows from top to bottom and kills its host — is certainly curious. Another fig tree, the banyon of tropical Asia, has to be the most amazing tree I've come across in literature. It sends prop roots down from its horizontal branches, and the roots enlarge and function as additional trunks in holding up the ever more sprawling tree. These trees can get immense: the Banians of Persia built a pagoda under one such tree, giving rise to one of the species's common names. Even more incredible, it is said that Alexander the Great and an army of 7,000 men camped under a single banyan, which, when visited in 1813 after floods had destroyed a large chunk of it, still had more than 3,000 trunks and a crown 2,000 feet in circumference.

Admittedly, the second forest type found in El Yunque has no trees on that scale, but its namesake, the palo colorado tree, does have several curious features. Distinguished by sword-shaped leaves clustered primarily at the top of the tree and long stalks of small white flowers, this tree, scientifically known as *Cyrilla racemiflora*, has an exceptionally wide range. It grows as far north as Virginia, where it is called swamp cyrilla, and as far south as northern Brazil. In most places it is a mere shrub, but in the Greater Antilles it has blossomed into a full-sized tree, reaching a height of up to 50 feet. Though the palo colorado is an evergreen, its leaves turn red when they are about to drop off, giving islanders a taste of temperate autumn. Unlike the stately tabonuco, the tree's reddish-brown trunk is gnarled, its branches twisted, and it grows much more slowly. A 91-inch-diameter tabonuco, for example, would be estimated to be 420 years old while the same sized palo colorado would be 1,200 years old. Its trees rank among the oldest in the Luquillo forest, with a few over 1,000 years and one specimen that a romantic or two consider more than 3,500 years old. Such curiosities have given this tree more cachet than its neighbors. As a result, the forest type has been named palo colorado even though there are actually several other tree species that are more numerous. Few, though, reach the size of the palo colorado. Never a lumber tree, it was once commonly cut for charcoal and fence posts, and for the honey which bees would store in its many cavities.

These cavities feature in one of the more ironic anecdotes of forest management in El Yunque. In the decade before World War II, when Forest Service personnel and Civilian Conservation Corps workers performed miracles in restoring forest to the Luquillo Mountains, they removed many dead or decrepit trees in order to improve existing stands. Aging palo colorados, gnarled and pocked with apparently useless cavities, seemed the perfect target, especially so since their wood could be used by local residents for much-needed charcoal. Several decades later, when the native Puerto Rican parrot was fast approaching extinction in its final refuge in the Luquillo Mountains and scientists were scurrying to research the bird's life and habitat, it was discovered that palo colorado cavities were the parrot's preferred nesting site. Their destruction had proved to be a factor in the decline in the parrots in the mountains. Today, these cavities are sacrosanct.

Though the average person hiking in the forest is not going to exclaim when leaving one forest type and entering another, palo colorado forest does differ from tabonuco in a number of ways. First, it grows on gentle slopes and in valleys at higher altitudes (above 2,000 feet), where rainfall is greater (130 to 170 inches), temperatures lower and soils deep but poorly drained. It covers a smaller range, 17 percent of the Luquillo Mountains. Its trees are not as tall, reaching only 50 feet, and they fall into two general layers instead of three. Wadsworth found that, while there are more trees per acre in palo colorado forest (73 above 12 inches in diameter), there are fewer species (23), and the entire palo colorado forest has only one-third (53) the number of species found in the tabonuco type. This is true of tropical forests in general: higher altitudes produce more trees but fewer species, shorter heights and smaller diameters, probably due to poorer growing conditions. As a result, more light gets through the canopy in palo colorado forest, enabling more plants to grow on the ground. Extensive root networks snake among the plants; in places, decaying leaves form spongy mats over them. Because of the ground clutter, trees take some time to get started in this forest. Even survival patterns differ between the two forests: the largest trees in palo colorado forest are found in the valleys, protected from high winds, while the largest in the tabonuco type are found on the upper slopes and ridges.

If you can identify any of the following trees — caimitillo (*Micropholis chrysophylloides*), caimitillo verde (*Micropholis garcinifolia*), nemocá (*Ocotea spathulata*), and of course palo colorado — you will have a good idea when you are entering palo colorado forest. These are indicator species, trees more common here than in other parts of the forest. Indeed, both caimitillo and caimitillo verde are more numerous than palo colorado. Caimitillo verde, found only in the eastern mountains of Puerto Rico, is known by its small, thick and leathery leaves, which are shaped like those round straw fans once common in church pews in the summer.

The nemocá is a medium-sized mountain laurel found only in Cuba and Puerto Rico. The tree itself bears horizontally layered branches with spoon-shaped leaves. Its wood must rank among the most bizarrely beautiful in the Western Hemisphere. Subtle hues of pink, yellow and green add unusual colorations to the basic brown wood, which is flecked with dark spots, stripes and irregular lines. It reminds me of a Joan Miró painting. In this age of uniform pine and pasteboard, it would be refreshing to own nemocá furniture, to have people point to your table or dining set and ask, "What's that?" Who even notices most contemporary wood products? However, nemocá, though strong, is susceptible to drywood termites; in addition, most of the trees are too small for anything larger than dolls' furniture.

Though I've never made a serious attempt to find the line of demarcation between forest types, I remember one time when I did notice the differences between tabonuco and palo colorado. Ecologist Miguel Canals and I were taking a little-used secondary trail down the mountains in a northwesterly direction toward the Río Espíritu Santo. Though the distance, as the crow flies, was only five miles, the hike took some nine hours. Like many of the secondary trails, this one started out with great promise, but soon deteriorated and eventually vanished. At one point we became disoriented, and Canals regaled me with a tale of how he once got lost in this very region for three days. At another point we had to rock-hop along the thousands of rocks and boulders which nature has dumped into the river over the eons, rocks which, I might add, were slick from newly fallen rain.

Before the trail vanished, we were in the heart of palo colorado country. Marking the trail head is a thick, moss-cloaked palo colorado Canals estimated to be more than 1,000 years old. He also pointed out a guayabota (*Eugenia stahlii*), a Puerto Rican member of the myrtle family; camasey shrubs (*Miconia impetiolaris*) with pronounced leaf veins; *Marcgravia rectiflora* vines, one of the most common vines in the forest, locally known as pegapalma for the way they attach themselves to sierra palm trees; and the dense, deep-green crowns of caimitillo trees. When the trail deteriorated, we had to step around an unruly tangle of fallen branches, root networks hidden under decaying leaves, encroaching razor grass, and, at one point, a veritable garden of bromeliads, large bouquets of arching green leaves with peach-colored bracts in the center.

There must have been 300 of them, in branches, tangled in vines, on the ground.

Eventually we abandoned the forest for the river, and later we abandoned the river in favor of a small path which suddenly appeared. We seemed in a different forest. Here were signs of civilization — an abandoned campsite, a concrete dam, a road in ruins, and a beautiful stand of hibiscus which someone had worked into a tunnel shape. The trees had a more refined look about them: the gnarls and twists of branches at higher elevations had been straightened, and the trunks held themselves more erect. Fewer roots and less underbrush got in our way, and the ground sloped more gently. Smells of wet earth, prodominant for most of the day, gave way to a refreshing smell of leaves. We spotted a motillo tree, silvery in the late afternoon light, which looked almost feminine with its skirtlike root buttresses. This was tabonuco forest.

SIERRA PALM

The sierra palm deserves to be named the official tree of El Yunque. It may come as a surprise to know these mountain palms comprise a separate forest type since they are actually found just about everywhere in the forest. Stand in a hundred different places, a thousand different places, and you will see sierra palms nearby. *Prestoea montana* heads the numbers lists in both tabonuco and palo colorado forest types; in fact, sierra palms outnumber tabonucos by a factor of three and palo colorados by a factor of four on an average plot of land. Barbara Bannister, in a study of the life cycle of sierra palms, calculated the densities of seeds, seedlings, young and mature trees on a square meter of forest in El Yunque. She estimated an average of 1.41

seeds, .75 seedlings, .24 young trees and .006 mature ones. If I take a few liberties —assuming that Bannister's meter is typical of the forest and calculating that a square yard is slightly less than a meter (which is 39.37 inches), that 4,840 square yards are in an acre and 28,000 acres are in the forest — I can make a very rough estimate of almost two hundred million sierra palm seeds within the Caribbean National Forest, more than 100 million seedlings, 32 and a half million young trees and slightly more than 800,000 mature trees.

The sierra palm also merits official-tree status because of its appearance. The most inept tree watcher can spot its large floppy quill-like fronds arching over a slender, ringed trunk. White pompomlike clusters of flowers grow below the fronds, and dense networks of prop roots on the ground look like fingers digging into soil. Sierra palms are unmistakable, and unmistakably tropical. Temperate rain forests have their ferns and mosses and dense vegetation and ever-present rains, but they have no palms.

When the sierra palm is a mere seedling, its leaves — flat and notched to resemble a V — look nothing like the majestic hovering fronds. Not until the plant reaches a height of one and a half feet do the leaves begin to transform into fronds. A blade grows out of the trunk, and narrow leaflets up to a yard long extend on both sides of the blade. Each year new blades open at the top of the palm while the lower ones

shed, forming raised scars around the trunk. As the palm grows, it acquires more scars and a longer trunk. Yet the fronds reach their mature size, as much as 20 feet long, even on relatively young trees. Short, almost trunkless palms can be seen squatting next to palms the height of a five-story building, both with the same long fronds.

The native sierra palm has no nut to match that of the imported coconut palm. Its lone edible offering is a bud, the heart of the palm, which can be used in salads but at the expense of the entire tree. Small black fruits growing from the flower clusters appeal to Puerto Rican parrots, which have made the fruit a staple of their diet. Even without coconuts, this is a versatile tree. People who lived in the forest in the early decades of this century remember its many uses — leaves for thatch, wood for narrow boards, canoe-shaped sheaths for children's play.

The sierra palm forest type cannot be as neatly classified as the first two types. The first two are based primarily on elevation ranges while the palm type is based on slope and soil conditions. Common to Caribbean montane (mountain) forests from Cuba to Tobago, the trees are especially common on steep slopes and stream banks above 1,500 feet where other trees have difficulty growing due to unstable, shallow and erosion-prone soils. These denser groupings, found as patches within both the tabonuco and palo colorado forests, form the third forest

SIERRA PALM IN DWARF FOREST

type. Such patches cover some 11 percent of the Luquillo Mountains.

Some scientists consider the sierra palm as a successional species, like Cecropia (yagrumo), which moves into open clearings and pioneers new forest growth, rather than as a separate forest type. But Bannister points out that sierra palms, contrary to what one would expect in a tropical forest, are astoundingly slow growers. While a Cecropia seedling can grow more than six feet in the same number of months, a palm seedling under average conditions increases only slightly more than an inch during that time. Even leaf litter can accumulate faster, burying fledgling trees in the process. Older trees fare little better, creeping upward at slightly more than half a foot a year. It takes sierra palms at least 20 to 25 years to reach reproductive size (18 feet), at least 53 years to touch the forest canopy. They have a curious mechanism in which the seedlings and young trees can remain in an almost dormant state under certain conditions, primarily in areas of deep shade, waiting patiently for increased light to nudge their growth. For this reason there is such a disproportionately large number of young palms compared to mature ones. More than half the seeds become seedlings; almost one-third of the seedlings becomes young trees; but only .3 percent of the young trees reach reproductive size, which is considered maturity. They are the Peter Pans of the forest community; in no hurry to grow up, they undoubtedly shake their fronds in disapproval at young eager beavers like Cecropia.

Tropical forests are impatient habitats, not about to wait around for such slow growers to rebuild their damaged areas. Sierra palm forest seems to exist where other trees cannot grow — on steep, high-elevation, wind-ward-facing slopes. Their anchorlike roots give them a great advantage in the unstable soils. Sierra palms not only survive but do well in eroded areas, where the unblocked sunlight provides optimum growing conditions. Regardless of the reasons they are there, palms are extremely helpful in protecting watersheds and stopping further soil damage. Some 26 of the tree species found in tabonuco and palo colorado forests also grow in the palm type, but the sierra palm is clearly dominant.

DWARF FOREST

On the tops of the mountains lies a neverland of stunted trees and dripping air plants, often barely glimpsed through thick cloakings of fog. It is called dwarf forest, the last of Luquillo's four forest types. The other types have been named in a logical fashion for their prominent trees, but scientists bowed to romance in dubbing the vegetation of the summits. Throughout the tropical world, this summit vegetation is known by several names — dwarf forest, elfin woodland, mountain thicket, cloud forest or mossy forest — all of which describe specific characteristics but fail to convey the total picture. To be accurate, though, local scientists only partially bowed to romance, for in fact there is no prominent tree in Luquillo's dwarf forest. Forest researcher Peter Weaver has studied the dwarf forest extensively. When I asked him his choice for the most interesting or distinctive dwarf forest tree, he stalled for a moment before deciding on two choices — roble de sierra (*Tabebuia rigida*) and nemocá. Roble de sierra translates as mountain oak although it is actually a member of the bignonia family. It is a small tree, found solely in the upper Luquillo Mountains, and the only member of its genus to have a single leaf rather than a cluster of leaves on each stalk. Nemocá is the tree with the unusual wood grain. Weaver likes it for its pagodalike branching and attractive wood buttresses. Later, he added a third — guayabota de sierra (*Eugenia borinquensis*), a small tree with round leaves that is found only in eastern Puerto Rican mountains. These trees, and in fact all trees found in dwarf forest, are actually stunted versions of trees also found in the lower palo colorado forest. A few scientists consider dwarf forest as merely a subdivision of palo colorado, made different by very special conditions, conditions found on only two percent of the Luquillo Mountains.

The conditions are these: Dwarf forest exists on peaks and ridges with elevations greater than 2,500 feet. Temperatures are relatively cool; in fact, the 66 degrees Fahrenheit average recorded on one peak puts dwarf forest in a temperate rather than a tropical climate. Cottony cumulus clouds enshroud the peaks as they move across the island. The cloud base is usually some 1,800 to 2,250 feet above sea level, well below the dwarf forest. The clouds and the accompanying fogs and mists contribute to the low temperatures, for they shut off almost half the amount of sunlight that reaches the coast. They also bring the rains, an average 180 inches a year. Additional moisture, some ten percent of the rainfall, reaches the vegetation through droplets of water that has condensed from the fog. Relative humidity averages 98.5 percent. Soil becomes extremely saturated, resembling that found in a swamp.

The trade winds bring the clouds. These winds are very predictable, continually buffeting the mountains from the northeast. Only occasional storm systems cause a change in this pattern. One group of scientists feels the winds are the dominant force behind dwarf forest. They point out that dwarf forest exists on the wind-exposed sides of the mountains; on the leeward sides, where the grounds are wet but the winds not so strong, sierra palms predominate. But other scientists disagree, citing the unrelenting fog, cool temperature and saturated soils as the primary dwarf-forest makers.

But how does the fog, and the accompanying high humidity, actually dwarf these trees? In such dampness, trees sweat less, and transpiration (sweating) is essential to growth. With little transpiration, minerals get pumped through the systems slowly, and trees don't grow properly. The reduced light caused by cloud cover in turn reduces the amount of photosynthesis that goes on. Saturated soils also impede growth. Roots growing in the dense muck can't breathe well; moreover, organic matter breaks down slowly, returning nutrients to the soil slowly; consequently, the roots develop poorly and remain shallow. In order to survive such conditions, trees adapt, developing stunted trunks, interconnected root systems and leathery leaves. Some species don't survive at all; palo colorado, for one, is virtually never found in the dwarf forest. The number of tree species that do grow here, 43, is small for tropical forests, and the common species are far fewer.

The interconnected root systems along with the forest's tangled branches and vines seem to work together as a brace to protect the trees in times of crisis. Then these rugged dwarfs resemble football linebacks; with their arms linked and their feet well planted on the soil, they tend to weather hurricane-strength winds and rain better than many of the trees at lower elevations. And well they should, for, once the forest is destroyed, it takes new trees a very long time to grow back. In 1968, a small plane crashed into the side of East Peak. There were no survivors, and a portion of dwarf forest was shaved away. Weaver subsequently studied the area. He found that certain aspects of the forest had recovered within three years. There was an abundance of byrophytes, lichens, algae and ferns, more species than found in the neighboring forests, but these are small plants, not trees. Even now, trees have yet to take hold, and he estimates it will take a couple of centuries for the forest to recover completely from this crash.

While tabonuco forest, with its great diversity of stately trees, is an impressive, well-heeled sort place, dwarf forest is intriguingly eccentric. The fog does much to create this intrigue. Many visitors to El Yunque, especially those with cameras, consider it great luck to reach the peaks when there is no fog and views extend down tiers of greenery patched together by stands of sierra palms and the silvery undersides of Cecropia.

But the fog is a trademark of tropical rain forests. When one is in the proper mood, it seems more silent, more mysterious and more magical than the gentlest of snowstorms. Unlike the tip-toeing-cat-feet fog of Sandburg, El Yunque's fog moves in briskly, hurried along by the winds, more in the style of a Mary Poppins. The world whitens out, the dramatic views vanish, and you suddenly find yourself on intimate terms with the immediate vegetation. Trees look like shrubs, rarely growing more than 12 feet high and sometimes as short as three or four feet. You are on eye level with the forest. Trunks curve their short way skyward, and twisted branches seem to gesticulate to each other. Tree barks, even leaves, are mottled with lichens, mosses, algae, ferns and

liverworts. Bromeliads of all sizes crowd branches and trunks, leaving room for a few spindly anthurium and tiny orchids. In short, a miniature forest grows on each tree. Some of the air plants lie flat against the bark like paint on a palette, others hang down like beards. All look very wet: when you squeeze them, water trickles down your wrist. The environment is so wet, in fact, that algae growing on branches and other vegetation are the sorts normally found in freshwater ponds. Random roots shoot down from branches, and new shoots rise out of fallen trees. Ground-level roots weave intricate patterns, and it is often hard to tell which roots belong to which trees. The ground itself is covered with a carpet of decaying logs and leaves and the same potpourri of mosses and other plants that cover the trees. In places, walking on the ground feels like walking on a foam mattress, but it is much more treacherous. This is perhaps the extreme in vegetative chaos. As you begin to get a feel for the place, the wind suddenly whisks the fog away, the rest of the world dramatically reappears, and the dwarf forest fades into the background.

Due to its inaccessible nature, dwarf forest has been studied less than other regions of tropical forests, which in turn have been studied less than temperate forests. Roads built to El Yunque Peak in the 1930s and East Peak in the 1960s have given scientists like Weaver unique opportunities to learn more. Both peaks were altered by the arrival of the roads and subsequent communications facilities, but West Peak, just off the East Peak Road at an elevation of 3,445 feet, remains basically untouched. In the 1960s Richard Howard of Arnold Arboretum in Massachusetts chose West Peak for a decade-long study of dwarf

*Tabonuco
trunk and its
epiphytic
lodgers.*

forest vegetation. An old footpath which crossed the peak was revitalized, and specific plants along the path were identified for study. A small shelter was established at the top to store instruments, shelter scientists and serve as a lookout. Within a year, the intense humidity had resulted in the corrosion and electrical failure of most equipment, but by then enough data had been taken. Dozens of participating scientists collected everything from rainfall to liverworts; studied roots, algae, lichen and mosses; and analyzed the chemical components of a variety of plants. The results of their studies were presented in 17 articles that spanned various issues of the *Journal of the Arnold Arboretum.*

All they wanted to do, Howard wrote, was to answer three basic questions: "What was present; under what conditions did it live; and what was it doing?" Along the way they answered thousands of variations on their three questions. As I looked through the articles, I jotted down a few of the results, which now seem like the details one might find on an Arnold Arboretum dwarf forest study trivia game.

A measurable amount of rain falls on the peak an impressive 350 days a year, they discovered. Clouds cover the peak 60 percent of daytime hours, 100 percent of nighttime hours. Winds are strongest at night, weakest in the afternoon. The peak shelters at least 126 types of epiphytic algae, algae that need the mechanical support of other plants or objects. Aerial roots, rare in temperate regions, are prolific here, dangling from trees, shrubs, vines, small plants. Earthworms up to 24 inches long are common in the clay-rich surface soil. Axillary stems, such as those on Marcgravia vines, can change from young to mature forms and back again; the Marcgravia

vines often convert back to their young form when they contact a new tree. The peak cannot be called a mossy forest, for mosses actually take a back seat to the liverworts, a moss relative. While there are some 18 species of mosses here, there are probably more than 100 species of liverworts. On the peak's windy eastern face, the vegetation is the most tangled and the shortest, less than six feet in height; on the summit the canopy reaches 12 feet, on protected slopes, 15 feet; and on the lee side sierra palms and other trees reach up to 30 feet. One third of the plants studied grow only in Puerto Rico.

In summing up the studies, Howard wrote, "the summit dwarfed forests of the Caribbean islands, being small in extent and occurring on small land masses, are different from the mossy forest, the cloud forests, the upper montane rain forests and similar formations previously described in other parts of the world. Their characteristics, however, are similar and the idea of a selection of species within a microclimate is an appropriate one. This is indeed a special ecological niche."

El Toro Trail loops its way through all four forest types in the Luquillo Mountains. This is the longest maintained trail in the national forest, and on the island. It follows the ridge of Luquillo's primary mountain chain, connecting Road 191 in the heart of the forest with Road 186 to the southwest. The region it crosses is quite rugged and remote, inaccessible except by foot and then only along the trail. To leave the trail is to enter a maze of valleys and tousled vegetation that is difficult to penetrate. It is the sort of place a group might (and once did) choose to train for a Himalayan expedition. El Toro Trail is not heavily used, and you can often travel its six-mile length and see no one else.

On maps the trail has two names. East of El Toro Peak is officially known as the Tradewinds National Recreation Trail, west of the peak as El Toro National Recreation Trail. It seems, according to one source, Forest Service personnel had to come up with a minimum of two national recreation trails within the forest; since El Toro was apparently the only one that met the criteria, it was divided and named twice.

El Toro provides a good example of the difficulties of trail maintenance in the tropics. Originally built by the Civilian Conservation Corps in the 1930s, it provided an access for people who were working in the forest and living in nearby communities. Roads and cars eventually eliminated most of its use. Without hikers, the trail deteriorated. Heavy rainfall, landslides and hurricanes sped up the deterioration, and fast-growing, light-loving vegetation obscured much of the route. I first walked along El Toro in the mid-1970s. New to the island, I was accompanying a friend and several foresters who were interested in resurrecting the trail. As it turned out, it was not a hike as I, having come from the deserts of Arizona, understood hikes to be. We didn't seem to be taking an old trail but creating a new one — cutting at vines and ferns with a machete, stepping over landslides, wriggling our way through shrubs, tearing at cobwebs, forever backtracking.

Six years later I took the trail again. Much had improved. Some 60 young people from the Young Adult Conservation Corps (YACC) had recently worked for more than two and a half months (when funding expired) to repair the trail. Trail repair is no easy task in a rain forest. Drainage ditches must be dug, gravel spread to prevent erosion, landslides bolstered up, all the while preserving the natural forest beauty. When the YACC left, one-third of the route was neatly completed, with ditches, gravel, rock borders and several rain shelters. Beyond, the trail was equally easy to follow but harder to hike, an occasional obstacle course of squishy mud, mossy rocks, small landslides and overhanging plants. On a third trip several years later I found El Toro basically unchanged. Its designation as a national recreation trail, as two national recreation trails in fact, has promoted El Toro to primary trail status, assuring its continued maintenance.

El Toro is one of those trails along which you tend to amble at a leisurely pace — stopping to take in the thick stands of sierra palms, noticing the parasol shapes of tree ferns, examining a UFO-shaped rock, touching moss on a tree, contemplating lizards on rocks — before you suddenly realize you still have a long way to go. This early part of the trail meanders through palo colorado forest type, interspersed with occasional patches of sierra palm forest along the ravines. You realize your hike is far from over when you round the umpteenth bend and see, through a break in the trees, miles of jungly forest and a humped peak in the distance. The peak is El Toro, presumably so-named because it is shaped like a bull. As the trail approaches El Toro, it offers a couple of far-flung views east to the San Juan metropolitan area, but by then leisurely curiosity has for the most part given way to a dogged determination to reach your destination. By the time you loop your way up the slick slopes leading to the peak, you are in the realm of the dwarf forest type, but you may be in no mood to notice. Standing at the top, you have completed two-thirds of the journey (unless you have to retrace your steps to get back to your car); beyond, the trail descends in straightforward fashion to Road 186. The final forest type, tabonuco, lies in the lower elevations near 186.

Grass, several boulders and low-lying thicket top El Toro, highest peak in the Luquillo Mountains at 3,524 feet. It is the odd-peak-out in Puerto Rico, for no media antenna towers over it. A collapsed metal shelter once detracted from the pristine setting, but it has since been removed. When you reach the summit, you have reached the top of eastern Puerto Rico. Views unfurl southeasterly to the Humacao valley and the Caribbean Sea, easterly to the Navy's Roosevelt Roads and two offshore islands, northeasterly to San Juan and the Atlantic Ocean. If you really want to see these landmarks, bring along a good book, for the peak will be draped in fog much of the time.

When Antillean temperatures soar into the 90s and the humidity follows close behind, it is time to visit the Río Mameyes or one of its tributaries in the northeastern section of the Caribbean National Forest, where many of the very best swimming holes on the island can be found. It is time to cool off, to slip into crisp mountain water and sun atop giant boulders. It is not the time to notice several majestic trees in the area, trees with straight trunks and rough bark and leaves high in the canopy, trees which are probably the most alluring and valuable of all the trees in tropical America. Forget about trees for the moment: go swimming first.

The Mameyes Pool is the best-known of the forest's swimming holes. Some 15 feet wide, 60 feet long and relatively shallow, it is wedged between jagged rock on one side and a swampy plain on the other. The Río Mameyes slips rather than plunges into it, making its water clear and still and its pebbly bottom visible even at the deepest point of six feet. A spindly ausubo tree arches over the center of the pool.

When there is no flooding, a swampy plain behind the Mameyes Pool is a favored local campground. Hundreds of sierra palms crowd the plain, and there are also a number of Pterocarpus trees. This is the island's largest mountain stand of *Pterocarpus officinalis*, a tree of eerie beauty. In English, it is named swamp bloodwood for the blood-red latex in its bark. One of its Spanish names, sangre de dragón (dragon's blood), also alludes to this characteristic; a second, palo de pollo (chicken's feet), refers to the relatively straight trunk and the tree's massive buttress roots. These support roots are immense: growing to 15 feet up the trunk and 10 feet along the ground, they resemble planks distorted by a fun-house mirror. In one place dozens of Pterocarpus seem to have grown in a circle. Buttress roots swirl out from all sides of the trees, and ferns grow out of the roots. All that is missing to complete the strange setting is a cauldron in the center of the circle.

I'm sorry, I forgot: you are swimming, not tree watching.

Another pool I have visited is about a half-hour's hike away along the Río de la Mina, a tributary of the Mameyes. Almost circular in shape and some 25 feet in diameter, it is fed by a 60-foot-high waterfall that plunges between cliffs. Strata lines on the cliffs resemble petroglyphs, and a large rock in the center looks like a hump-shaped Taino cemí figure. The vegetation forms an amphitheater around the pool: mosses and ferns grow in the cliffs while vines, tree ferns and the bright yellow bracts of wild plantain add exotic detail to the forest.

One of the most dramatic (and hardest to reach) pools is downriver from the Mameyes Pool, along a canyonlike stretch of river where huge boulders derail the water, and pools, chutes and waterfalls are a dime a dozen. At one point the river slips along an S-shaped curve, then disappears between an eight-foot-wide chasm. From a keyholelike vantage point at the right of the curve, one looks far down into an oblong pool, perhaps 35 feet long, wedged between sheer mossy cliffs topped by jungly forest. In the distance is yet another pool.

The prettiest route to these and other pools in this remote region of the forest is along La Coca Trail. It starts at Road 191 below Yokahú Tower, wending its way through forest to the Río Mameyes and the start of the Bisley Trail, which in turn connects with an old logging road, now rutted and closed to traffic. Beyond, a narrow, paved road leads to the community of Sabana at the northeast edge of the forest. Both La Coca and Bisley are referred to by foresters as secondary (less used) trails. About half the trails in El Yunque, totaling more than 15 miles, are secondary. Since they receive fewer hikers than the primary trails, they also receive less maintenance. Their condition depends on the vagaries of nature and the work load of Forest Service personnel. La Coca crosses Quebrada La Coca twice and Río de la Mina once before it reaches the Río Mameyes. Heavy rains turn the quebrada (stream) into a river and the rivers into torrents; afterwards, the trail tends to vanish on both sides of the banks. These secondary trails perform disappearing acts on dry land as well. One moment the path is wide and well defined, as if trod on by many hikers, and one moves along with great confidence; the next minute it is gone, replaced by an unbroken maze of forest. Flooding, the slope of the land and the tropic's prolific growing capabilities have been suggested as reasons for this now-you-see-it-now-you-don't peculiarity, but the moments in which the trails choose to vanish seem a bit more whimsical to me, not quite so prone to logical explanation. The first time I hiked along La Coca, I noticed a wooden sign at the trailhead, optimistically pointing the way to Río Mameyes, 2.7 kilometers; Bisley Trail, 4.5; Sabana, 8.4. Several hours later, having gone in circles for much of the afternoon, I returned to the trailhead and studied the sign more carefully. Another exasperated soul had crisscrossed the word "Sabana" with knife cuts; at that point, I understood why.

On your return trip along La Coca Trail, after you have cooled off in one of the pools, take some time to look at the forest around you. Like the trail, most of it is secondary — secondary tabonuco forest type. In this case, "secondary" means forest that has grown back on land that was deforested. Trees are relatively young and short, the underbrush dense. Occasional banana plants and citrus trees remain from earlier farming efforts. New, fast-growing species mingle with a few resilient native timber trees such as guaraguao (*Guarea guidonia*, known in English as American muskwood) and granadillo (*Buchenavia capitata*). The forest's namesake, the tabonuco tree, has not been able to make a comeback here. In its place are a number of mahogany trees.

The Caribbean National Forest is, as its name states, a national forest. It is not a national park. National parks were established as lands to be set aside for preservation and recreational enjoyment. National forests, run by the U.S. Forest Service, were created so that their resources — timber, water, recreation, wildlife and others — would be wisely managed. In the decade prior to World War II, the Forest Service and the local Civilian Conservation Corps planted much of the forest that now dominates the region around La Coca Trail. With an eye to harvesting the mature trees decades later, Luquillo foresters tested native (natural) and exotic (non-native) species with good lumber potential. Of all the exotic species tested, mahogany was felt to have the greatest promise. Between 1933 and 1945 two million seedlings were planted on these lower slopes. Mahogany had reached the Luquillo Mountains.

🌿 Along Road 988 near the community of Sabana, less than a mile north of La Coca Trail, lies a mahogany plantation. A wall of exceptionally tall tree ferns along the southern side of the narrow road bends toward the sunlight. No signs announce the plantation, no roads wind through it. The path leading into it is a path in name only; passersby would not notice the flattened vegetation which marks its start. Ferns and other plants cover the ground, and scattered large trees grow above the young ones. It looks like youthful forest. I would never guess it was a plantation.

"I prefer to call them plantings," forester Jerry Bauer tells me. It is the autumn of 1988. Bauer and I have taken many weekend hikes into the forest; today he is showing me some of what he does during the week. He prepared his Master of Science thesis for the State University of New York on the development and growth of mahogany in line plantings, and he used this site in his research. The word plantation, he feels, conjures up an image of bare ground under symmetrical rows of trees, and the Caribbean National Forest, with its exuberant capacity for growth, has no such staid plots. Line plantings, trees planted in parallel lines while the rest of the forest is left untouched, is the most promising technique for growing timber in tropical forests. This method produces desirable tree species while maintaining the natural forest. The natural forest in turn acts as protection for the newly planted trees, which eventually grow and form a closed canopy over the site.

Dressed in his Forest Service garb — cap and buckle with FS insignia along with a teeshirt, khaki-green pants, heavy boots — Bauer is a youthful-looking man around forty years old who has a partiality to chewing tobacco and a propensity to speaking his mind. He came to Puerto Rico from farm country in southern Illinois by way of a stint in Honduran forests with the Peace Corps. Southern Illinois is apparently far enough south to produce a strong Southern accent in its residents, and when he speaks, Bauer often violates certain basic grammatical rules like subject-verb agreement. This roughhewn English belies a clear, bright and highly organized mind, one that can make an impromptu talk in the forest sound like an outlined lecture.

A forester from the island of St. Vincent named Rob and Bauer's eight-year-old son Nestor have joined Bauer and me on this outing. We stand within the muggy, gnat-laced environs of the plantings. "When the Forest Service purchased this plot, in December, 1935, it was bare land, planted in root crops like ñame and yuca. All the land in this area was either bare or high graded." High graded means the best trees had been cut and taken out.

Bauer speaks of the mahogany that was planted between 1933 and 1945. Initially, foresters encountered difficulties in establishing mahogany within the forest. Bauer lists sev-

Jerry Bauer inspecting a 13-year-old mahogany line planting in the Zarzal area.

eral reasons. "First, one of the species of mahogany they used grows primarily in dry areas; the rain forest was too wet for it. And at that time the land was all bare and open." Although mahogany trees seem to need some kind of forest disturbance in order to get started, they perhaps found growth difficult on those open sites. "Also, the soil probably lacked the right nutrients after decades of being farmed."

For the current planting, Bauer made an inventory of the tract. If a tract has 40 or more trees of desirable species per acre, foresters leave it alone or manage it to help it grow naturally. If there are fewer, foresters plant. His tract didn't have the minimum number. Most of the existing trees were robles (*Tabebuia heterophylla*), which is a pioneer species, that is, one of the first species to grow on forest that has been cleared. Today, most robles are

small, good only for posts and of little importance to wildlife. So he planted. Desirable trees within the strip were not touched. Bauer points to a native maría (*Calophyllum calaba*) which remains.

I ask him why foresters like to plant and arrange, rather than let nature take over. By managing, Bauer explains, "we can do in ten years what would take 25 to 30 naturally." By planting, "we're finding that when we open

up the forest for a species like mahogany, the light coming in also helps other trees. I now see a couple of ausubo that weren't there before we started planting. Birds are coming in — there's a nest in one of the mahoganies — to eat fruits of plants like cachimbó, camasey, rabo de ratón, and they drop the seeds in other places. Foresters aren't just helping mahogany. They might thin a mahogany if it meant letting an important native species grow better."

Top left:
Mature mahogany seeds inside the seed capsule.
Botton left:
Forester Monty Maldonado and forest worker planting a young mahogany seedling in a cleared "strip" in secondary forest.

Top right:
Forestry technicians Rafael Corcino and Miguel Figuroa measuring 6-year-old mahogany line planting.
Botton right:
Mahogany in the Bisley canopy.

And what about this concept of desirable species? What makes one species more important than another? Who decides? "Wadsworth did the early major studies, compiling a list of important species. That list is continually updated, a consensus of a number of people working in the forest. They consider lumber quality, wildlife, watershed protection, aesthetics, whether or not the tree is endemic [native and restricted to the area]. The maría tree in my plot, for example, was left because it was a food source for wildlife. Sure, there can be differences of opinion. Someone might take out a tree I would consider should be left, but the benefits of management far outweigh such incidents." And they are? "By managing we can produce goods and services needed by the people, and by protecting environmental integrity, we can enhance the forest."

And why plant mahogany, which is not native to Puerto Rico? "After its initial problems, foresters made some changes, and mahogany began to show success. It has a high market value, it's always in demand. And it can be planted under a system that is ecologically sound and aesthetically pleasing." Later in the day, Bauer gives additional reasons justifying mahogany plantings. Though not native to Puerto Rico, mahogany is common in similar types of forest elsewhere in tropical America. One species of mahogany has existed on the island for almost a quarter millennium, and the trees have been naturalized (regenerating naturally) in Puerto Rico for most of this century. In addition, it has a cousin, the guaraguao, also of the mahogany family, which is native to the island.

Frank Wadsworth, former director of the Caribbean National Forest, and, as Bauer mentions, author of the early lists of important forest trees, later expands on this topic of planting exotic species in the forest. Wadsworth feels it is valid to plant exotic species if native species have been tried first and haven't worked. "Less than one percent of tropical species are on our site. Do we blame insularity? Do we exclude other species just because they couldn't make it across the water to reach Puerto Rico?" He gives as an example the eucalyptus tree, native to Australia. "Eucalyptus was planted in Brazil during the last century, and there now have been some five generations. I've heard that Australians who go to Brazil can't even identify it anymore." This is partly because the Brazilian eucalyptus is a hybrid of various Australian species which were planted side by side.

Wadsworth gives two reasons why exotics are often more promising than native species, "promising" in this case meaning trees that are healthy, are growing well and reasonably fast, and can produce marketable timber. "First, natives all over the world are products of survival, not growth rate, and they tend to be slow growers." Some of Luquillo's native trees have astoundingly slow growth rates. "The average [native] tree growth is .07 inch a year. Nobody can wait for that, so why take [those] trees out? Secondly, being native, natives have their enemies in the forest, while the exotics don't, yet. The eucalyptus grows well in Brazil and hasn't been seriously attacked by insects. Foresters tell me they will keep using it as long as it works, then they will try something else."

Take, as a case in point, Spanish cedar (cedro hembra, *Cedrela odorata*), a species of the mahogany family that exists throughout the low rain forests of tropical America and is native to Puerto Rico. It is considered one of the most important timbers for local use in tropical America, having been used for everything from dugout canoes to carved saint figures. But it had trouble with Luquillo's wet soils, and few seedlings survived. "Holdridge [a research forester involved in the pre-World War II reforestation program] planted some 2,000 acres of Spanish cedar," Wadsworth reminisces, "which was almost an entire failure. The insects attacked it. The trees looked yellow and hung willowy. Some think it was aluminum toxicity in the soil. Holdridge kept saying, 'You have to find the perfect site.'" The perfect site was never found. Conversely, "Spanish cedar is a wonder in Africa [where it was introduced]." In short, "Foresters in Africa are planting our trees, and we theirs. Mahogany there doesn't have the shoot-borer that is a problem here. On the other hand, Asian cedar works well here."

Bauer started his mahogany plantings by calculating a line that ran from the road in a straight east-west direction. Flagging tape tied to poles marks the line, called a strip. He then marked a series of parallel strips some 33 feet (11 meters) apart. A crew came in with machetes and chainsaws to clear a nine-foot swath along each strip. They rid the swath of plants and felled or girdled the trees. Girdling, which is safer than felling for the crew, involves cutting a band of bark around a tree. Nutrients manufactured by the tree's leaves can no longer travel down the trunk to the roots, which eventually starve. To help things along, Bauer added the herbicide Roundup to the girdles. Between each strip lie some 24 feet of forest.

Meanwhile at the forest's small nursery, seed capsules collected from mature mahogany trees in the forest were set out in the sun to dry. When they split, the inner seeds were extracted, dried an additional day or two and eventually planted in tilled, weed-free seedbeds. Within a month, they germinated; within a year, they were three feet tall and ready to be transferred to the field. Lifted from the soil with a spade, stripped of leaves, pruned of a few roots and packed in cloth bags filled with wet spagnum moss, they were delivered to Bauer's tract and planted seven and a half feet apart along the strips. The trick of line planting is to give the trees enough open light so they will grow optimally and enough shade along the sides so they will head for the light in a straight line. At least once a year, for three to five years, the strips had to be cleared with a machete in order to free the young mahogany.

The trees in Bauer's tract are almost six years old when we see them. Bauer pronounces them established in the forest. The underbrush, no longer cut, already rises to our thighs, and the trees themselves measure some 15 feet tall. Lichens and mosses give the bark the mottled look most forest flora gets. They are nice trees from a forester's point of view: almost all have forked above ten feet, which is the minimum height for lumbering specifications.

Rob asks about the shoot borer, a moth considered the single most damaging problem for mahogany. The insect enters the tree and lays eggs which soon become larvae. The larvae feed on the tender part of the wood, often the newly-forming central shoot, causing it to branch. Though not usually fatal, shoot borer can disfigure trees so that they look more like orchard than lumber trees, making them unacceptable for harvesting specifications. Bauer feels shoot borer is more of a problem on the mainland than on islands.

In addition, "it gets exaggerated and mistaken for other problems, such as poor management." When Bauer's mahogany trees were three years old, he checked for the pest. Eighteen percent of the trees had been attacked; they were pruned back. Only five percent were attacked again, a positive sign.

At about this point in the lecture Nestor writhes with the impatience of a young boy forced to listen to interminable adult conversations. We get into Bauer's yellow Volkswagon to drive to a second site.

🍃 Mahogany is probably the best-known and most highly esteemed wood ever dragged out of a forest. The very word, mahogany, and its Spanish equivalent, caoba, conjure up visions of exotic elegance. In an interesting book titled *Mahogany of Tropical America*, Bruce Lamb, who worked with the Forest Service in Puerto Rico for a year and a half in the 1950s, traces the origins of these words. The Spanish word comes from "caoban", the name the Arawak Indians of Hispaniola used for the tree. "Mahogany" derives from the Nigerian word for African mahogany. Slaves captured from the Yoruba tribe and brought to Jamaica noticed a tree which resembled one they knew in Africa. Though not the same species, the African version does belong to the same general family of trees, the Meliaceae (mahogany) family. This family includes 15 species in Africa and three in the New World tropics. The slaves called the new tree "m'oganwo", and by 1700 Europeans were using the word we use today.

Of the three New World species, *Swietenia macrophylla* (Swietenia refers to a Dutch naturalist, Baron Gerard Swieten) has the largest distribution, ranging from central Mexico down to Bolivia and southern Brazil. Known commonly as big-leaf or Honduran mahogany, it is considered the oldest of the species, most likely originating in South America, then moving up into Central America and eventually over to the West Indies. The West Indian species, known as *Swietenia mahogoni*, Dominican or small-leaf mahogany, is native to southern Florida, the Bahamas, Cuba, Jamaica and Hispaniola (Haiti and the Dominican Republic). It arrived in the Caribbean far enough in the past to evolve into a separate species but recently enough to be able to fertilize naturally with its ancestor, big-leaf mahogany. One can only wonder why the small-leaf species never made it from Hispaniola to Puerto Rico. Perhaps the Mona Passage proved too wide, or perhaps it would have, given another millennium or so. A third type, *Swietenia humilis*, hugs the western coast of Central America and plays a minor role in the mahogany drama.

Because of its extensive distribution and hardy nature, big-leaf mahogany has become the most important species for commercial purposes. Although the wood of small-leaf mahogany is considered superior in terms of wood quality, it has been removed from just about all of its original range and has proved delicate in adapting to new conditions. Interestingly, a hybrid of the two, known, logically, as medium-leaf mahogany, has sprung up on plantations where big-leaf and small-leaf mahogany coexist. The hybrid seems to have the hardiness of the former and the superior wood of the latter, a promising combination.

For centuries, Indians throughout the Americas made use of mahogany trunks, carving them into large dugout canoes. From the moment the Spaniards spied the tree on Hispaniola, they realized its value as a lumber wood. Lamb quotes Oviedo, who wrote prophetically in 1535, "caoban is a tree with the best wood found on Hispaniola, other islands and the mainland. This wood would be esteemed in all parts of the world." The cathedral in Santo Domingo, dating back to the early 1500s, provides the earliest existing example of mahogany used in the New World. Its cross and carved woodwork remain in excellent condition. A half century later, mahogany was being used for trim and furniture in Spain's prestigious Escorial. Ship builders appreciated the timber's many qualities, and they used mahogany in constructing most of the larger ships in the Spanish Armada. Cuba flourished as a ship-building center. England, though long-time enemy of Spain, came to hold mahogany in the same esteem. They, too, used it in ship building. It soon overtook walnut and oak as a preferred furniture wood. Jamaica became England's original supplier of mahogany, and British Jamaicans later established a colony in Belize, formerly British Honduras, primarily to extract mahogany from its forests. The wood became so well known that aggressive lumber merchants in other parts of the world, particularly the Philippines, used the name mahogany to promote unrelated species. Today, the demand remains strong, but the once-vast natural supply has been reduced to stands in remote areas. Most mahogany is now grown on plantations.

Both the small-leaf and big-leaf mahogany were protagonists in the 1933-45 reforestation pro-

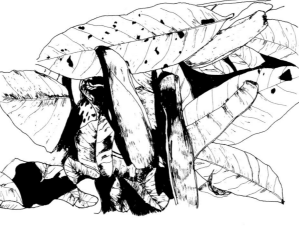

MAHOGANY SEEDS ON FOREST FLOOR

gram in Luquillo. About a million seedlings of each were planted. One would have expected the small-leaf mahogany to do well, being native to the West Indies, but it is a tree of dry coastal regions. This was the species which, Bauer explains, couldn't adapt to the poor soil conditions resulting from the forest's high rainfall. Its survival rate was low to medium, its growth rate slow, and when it did grow, the result was a stunted little specimen, not what one would want in a timber tree. On the other hand, the big-leaf mahogany did do well initially, with a high survival rate and a medium growth rate, and foresters recommended introducing it into the natural forest, not merely in plantations. But, as Wadsworth points out in a later conversation, even the big-leaf mahogany became stagnated for a time, its growth slowed down, its crowns small, its branches deformed by repeated attacks of the shoot-borer. Yet most did survive and even flourish, developing trunks that could provide useful logs, and today, with experiments such as Bauer's, mahogany is showing good potential within the forest.

The second site we visit, also on the Sabana road, shows the results of letting nature take control. Mahogany has been planted here without benefit of management. The overhead canopy is dense, permitting little light to reach the ground. As a result, ground vegetation is sparse. This patch of forest looks darker, feels cooler and appears more tranquil than the first. Its mahogany trees are the same age as those we have just seen. "What do I got, look."

What Bauer has are trees no more than six feet tall with trunks the size of twigs, runty relations to the first group. In his book on mahogany, Lamb mentions that seedlings can persist for many years in medium shade but develop very slowly.

Bauer is a confirmed forester. He truly believes in the benefits of management, and he can get impatient with those who don't. He speaks of a 1985 survey. Six plots were measured for every tree or plant that was more than five feet tall. Contrary to what most would expect, secondary forest that had been left unmanaged showed less diversity of plants and trees than managed forest. "It's not just the numbers that count," he adds. "You have to look at what the forest is made of. One site may have more stems, but if they're all something like Calophyllum [maría], of which there're millions in the forest, who gives a damn?"

The third site we visit is on a slope behind the community of Sabana. This is a plantation. Here the mahogany trees are up to 50 feet tall, with trunks around which you can wrap your arms. They are beginning to reflect the majesty of the climax trees Oviedo once saw and foresters see today in remote tropical regions. Lamb describes the trunks of such trees — often over 100 feet in height and up to five feet in diameter, straight and clear of branches for up to 60 feet, supported by buttresses that can extend 15 feet up the trunk. Vines and epiphytes weave their own sort of lacework down the trunks. The shiny dark green leaves, made up of pairs of smaller leaflets and from eight to 16 inches long on the big-leaf mahogany, look tiny when seen from ground level. At certain times of year the leaves

turn a reddish-brown, and the tree can be easily spotted when flying over the forest canopy. This is one way foresters spot stands of mahogany in remote regions. Originally, the site where we stand was farm land, converted to a mahogany plantation in 1967. Bauer notes it must have had very few trees at the time of planting because there are no remaining stumps.

"This stand has set still the last ten years," he adds with an itchy tone to his voice. "It needs to be thinned so the trees will grow faster." Commercial thinning is done to ensure most trees are of uniform size when harvested, to give trees more breathing space so they will grow faster, and to rid the plot of poorly formed or diseased specimens. The thinned wood is usually removed and used, which is what Bauer would like to see happen. However, at the time of our visit a forest management plan that advocated a limited amount of harvesting has, after pressure from environmental groups, been relegated back to the drawing board, and a new plan hasn't yet been approved. Until it is, no cutting is being done in the forest. Bauer's frustration over this decision is evident.

To visit a third mahogany plantation we ford the Río Chiquito, stepping around a car being washed in the river. The plantation, on a slope next to the river, was created in 1963. Though these trees were more closely spaced than current line plantings, the forest has lost all signs of symmetry. The mahogany trees are up to 90 feet tall. Now the forest is regenerating itself, reproducing primarily young mahogany but also other tree species. Crowns touching each other mean these trees also need to be thinned. "After thinning, another 15 years and this plot will be ready to cut." He and Rob agree the site

Mahogany.

would be easy to work, being relatively flat and close to the road.

Ideally, mahogany trees should be harvested when they reach 40 to 50 years, with an average diameter of 60 centimeters (24 inches). In his book, Lamb points out that damage to the forest doesn't occur so much when trees are cut as when they are dragged out of the forest. He records a parallel between increased logging technology and increased forest damage, from early loggers who merely felled trees, rolled them by hand into a river and rafted them to the coast, to companies which invest big money in road-building equipment, tractors and log-hauling trucks. Trees of 24-inch diameters are large enough to meet lumber specifications, yet small enough to do a minimum of damage. As we leave the site, Bauer points toward the other side of the road. Private land, it is denuded for the most part, either abandoned or used as pasture. This is another unspoken plug for forest management.

Bauer is not against preserving some forest (that is, leaving it untouched). Many of those who are against lumbering in El Yunque would like to see the entire forest remain untouched. Bauer agrees with other foresters that preservation is a part of management. The problem comes in over how much. For Bauer, conservation is the wise use of an area, maximizing a variety of forest uses rather than optimizing any one resource. "El Yunque isn't here because we've done nothing," he notes. "It's here because we've managed."

"People tell me," he goes on, "'you cut down one or two trees and you'll change the environment.' I feel like shoving a satellite photo of eastern Puerto Rico in their faces." I've seen the photograph he is referring to: the forest boundaries are clearly visible. "There ain't no goddamn trees in eastern Puerto Rico except for the Caribbean National Forest. I can't buy that managing the forest is going to damage it." He has answers for other concerns about lumbering. To those who feel El Yunque is too small to give some forest up to lumbering: "Small is relative. Twenty eight thousand acres is small in the U.S., but it's humungous in Europe, where areas as small as five acres are managed." To those who feel that the targeted forest, though admittedly not virgin vegetation, is now well-developed, mature rain forest, the habitat of much wildlife, and should be left undisturbed: "You see? That means management has been successful, so give us a chance to do a second planting. The second will be even more successful."

Bauer mentions one opponent of timber harvesting who visited the forest and remarked that no trees should be planted. In his inimitable way, Bauer reminded the opponent he was using paper and writing with a pencil, and he asked him if he used toilet paper. "Trees must be grown. There is need for their products and someone must grow them. Our job as professionals is to meet the demands of society." He disputes the fairness of keeping the remaining U.S. forests pristine while buying lumber from Third World countries, and he disputes the effectiveness of telling Third World countries like Brazil, plagued with population explosions and economic and social crises, not to harvest timber. "Go ahead, tell them don't touch the forests, and we lose all. If we tell them, use some, we may lose some species, but we save others." Management, he feels, is the answer. "What more can we do for tropical America than show them how to use their forests?"

Rob, a Peace Corps worker and St. Vincent's lone forester, agrees. St. Vincent, he explains, is having no success in planting mahogany. After seeing the success here and talking to Bauer and others, he understands some of the mistakes being made on St. Vincent — using the wrong species, planting trees too young to compete with other vegetation, not checking for shoot borer before moving trees from the nursery. He is ready to go back and try some of the things he has learned.

Bauer wants to show us one last site. We take the Sabana road to the main forest road, start up the mountains, then jog to the right on a small, winding, rutted road toward the El Verde Field Station in the northwest part of the forest. When we reach the El Verde road, we detour slightly down the mountain to El Chapín Restaurant. Nestor, who has been reduced to chafing impatience over this circuitous morning outing, picks up slightly. Chapín is the name of a local marine fish. For years the small, tidy restaurant has been known for its excellent empanadillas (fried pastry shells) stuffed with chapín. It has been redecorated since I was last there; paintings of seascapes more New England than Puerto Rican hang on the walls. After having several empanadillas washed down with soft drinks, we feel better equipped to make our last stop.

This plot actually has a name. It is called Harvey's Plantation, for the man who created it back in 1931, before the Forest Service bought the land. At the entrance a dead tree has been blown from its trunk and is dangling in the branches of another tree, forming a monumental mobile. The plantation's trees, originally planted seven and a half feet apart, have been thinned a couple of times. Now they reproduce naturally. The mature trees range up to three feet in diameter. This is the goal of

every conscientious forester — to make a forest sustainable, able to maintain itself indefinitely while producing marketable timber. Harvey's Plantation is one of the 1933-45 mahogany plots which have been successful. The apparent reason is that, when foresters brought mahogany over from a plantation on St. Croix to be planted here, they inadvertently brought the hardier hybrid medium-leaf species. Over the decades, these surviving trees as well as more recently planted big-leaf and small-leaf species have intermingled throughout the forest, and it is now hard to find seeds which are not hybridized.

Like all the old plots, Bauer feels this one needs work to give the trees space to grow. "These big trees should be taken out," he fusses. "If not, a hurricane's going to get them." This is the most diverse of the plots we visit: ausubo, motillo and royal palms (*Roystonea borinquena*) grow along with the mahogany. Bauer explains that fully grown line plantings would look even more natural than this. He stoops to pick up a mahogany seed capsule, not yet mature, which a recent storm had knocked down. It looks like an elongated top. The outer shell, or pericarp, is sectioned into five sides; up to 70 flat, winged seeds are fitted between the pericarp and an inner core, which resembles finished mahogany wood in both color and pattern. When ripe, the pericarp sections curl back, and the wind picks up the seeds and scatters them through the forest.

As a finale to the day's outing, Bauer, always eager to make a point, drives us down the mountains through an area known as Guzmán. An extensive valley clefts the mountains, and steep slopes rise on both sides. Rivers flow down the slopes, eventually joining to form the Río Espíritu Santo. This valley reminds me of photographs I have seen of Haiti. The mountains are steep yet smooth and covered with a rich tropical green that looks like velvet. It is a very pretty landscape, but as you look more closely, you realize something is missing. The green comes from grasses, shrubs, crops. It is land devoid of trees. Here, cattle graze in pastures, and crops, in particular bananas, grow along the slopes. Bananas, Bauer mentions, create a lot of erosion and soak up a good amount of pesticides. "Now how can limited logging in the forest affect the watershed, as some claim, when the rivers pass through this farmland? That's where the pollution and sedimentation come from." As we descend, the Caribbean National Forest disappears behind us.

❧ A year after my visit to the mahogany plantings with Bauer, Hurricane Hugo passed over the Luquillo Mountains. About 80 percent of his plantings survived the hurricane, suffering primarily from broken branches. Most the casualties were caused by larger neighboring trees that toppled over. Bauer has now been gone from El Yunque for several years. The plantings, unattended and rarely visited, continue to grow, as do all the plantations we visited that day. In the current revised forest management plan, timber harvesting would occur on a much smaller scale than indicated in the 1980s plan, and for demonstration (not commercial) purposes only. As of 1996, it is not known whether or not this revised plan will be approved. The odds are good that the mahoganies Bauer had been so eager to harvest will succumb to senescence, not to the woodcutter's saw.

CHAPTER 9
A TROPICAL GREENERY

Most visitors to El Yunque have seen the Baño Grande Pool in the heart of the picnic area, and numerous hikers have cooled their feet on the banks of the Mameyes Pool. Yet within the forest there are a vast number of intriguing swimming holes, usually referred to as tanks, that remain uncharted and unexplored, perched for the most part high above human scrutiny. These tanks are actually collections of smaller pools clustered together in a rosette pattern and separated from each other by green walls. Visitors make their way down the walls to reach the pools, where they splash around for a bit, sip the water, and perhaps socialize with the pool's residents. In spite of the tanks' symmetrical beauty, humans wouldn't find them of great recreational value, for they rarely hold more than a gallon of water. Yet those who do use them — spiders, lizards and the like — undoubtedly rank them among the best of swimming holes. The tanks collect in bromeliads, one of the many tree-hugging plants that form part of the vast plant community in the Luquillo Mountains.

The sierra palm may be the most unmistakably tropical of El Yunque's tree species, but epiphytes — plants that grow on other plants, trees or objects and depend on them for support, from the Greek for "upon plant"

— make each and every tree trunk in the Luquillo Mountains markedly different from those of temperate forests. In temperate regions, tree trunks reign in a hiker's eye-level view of a forest, but in tropical regions, trunks scarcely figure into the picture. Much more conspicuous is the lush cloak of epiphytic plants covering the trunks. While the tropical forest floor contains more plants than the temperate floor, tropical trees host even more plants than the tropical floor. Which means that a lot of plants in the tropics are epiphytes.

By plants, I mean the leafy things often coaxed to maturity from a pot — the layman's, not the scientist's, definition of the word. To scientists, plants include all members of the vegetable kingdom. Herbs are plants with no permanent woody stems, shrubs are low-lying woody plants with several stems rather than a trunk, and trees are — usually — tall woody plants with a trunk.

No visual picture of a tropical forest is complete without the epiphytic plants that cling, climb, drop, dangle, arc, entwine, encircle and extend from trunks, branches, leaves, rocks and other epiphytes. Little sunlight reaches the forest floor in the tropics, and plants that want their place in the sun have had to climb. Though often called air plants, epiphytes live on more than air alone.

The forest's high rainfall and humidity have made their climb possible by ensuring a fairly constant supply of moisture, and the plants have developed other mechanisms to guarantee a proper balance of nutrients. Unlike parasitic plants, epiphytes use the trees merely for mechanical support. They request lodging from their hosts, not board.

The dwarf forests, with more-than-excessive humidity, produce the most exotic piggyback arrangements, but epiphytes are found throughout the mountains. Virtually every plant family in the forest has species which are epiphytic lodgers or parasitic boarders. They range from single-celled algae to hundred-foot-long lianas sprouting yard-long leaves. Mosses and mosslike liverworts set down carpets on trees and rocks. Lichens color tree bark with what looks like a well-weathered, rusting coat of white paint. Ferns in assorted degrees of delicacy angle out of trees like little flags. Tiny orchids perch on branches, oblivious as to whether the branches are dead or alive. Slender anthuriums, prized in floral shops for their statuesque heart-shaped flowers, make the most of litter collected in the crotches of trees. Bromeliads space themselves along branches as regularly as Christmas lights. Vines and the thicker lianas, perhaps the most characteristically tropical of all epiphytes, creep their way from the ground to sunny forest canopies, and young strangler figs send aerial roots from the canopies down to the ground.

Despite the preponderance of epiphytes, El Yunque also has its share of plants that grow on terra firma. Ferns mass together on patches of sunlit soil. Plants with edible tuber roots — yautía, ñame, and malanga among the most common — are easily recognized by their floppy leaves which grow in the shape, and almost the size, of an elephant's ear. Begonias — named for Michel Bégon, seventeenth-century governor of neighboring Santo Domingo — enliven the forest with their brightly veined leaves and waxy flowers. Also waxy are the rocket-shaped bracts of the ginger plants. Though not the commercial ginger species, their knobby roots give off the scent of the famous spice.

Heliconia caribaea holds a special place in the Luquillo plant community. In the same spirit that sierra palms should rank as the official tree of the forest, Heliconia, also referred to as wild plantain, should be named the official plant. In dank-green, canopy-darkened recesses of the forest, visitors come upon stunning natural gardens of Heliconia. Members of the banana family, these plants have similar paddle-shaped leaves, but no bananas. Instead, they produce splendid yellow or red bracts up to a foot long. Shaped like lobster claws piled on top of each other, the bracts resemble simpler versions of the bird of paradise flower. Heliconia often grow together in groupings of a dozen or more plants. Tiny pools of water collect within the bracts; hummingbirds use the water and, in thanks, aid in the plant's pollination.

Though they take a back seat to trees in the rain forest, plants have an even greater diversity of species, numbering in the thousands. Pity the poor specimens that don't have the showy bract of a Heliconia or the fancy design of a fern, for they go scarcely noticed in the greenery.

In an ironical touch that is nevertheless typical of the complex tropics, one of the most beloved plants in El Yunque is actually thought to be a tree. It is an outsized member of the class Filicinae, commonly known as the tree fern. These delicate parasols stand out like stilt walkers in sunny patches of forest and cling together like demure belles in protected portions of the upper mountains. Though tree fern trunks can grow well over 30 feet high, they are not "normal". Unlike most tree trunks, they do not expand as they grow; instead, they remain slender poles that rarely exceed five inches in diameter. The trunks are actually bundles of exceptionally elongated roots held together with pith and contained within a dark and scaly outer layer that is often decked with mosses, liverworts and smaller ferns. Though spindly, the trunks are sturdy and long lasting, and older mountain residents remember once using them to build homes. Carib Indians apparently used them to transport fire, which could somehow be kept within the trunk for hours without causing flame or smoke. A dozen or more fronds flop over the top of the trunks. Starting as tightly coiled fists, these elegant fronds unroll into majestic quills up to 12 feet long.

There are several species of tree-sized ferns in the Luquillo Mountains. The most common, *Cyathea arborea*, grows abundantly along Luquillo roads. Its trunk is spineless; a spiny relative found deep within the forest is the bane of cross-country hikers, who grab it for support — once. Ferns can be found most everywhere on the planet, but tree ferns have developed solely in moist tropical areas where their roots can be continually pampered in warm, water-logged, clayey soil.

🌿 A small stream known as Quebrada Juan Diego forms near El Yunque Peak and empties into Río de la Mina, one and a half miles below. Clear in dry weather but cappucino-colored after heavy rains, Juan Diego navigates a maze of moss- and algae-covered rocks. A short path starting at a bend

in Road 191 briefly parallels the stream through forest unaltered by man. Plants and shrubs grow down to water's edge, trees up to 80 feet high climb the slopes, and vines and aerial roots drop from branches. In several minutes, the path reaches two pools wedged against cliffs and separated by a ten-foot waterfall. Moisture darkens the cliffs, and plants have sprouted between stratum layers. Another fall can be glimpsed higher upstream, but the path ends at the pools.

Botanist George Proctor brings visitors to this path along Juan Diego to look at ferns, and he shows me the site one warm October day. The pools are surrounded by "an exceptionally large number of species, some of them rather interesting." When asked what constitutes an exceptionally large number, he says he would have to sit down and make a list, but he wouldn't be surprised if there were 100 species. We stop for a moment along the path. At first, it is hard to focus solely on ferns when surrounded by so much vegetation, but when I do, I see them in any number of places — on rocks, trunks, stems, the ground, even in the river.

Proctor, a slight man with elfish features, alert eyes and the somewhat disheveled look of a scientist immersed for decades in his research, quickly rattles off the scientific names of six species within hand's reach of us and 12 in the immediate area. He doesn't bother to learn common names for ferns, nor for any other plants. For one reason, many of the diverse tropical species are rare, and few have been fussed over to the point of receiving a common name. Also, scientific names are more practical; they are universally known and much more descriptive to the scientist. Plants are classified into categories. The two narrowest categories are genera and species,

*Bromeliads
on
sierra palm
trees.*

Tree fern.

Wild ginger.

which make up the Latinized scientific name of a plant.

Of the ferns we see, some look like trailing ribbons or lacy nosegays, others like serrated knives. Proctor points to a small fern attached to a rock in the middle of the stream. "*Calyptus rheophytus.*" A rheophyte is a plant which lives in an underwater habitat part of the time, in this case when the stream floods. Another species, seen upstream, grows almost exclusively under waterfalls. Several types of ferns are growing atop a tree that has fallen. Fallen trees provide great opportunities for collectors, who can examine species normally out of reach. He shows me a delicate cluster some five inches long. For a long time this species had been mistaken for another; Proctor realized the mistake by examining both ferns in living situations and noticing their different ranges and structures.

He peruses a tree trunk for the world's smallest fern. It is fan-shaped, wet, dark green and somewhat translucent; the average leaf is less than half an inch long. "*Trichonanes ovale.*" He mentions all names in a quick, off-hand manner and seems puzzled when I have to ask him to spell them. Nearby, a fern with large trailing leaves pokes out of a rock against a backdrop of liverworts. On the ground, a salaginella resembles tiny spinach rotini. We search for a certain ground fern. First identified in 1907, the species was not seen again until Proctor found one specimen, here, in 1987. Proctor combs the grasses, becoming increasingly fretful, until he finds it. It measures a foot long, with long oval leaves, serrated edges and deeply etched veins. "*Diplazium grandefolium.*"

Though it takes a bit of prodding to get him to admit it, George Proctor probably knows more about West Indian ferns than any

other person. Since he started fern hunting in Puerto Rico several years earlier for the island's Department of Natural Resources, he has discovered 80 species and hybrids, 13 of which grow only in Puerto Rico, bringing the total number on the island to 408. That, he is delighted to report, is two more than the entire number of fern species found in all of North America above Mexico. It is also almost a quarter of the island's known fern species, many of which may have continued to go undetected in the tropical greenery without a botanist of Proctor's stature on the scene.

How Proctor came to be an authority on Caribbean ferns makes an interesting story, one he doesn't mind telling me when we drive out to the forest earlier in the day. One cold winter morning in Boston in the 1930s, when the temperature hovered at 20 degrees below zero, Proctor, a young lad of 13, was shoveling 18 inches of snow from the front of his house. Six minutes into the unpleasant job — not five, not seven — he vowed he would move to the tropics one day. He had read a lot about them, and they fascinated him. While other boys doodled cars, Proctor doodled palm trees. For his sixteenth birthday he received a copy of the *Field Book of Common Ferns*, and he spent his spare time in the White Mountains that summer in search of ferns to identify. Fifty years ago he joined the American Fern Society; he imagines he is one of their oldest members. One of his mentors, William Maxon of the Smithsonian, had a lifelong interest in the ferns of Jamaica but never published his research. When Maxon died in 1947, Proctor decided to continue Maxon's work.

His introduction to the West Indies came as an extravagant coming-of-age experience that Proctor has often been tempted to write about. While completing graduate work at the University of Pennsylvania, he met the ornithologist James Bond at a luncheon at the Philadelphia Botanical Garden. When the Academy of Natural Sciences organized an expedition to the West Indies in 1948, Bond backed Proctor, who became the group's botanist. A Philadelphia millionaire chartered a yacht and sponsored the expedition as a tax write-off. Some of the journey's more memorable moments for the young Proctor included a wedding which everyone attended barefoot; Proctor's first plane ride, to Cienfuegos, Cuba, with Bond; and an encounter on San Andrés Island (off the coast of Nicaragua) with a Chinese market owner who, they realized in the course of their conversations, had the same Boston sea captain great-grandfather as Proctor. On nearby Providencia Island the millionaire remembered a wedding he had to attend in Philadelphia; the yacht returned north, leaving Proctor there to finish his study and find his own roundabout way home.

A year later, Proctor was living in Jamaica. Working on his doctoral thesis, he struggled to get by on $14 a week, lodging with a local family. He stayed on the island through several grants and a job as botanist with the Institute of Jamaica. He has published books on the ferns of Jamaica and the Lesser Antilles, the flora of the Cayman Islands, and a chapter on monocots as part of the flora of Barbados. In between botanical expeditions, Proctor married a Jamaican woman; they have five children, three of whom are adopted. They lived, and those remaining in Jamaica still live, in an old wooden house in Kingston which has survived three hurricanes, including the 1988 Gilbert.

At age 60, Proctor was forced to retire — "that was ridiculous, I was just getting

going" — so he came to Puerto Rico to work on the ferns of Puerto Rico and the Virgin Islands. His wife remains in Jamaica. He doesn't get to Jamaica often because the flight is expensive, and he would have to buy gifts for everyone; instead, he sends his wife the money.

❦ I first met Proctor a decade ago in a local travel agency where, coincidentally, we both brought copies of books we had recently published. In celebration, the travel agent opened a bottle of champagne. Half a decade ago I called him to ask if he would go with me to El Yunque to help me unravel its jumble of ferns. He agreed, and that trip forms the basis of this chapter. Proctor enjoys humor: he delivers it with deadpan seriousness, and it is never far below the surface of his conversations. While we were talking on the telephone, he gave me a tongue-in-cheek summary of what he was doing. He had finished working on the ferns of Puerto Rico and the Virgin Islands, a five-year project, Proctor began. (This study was recently published in book form as a special memoir edition by the New York Botanical Garden.) Now he was in the middle of another five-year project, on monocots. After that, he continued, he would go on to the dicots, which would be a ten-year project and would bring him to the ripe age of 80. From there he would tackle the little-studied ferns of Brazil, which would take him up to 100. I laughed along with him, then admitted I had no idea what "monocot" and "dicot" meant. Monocots, he explained, are flowering plants that sprout one leaf — grasses, corn plants, most grains. Dicots are flowering plants that sprout two leaves, and they include bean plants and virtually all trees.

Shamed in not knowing something as obviously basic as "monocot" and "dicot", I decided it was time to make some order out of the confusion of the scientists' plant kingdom. The Forest Service tropical forestry library stores several old botany textbooks, and I borrowed one of them. The book, by one Professor Raymond Pool, was a half century old, but I imagined (erroneously as it turned out) that the "foundations of plant science", the sub-title of the book, had not changed measurably. The godsend of the book was a family tree of the plant kingdom. Here all the taxonomic categories of this vast world were neatly hung on various willowy branches, from primitive phylums (divisions) hovering near the trunk to complex families topping the upper canopy. Each branch in turn was ordered from primitive to complex species. This I could understand.

At the bottom of this family tree bloblike slime molds hugged the ground opposite a severed branch which apparently symbolized some category now extinct. Two low-lying branches extending from opposite sides of the trunk represented the thallophyte phylum. One side supported algae, the earliest life form found on Earth, aquatic plants that lack true stems, roots and leaves but contain chlorophyll and can make their own food through photosynthesis. The other side supported fungi, which lack chlorophyll and must get their food from living or dead hosts. (Though a fungus, the slime molds were apparently too lowly to merit a position on the branch.)

A slightly higher branch held the bryophytes — mosses and liverworts. Though more developed than the thallophytes, bryophytes lack the vascular tissue (necessary to circulate fluids) of higher plants. They act as a link between the characteristically aquatic forms of primitive plant life and the more highly developed land-based plants. Above the bryophytes were the pteridophytes, the ferns, which reproduce with spores. The rest of the family tree dealt with the spermatophytes, encompassing all plants which reproduce with seeds. The gymnosperms, also known as the conifer family, were placed along the lowest of the upper branches, being the most primitive of the seed-bearing plants. The top branches held the angiosperms, the flowering plants. Here the trunk divided in two. A smaller branch represented the single-sprout monocots, crowned by complexly structured orchids; a larger branch represented the double-sprout dicots, crowned by sunflowers.

The order and visual clarity of this tree pleased me, and I often returned to it, though I did have a nagging suspicion that a few botanical differences may have surfaced over the decades. Later, when I mentioned the book to Proctor, he confirmed that there have indeed been changes in the foundations of plant science. The latest edition of the Encyclopaedia Britannica concurs, stating that advances in biochemical and electron microscopic techniques along with genetic testing have redefined the old taxonomic relationships. Gone are the simple plant and animal kingdoms, replaced in still-evolving classifications by five kingdoms —Monera (bacteria, blue-green algae), Protista (other algae, protozoa, slime molds), Fungi (funguses), Plantae (nonvascular, vascular plants) and Animalia (animals).

In spite of its outdated facets, the family tree did give me an overview of basic differences among the major plant kingdom divisions. To return to ferns, they differ from most other plants in that they reproduce from spores rather than seeds. Even more curious, the fern life cycle involves two generations of totally different plants, one which reproduces sexually, the other asexually. Briefly explained, ferns (the asexual plant) have tiny fruit dots on the undersides of their leaves which store spores. When mature, the spores fall to the ground and germinate into a prothallium, a small, heart-shaped green leaf which attaches to the ground through rootlike hairs (rhizoids). Prothalli have male and female organs on opposite ends of the leaf. When the plant is mature and the underside of the prothallium is wet from rain or dew, spiral cells from the male organ "swim" over to the female organ, resulting in an egg cell which becomes a fern embryo. Eventually, the embryo becomes a fern, and the prothallium, its job done, fades away.

Ferns' primary contribution to the well-being of forests is their pioneering nature. They quickly invade patches of bare, sterilized soils, such as those found after manmade road building or hurricane-induced landslides. By doing so, they prevent erosion, bind the soil together and prepare it for other vegetation. Their primary contribution to the well-being of humans has been the creation of coal. Hundreds of millions of years before Puerto Rico rose above the ocean floor, during the Carboniferous period, ferns dominated the world's vegetation. Picture forests of gigantic selaginella, of pine-shaped club mosses up to 150 feet high, of huge tree ferns and sprawling fern epiphytes, all proliferating in the vast swamps common throughout much of the world at that time. After fern forests gave way to forests of flowering plants and trees, nature worked a slow magic, transforming fern-filled sediments into coal beds. Today, only a few miniature species of these ancient ferns remain, relics in a vastly changed world. Ferns in general, however, continue to do well, claiming some 10,000 species worldwide. Tol-

erant of environments that range from snowy mountains to coastal deserts, they grow with greatest abandon in wet tropical regions.

Angela Kepler came to Puerto Rico in the late 1960s with her husband, Cameron Kepler, an ornithologist who set up and, for a time, directed a program to save the endangered Puerto Rican parrots in the Luquillo Mountains. Not content to pine away in the dank lushness of El Yunque, Kepler explored the local fern population. The result of her exploration is a book, *Common Ferns of Luquillo Forest, Puerto Rico*, published in 1975.

Ferns are, arguably, the most noticeable plants in the Luquillo Mountains, yet the large number of species — Kepler estimated 150 in the Luquillo Mountains and Proctor has discovered more —makes identification difficult. With Kepler's book, even the most inept plant watcher can identify many of them. As a general description, ferns are plants with ever-green, stalked leaves that bear fruit dot spores instead of flowers. Most leaves begin as tight coils called fiddleheads that slowly unwind.

The most fascinating of several key features which identify ferns is their leaf cuts. Cuts refer to deep divisions reaching from the outer edge to the central stem of each fern leaf, as if someone took a pair of scissors and snipped, snipped, snipped. Think of a long, flowing leaf resembling the trailer on a kite. This is an uncut fern leaf. Now take that same leaf and imagine making regular cuts along both sides of the stems, resulting in numerous leaflets that look like miniature versions of the large leaf. This is a once-cut leaf. Cut into the leaflets of a once-cut leaf and you have a twice-cut leaf — the basic leaf has been cut first lengthwise and again around each leaflet, producing delicate subleaflets. Cut into the subleaflets and you have a thrice-cut leaf, a rococo combination of leaflet, subleaflet and lobe. Thrice-cut leaves produce the well-known lacy look of many ferns.

Most of the common fern names in Kepler's book are her own creation. Uncut ferns take on such descriptive names as stag's tongue (*Elaphoglossum flaccidum*), ribbon fern (*Vittoria remota*) and snake polypody (*Polypodium piloselloides*). One creeping uncut species, the oleander fern (*Oleandra articulata*), is the most common epiphyte in the mountains and a frequent lodger in palo colorado trees. Once-cut ferns, such as the saw-toothed-shaped sword fern (*Nephrolepis exaltata*), are commonly seen on steep banks alongside the road, making attractive silk-purse gardens out of eroded sow's-ear soil. These ferns, fueled by the sun, grow grass-thick and waist- or even neck-high. Maiden-hair ferns are twice-cut. The most common maidenhair in the Luquillo Mountains has been dubbed glaucous maidenhair (*Adiantum latifolium*) for the whitish underside of its fan-shaped leaves. One of the most common ground ferns in Luquillo, named the eared woodfern (*Thelypteris deltoidea*), is also twice-cut. Most tree ferns are thrice-cut. Several other thrice-cut ferns, including the lacy mountain fern (*Dennstaedtia bipinnata*), are found in moist areas, especially along stream banks.

After visiting Quebrada Juan Diego, George Proctor and I drive up the mountain to one of the recreation area parking lots, where Proctor shows me a particular once-cut fern. "Named *Nephrolepis multiflora* [multi-flowered] because it has no flowers," he jokes with a straight face. Apparently, there are a number of plant and animal species that,

like this fern, have been misnamed for one reason or another. "The doctrine of negative correlation," Proctor calls it. Originally from Asia, N. multiflora was virtually unknown in the New World before 1940. But once it arrived, it multiplied, so much so that it is now Puerto Rico's most common fern, a mere weed. The great majority of ferns — as well as trees, animals and other plants — within El Yunque are native to the forest, "native" meaning they flourished here naturally when Columbus first sailed by. Today about one quarter of the native species, whose ancestors made their way to the island from mainland America eons ago, have evolved into species unique to the Caribbean. On the other hand, almost a tenth of the forest's fern species originated in Asia or Africa and were imported, occasionally unintentionally, in past centuries. Botanists call them introduced or exotic species. If exotic species find conditions to their liking and go about reproducing on their own, as N. multiflora did on a grand scale, they are said to have become naturalized.

Our next stop is along a road which follows the mountain ridge to East Peak. "In spite of the high elevation," Proctor mentions as we park, "many of the plants along this road are similar to those of the silica sands along the north coast." He presumes the similarities have to do with the soil's acidity and the area's continual moisture. At the edge of the road, I notice a common pungent smell that, for me, is the smell of Puerto Rico's mountains. The plant, it turns out, is Wynne grass. Another of its common names, molasses grass, describes the scent. Ironically, Wynne grass is native to Africa. It was introduced to the island to control erosion along the roads and has become naturalized. We leave the road and head north. Far below, coastal towns and the Atlantic Ocean gleam under the tropical sun. Where we are, clouds shadow the landscape and hover over nearby peaks. Insects buzz faintly and a lone tree frog keeps up its two-toned chant; otherwise, the mountains are silent.

We coax our way between tree branches and step over a healthy bed of pale green sphagnum moss, *Sphagnum portoricense*, the only species of sphagnum found in Puerto Rico's mountains. The moss is saturated; when Proctor wrings it, water falls to the ground in a trickle. Cavities in the leaves collect water, and the plant can hold up to 20 times its weight. Its absorbency plus its acidic, antiseptic nature makes it a good substitute for bandages. Decomposed, it forms the basis for commercial peat moss. Wet, poorly drained soils in the upper mountains have produced boglike conditions favoring the growth of sphagnum; in places, mossy mats cover thousands of square feet.

Shortly, we are beyond the trees in a small patch of savannah, one of several in the forest. The soil is a heavy yellow-beige water-soaked clay. Only grasses and sedges (grasslike plants with solid rather than hollow stems) can grow here. Proctor noses about in the brush bordering the savannah. He shows me a species of lycopodium, a mosslike fern which grows only in Luquillo Mountain savannahs. Proctor knows virtually every plant in the vicinity. This fern with leaf stems resembling baby

BROMELIAD

eels grows only on mossy branches. That fern grows only in subalpine savannahs. This tiny yellow orchid is *Epidendrum ramosa*. That dried pale green beard dangling from a tree is a lichen, a curiously symbiotic plant that gets its nutrition as an alga and its form as a parasitic fungus. The stems of this liverwort are covered with microscopic leaves. That bromeliad is of the Pitcairnia genus. The genus is named for bromeliad relations which inhabited the tiny South Pacific Pitcairn Island along with mutineers from the H.M.S. Bounty; the particular species Proctor shows me hasn't yet been identified. Proctor breaks off the bright red Pitcairnia flower and carries it back to the car along with several other specimens. When we return to the road, he snaps off a piece of sedge growing on the ground. "The last time I saw this particular sedge was in the area of Loíza along the north coast."

At the car, Proctor informs me of a "pressing" engagement. For a moment I am perplexed, wondering why our outing has so suddenly ended. He pulls a well-worn, briefcase-shaped, lattice-designed metal contraption out of the car. Its broken leather handle has been replaced by rope and metal clasps, and it is filled with newspaper and cardboard. He then explains: "This is a presser." The plant specimens are placed between the newspapers, face down in the order he found them; he will use the cardboard to separate locations. The presser dates from 1951,

137

A Tropical Greenery

Jamaica. It has pressed specimens from the West Indies, Central America and Ecuador. Back at his office, each specimen gets a number. The specimens are then put into a dryerlike machine in which a fan blows heat through the presser. Periodically, Proctor tightens the straps so the specimens dry flat and smooth. Within 24 hours, they are completely desiccated. Then he enters information for each specimen — the specifics of the locale, the date, the habitat and the collection number — into a notebook and attaches a label with similar information onto the specimen. Recently, he topped 45,100 collection numbers.

As we drive to another site, we pass a small bamboo tree along a rutted, leaf-splattered side road which connects the East Peak road with Road 191. That species of bamboo, Proctor mentions, has not yet been identified. There are three native bamboo species in Puerto Rico, only one of which is found in the Luquillo Mountains; all are small vinelike creepers. The tree-sized bamboos have been imported, planted primarily along the roads to check erosion. For hikers who get lost in the forest, the sight of willowy bamboo stems is a welcome one, for it means a road is nearby. Though members of the lowly grass family, these roadside bamboos grow up to 50 feet high, their hollow stems wide enough to serve as water pipes. Bamboo is the only monocot that grows to tree size. When the wind blows, the stems rub together, playing a haunting, creaking tune. Their leafy branches resemble ferns, and new shoots resemble oversized asparagus. Large bamboo are prodigious growers, shooting up as much as six inches in one day. Proctor is worried about the unidentified bamboo. Since large bamboo flower only once, some after a hundred years, and the

flowers are needed for positive identification, these species are harder to identify than most plants. In addition, there are few bamboo collections. Bamboo must be included in his survey of the monocots of Puerto Rico and the Virgin Islands, but he is not sure how he will identify them. At the moment there is no bamboo expert in the hemisphere: one died not long ago, and his successor died shortly afterwards. Orchids, on the other hand, will be no problem in Proctor's monocot survey: Jim Ackerman of the University of Puerto Rico will do orchids for him.

More people ask about Luquillo's orchids than about any other flowering plant, but few actually see them. The uninformed expect to stumble upon the sort of large splashy orchids they got, or bought, for the senior prom, most of which are commercially bred for their large round size and brilliant coloring. In the natural orchid world, small is normal. One of the largest orchid flowers in the Luquillo Mountains is scarcely two inches long, one of the smallest is less than a fifth of an inch. As for color, the forest's most common orchid hue is a somewhat drab greenish white. About half of Luquillo's orchid species are terrestrial, often partially hidden under litter or behind rocks; the other half are epiphytic, clinging to the trunks and branches of trees, often high above eye level. Small wonder, then, that they are hard to spot. Those who have the good fortune to look at a branch at just the right moment may be overwhelmed by a "large spray of yellow flowers that resemble a swarm of butterflies", as one forest brochure poetically describes them.

The average person enjoys orchids for the delicate beauty of their lionlike faces. But botanists like Jim Ackerman, Proctor's orchid expert, are also drawn to the plant's complexity. Several weeks after my fern expedition, I arranged for an interview with Ackerman at his university office. Ackerman is a natural teacher. As he added greatly to my slender knowledge of orchids, he used, almost as reflex, all sorts of props — lists of species, seeds in packets, seeds under a microscope, specimens in formaldehyde, drawings, diagrams, articles, books. Several years later he published much of his knowledge in a beautifully illustrated book about the orchids of Puerto Rico and the Virgin Islands.

One of the most recent and complex groups of plants in terms of evolution, orchids enjoy the highest position (as far as complexity) on the monocot branch of the botanical family tree. The flower that looks so pretty is an intricate arrangement of three sepals and three petals, one of them highly modified into a lip. Behind the flower is a column in which, unlike other plants, all the sexual organs are fused together — the seed-bearing ovary, the pollen-receiving stigma, and the style which connects the two as well as the stalklike filament and pollen-bearing anther. About one-quarter of the orchid species on the island do their own pollinating, with a little help from the winds and rains. The rest must rely on a pollinator — a bug or bird or butterfly, most of which cannot make use of the pollen they transport.

Contrary to other flowers, orchid seeds have no nutrition in them. Plants usually germinate using the nutrition found in their seeds; since orchid seeds have none, they must form a relationship with a fungus in order to germinate. Some orchid species need a specific fungus; others can use any fungus at all. The fungus infests the seeds, and the seeds send out enzymes to control it. The orchid

remains attached to the fungus until it is old enough to do its own photosynthesizing. Some terrestrial species remain underground for years, depending on the fungus all that time. Other orchids live life more quickly, flowering within a year, dying a year or two later. Still others live a very precarious existence. Twig epiphyte orchids, for example, find their life comes to a swift conclusion if the twig breaks. Stingy to their pollinators, dependent on a fungus — orchids seem to be rather spoiled forest beauties.

Like ferns, orchids are found virtually everywhere in the world — they form the largest family of flowering plants, claiming some 25,000 species. Like ferns, they show their greatest diversity in the moist forests of the tropics. Ackerman supplied me with a checklist of orchids in the Luquillo Mountains. Some 80 species from 40 genera, more than half of all species found in Puerto Rico, have been located in El Yunque. The Epidendrum genus has the largest number of species at 12. At least five species are quite common. The greatest number flourish in the lower-elevation tabonuco forest while the rarest cling to the upper reaches of the dwarf forest. Two species — *Brachionidium ciliolatum* and *Lepanthes eltoroensis* — inhabit separate peaks in the dwarf forest. They exist nowhere else in the world.

Three species of the genus Vanilla grow in the forest. Though most people are familiar with vanilla, few realize that the slender seed pod from which this aromatic flavoring is obtained is actually part of an orchid plant. The commercial vanilla species is one of a number of vanilla orchids native to the American tropics. Luquillo's three species produce vanilla beans, though not the commercial variety. One species Ackerman finds particularly attractive has dark green flowers edged in a dark maroon.

An orchid species Ackerman finds particularly curious is *Wullshlaegelia sphylla*, a terrestrial specimen of ghostly white color. Containing no chlorophyll, it apparently maintains a fungal relationship all its life. Another curious species is *Oeceoclades maculata*. Oeceoclades is an African genus, with species that have become colonized in the New World. Until the mid-1960s O. maculata wasn't even seen in Puerto Rico; now it is one of the island's most common species. Ackerman first discovered it in the Luquillo Mountains several months before we spoke. He has studied the plant's life cycle: it carries out its own pollinating, and its phenomenal spread suggests it is not tied to a specific species of fungus.

❦ After passing the bamboo tree along the roadside, Proctor and I continue on Road 191 through a gate (for which Proctor has a key) prohibiting further access by public vehicles. We almost immediately turn to the right, up a road that leads to El Yunque Peak. From the car, Proctor points to a fern on a tree trunk —"that one there" — and seems surprised when I cannot locate it among all the mosses, liverworts and leaves plastered onto the bark.

Near a short path to Mount Britton we stop, and Proctor shows me another specimen of the still-to-be-identified Pitcairnia bromeliad. Soon he will begin a thorough investigation to determine whether or not the species has been identified, examining its relatives and its distinguishing features, making a minute analysis. If he finds that it is, in fact, a new species, he will give it a scientific name. The first of the bromeliad's two names will be Pitcairnia, for the genus. He will have to be sure to use a new species name, one not used by any other species in the genus, no easy task

as Pitcairnia has some 1,000 species. I ask, using one of his deadpan expressions, if he will name it for himself. "No, no," he shakes his head quickly, "that would not be considered good form."

Proctor talks a bit about scientific names. The species suffix has specific meanings. *Ensis*, for example, refers to locality. The endemic orchid, *Lepanthes eltoroensis*, exists solely on El Toro Peak, thus its name. *Ai* means the name used refers to a person who was involved with the plant in some way. Proctor discovered a fern we had examined at the Juan Diego pool and named it *Calyptus hildai* for Hilda Díaz Soltero, director at the time of the Department of Natural Resources.

Ana means the name refers to a person who was not involved with the plant. Proctor stops the car and gets out to show me a small fern, six inches long, growing from a tree trunk. Some 25 stems arch out in the form of a bouquet from a cluster of beardlike roots. Leaves are once-cut, and ten tiny spore sacks symmetrically line the underside of each leaf. For years this species was mistaken for another species within the common genus Grammitis, but differences in the stalk, in hairs and spores, and, as the clincher, in a chromosome study separated it from the other species. Proctor discovered the differences and gave the fern its name, *Grammitis hanekeana*, in honor of Horst Haneke, a mutual friend of ours.

❦ Bromeliads, sheltering those preferred swimming holes of insects and other small creatures, opened this chapter, and it is fitting to close with a closer look at them. They are the best known of El Yunque's epiphytes. In fact, to many people the two words are synonymous. Though the great majority of bromeliads are epiphytic, some, like the unidentified Pitcairnia species, are terrestrial. The pineapple is another terrestrial example. A rosette arrangement of leaves from a base — in the case of the pineapple at the top of the fruit — characterizes all bromeliads. A product of the New World tropics, the bromeliad family encompasses some 44 genera with over 1,400 species.

Bromeliads' biggest claim to forest ecology fame is their ability to collect water. The Hohenbergia bromeliads, with exceptionally large leaves that fit together tightly at the base, hold up to a gallon or more of water, but all bromeliads store a certain amount. With the millions of bromeliads in the forest, this amounts to a lot of water, and the sheer weight of dozens of water-filled bromeliads on a single tree forces it to expend extra resources in fortifying its root system. By storing water, bromeliads can prevent soil erosion as well as provide water, especially during rainless periods, for the local forest community. Those that make use of bromeliads include algae, fungal bacteria, liverworts, mosses, single-celled protozoans, multi-celled rotifers, the aquatic larvae of many insects, small crustaceans, roundworms, flatworms, beetles, spiders, crabs, lizards and tiny tree frogs known as coquís.

"The exact mix of the animal life apparently depends on two factors, usually two, maybe three," Proctor explained at a later meeting in his office, a cluttered, somewhat dingy room in a once lovely but now rundown building that houses the island's newly-expanded Department of Natural and Environmental Resources, until recently the Department of Natural Resources. "First of all the ph, the acidity, of the water. Second the amount of oxygen that is dissolved in the water. And then third maybe the water temperature. Those three elements determine what

lives in the water." Those that live in the water pay their dues, for bromeliads seem to get their nutrients from the decayed litter which falls into the pools and from the wastes given off by residents and poolside guests.

One of the most common bromeliads in the lower elevations of the Luquillo Mountains also ranks among the showiest members of the family. The leaves of *Guzmania berteroniana* fan out up to several feet in diameter, and a spikelike bright red bract with small yellow flowers pokes up from the center of the leaves. Other bromeliads are so small they can fit in the palm of a hand. Virtually the only bromeliad species found in the upper dwarf forests is the red-leafed *Vriesea sintenisii*. The forest's middle elevations contain the greatest numbers of bromeliads.

I find it hard to resist asking experts about "the most interesting...", in spite of the mixed results the question has produced. Once I asked Angel Rosa, an older man who lives in the forest community of Sabana, about his most interesting experience in all the years he had worked in the forest. The question baffled him, and when he finally answered, at great prodding, he decided it was when he was harvesting lumber and a worker was sawed in half. When I asked Proctor his thoughts on the most interesting bromeliads in the Luquillo Mountains, he seemed equally baffled by the question. "Different species have interest in different kinds of ways. For instance, the Pitcairnia I think hasn't been named yet is interesting because it hasn't been named yet. Why hasn't somebody noticed it is different? Then the Guzmania berteroniana is interesting because the flowering spike is so showy, so spectacular. And the Vriesea sintenisii is exciting because the leaves are bright red. And the Holhenbergias are interesting because they have insects and other animal life growing in the water in their leaves, to a greater extent than the other species. So it's an interest that's varied, it isn't strictly comparable."

🌿 As George Proctor and I are about to leave the forest after our day's outing, we stop in front of a rock near the old rain forest restaurant in the recreation area. The rock is covered with greenery. I ask Proctor to identify the plants. He points out a small Marcgravia vine, wet and clinging to the rock; 15 ferns comprising four species; a liverwort; three species of moss; a flowering impatiens plant. He reaches down, picks off and hands me a small piece of *Tricomidis rigidem*, a terrestrial filmy fern. It is a beautiful leaf — wet, delicate and so lacy it seems to be cut a dozen times. I slip it in my pocket to show my family, but when I get home the fern is dried out, curled up, without a trace of its earlier beauty.

CHAPTER 10
TAMING THE FOREST

W e never found the house, though it is clearly marked on the Forest Service map — a tiny square symbol on the western side of La Coca Trail, near the merger of the Mameyes and La Mina rivers, the only such symbol within the entire northeastern boundary of the forest. My brother, visiting the island at the time, was curious to see it. At the indicated site, he canvassed the slope of the mountains, pushing through ferns and pulling aside vines. There was no sign of a house, not even the crumbling remains of a foundation, only a few wild orange trees and coffee bushes left from some prior cultivation. Trees were tall and their canopies dense, trapping moisture and filtering out all but a fraction of the light. Lianas dangled from upper branches, ancient-looking algae mottled rocks, decaying palm fronds littered the ground. The area looked more than abandoned: to the untrained eye, it looked as if it had never known the presence of humans. Yet the Forest Service map clearly shows a house by the side of the trail.

The house was a vestige of the decades, from the middle of the nineteenth century to the early part of this one, when people settled along the slopes of the Luquillo Mountains and eked out a modest living by making use of the forest that surrounded them. Those efforts at private, small-scale farming and forestry ended for the most part prior to the Second World War, and now the house, too, seems gone.

Life in Puerto Rico changed dramatically during the nineteenth century. If any one factor could be held responsible for this change, it would be the Real Cédula de Gracias (royal decree), approved by Spain in 1815. Through the Cédula, Spain encouraged colonization and trade. Roman Catholic subjects of friendly nations received enticements to settle here, and trade restrictions with other countries were relaxed. As a result, Puerto Rico's population increased, and settlements sprang up in previously unpopulated hills and valleys. Land was cleared for farming and grazing. By the end of the century, virtually all of the island had been tamed. One statistic tells the story: in the early 1800s, some two-thirds of Puerto Rico was covered by forest; by the turn of the century, only ten square miles — less than one-third of one percent — could be described as undisturbed forest. Eight of those square miles lay in the Luquillo Mountains.

Prior to the nineteenth century, the Luquillo Mountains formed the hinterland of a hinter-island. After pockets of rebellious Indians had died or fled in the late 1500s, the mountains officially became the property of the Spanish Crown. With its inaccessible terrain and lingering tales of marauding Caribs, the Luquillo region attracted few settlers, fewer than any other region of equal size on the island. The rare visitor would come upon an occasional isolated farm in the foothills. These creoles lived in a world apart, a remote, anonymous world that seldom made contact with the rest of the island.

Using a few detective skills, one can find a name or two connected to the Luquillo Mountains from the dormant seventeenth and eighteenth centuries. Forester Frank Wadsworth unearthed a few family names, which he mentions in his 1949 dissertation, *The Development of the Forest Land Resources of the Luquillo Mountains, Puerto Rico*. This dissertation, written for a doctoral degree at the University of Michigan, is so extensive that anyone who reads it imagines the young forester felt despair in ever finishing it. But finish it he did, and it remains the most important single source of information about the forest, the depository of thousands of details which would otherwise have slipped into oblivion. One detail concerns the Duke of Crillon.

In 1776, when the United States was declaring independence from Great Britain and the Spanish military was putting the finishing touches on the fortresses of Old San Juan, Spain handed out one of its first land concessions to a private individual in the Luquillo Mountains. It was given to Louis Balbo Bertone, the Duke of Crillon, a French admiral who had led a Spanish squadron in recapturing the Balearic Islands from England. To show his gratitude, King Charles III presented the Duke with some 20,000 acres in Puerto Rico, much of it in the Luquillo Mountains, on the condition that the land be cultivated within four years. Apparently the Duke was less than ecstatic about his gift, for he never went to Puerto Rico, never cultivated the land and didn't have a representative on the island during his lifetime. Even so, a number of place names in the mountains — Pico Duque, Barrio Duque, Sitio Duque — honor the old admiral. The Duke gave part of his grant, some 2,430 acres, to a Count Bernardo de Galvez; one can only wonder why. This land was inherited by his daughter, Matilde de Galvez, the Marchioness of Sonora, who in 1839 willed it to her daughter, the Countess Clotilde Capece Minutolo y Galvez. Though the countess with the unwieldy name never set foot in the Luquillo Mountains, she was shrewd enough to claim her property (and then some), to hire an agent, and to collect rent from the local dwellers. Her land apparently lay on the southwestern slope of the mountains; today, a patch of forest used for research by the International Institute of Tropical Forestry bears the name La Condesa.

Several years ago I unearthed another name when I was leafing through a local book, which, unfortunately, must remain anonymous since I failed to write down its title when I took the notes. In it, I came upon a footnote to a footnote in Puerto Rico's history. The primary footnote referred to the defense of the north-coast town of Arecibo against the British in 1702 by one Francisco de los Reyes Correa, a captain in the Spanish army. In the secondary footnote, Capitán Correa, in recognition of his heroic acts, was given a grant of land known as the San Luis de Canóvanas Plantation somewhere on the western half of the Luquillo Mountains. The concession was said to have been surveyed in 1787. In 1923 Correa's heirs made claim to the land, arguing they had been in possession of it up until 1896 and were cutting timber until 1912.

However, they couldn't establish their claim, and no evidence of timber cutting was ever found.

Though the Correa family apparently never harvested their trees, limited lumbering did occur in the Luquillo Mountains. From the moment Europeans arrived in the New World, they appreciated the forests which covered the Americas. As early as 1513, Wadsworth notes in his dissertation, King Ferdinand V of Spain offered land with the stipulation that part of it be planted in trees, yet for centuries Puerto Rico's forest resources were little utilized.

The rise of the island's population in the 1800s, along with a rise in entrepreneurial endeavors, resulted in the export of woods and wood products. Although fine timber trees populated the Luquillo Mountains, the region's steep terrain kept many of them from being felled. Prominent trees scattered along the more accessible slopes were cut, quartered and dragged down the mountain, but the timber industry remained relatively small-scale, in the same way that the gold mining operations of the nineteenth and early twentieth centuries were the ventures of individuals and small, short-lived companies.

Coffee, it turned out, became the industry which did the most to tame the lower slopes of the Luquillo Mountains. During the 1800s Puerto Rican coffee turned to gold. Early in the century, farmers, in particular the new immigrants, struggled to turn a profit on their land. In the process they experimented with a variety of tropical crops. Sugar cane did quite well in coastal regions, and coffee, they discovered, took to the conditions of Puerto Rico's hills and mountains. Most promising was a strain known as *Coffea arabica*. Down went tracts of forests in the Cordillera

Central of central and western Puerto Rico, and up grew coffee bushes no higher than a picker's outstretched arm. When the bushes were young, paddle-shaped plantain leaves tattered by wind and rain sheltered them from the intense tropical sun; later, specially planted trees provided the necessary shade. Throughout the year, dark green leaves covered the bushes. In the spring, fragrant white flowers brightened the hillsides; in the summer, green berries containing two brown beans replaced the flowers; in the autumn, the berries turned red and pickers, often barefooted, stripped them from the branches. The beans — depulped, fermented, rinsed, dried, roasted, polished and packed — reached the shores of Europe, where discriminating coffee drinkers declared them to be of excellent quality. More forests were felled, more coffee planted. The aromatic beans became the island's most important export. Puerto Rican coffee won numerous awards — Pope Leo XIII liked it so much that he bestowed the title of marquis on one grower — and owners of large plantations became enormously rich. More land was cleared for coffee, and eventually the coffee-growing fever reached the Luquillo Mountains.

Luquillo, however, never became a famous coffee region, never supported the large plantations found in the Cordillera Central. Once again its inaccessible terrain saved most of the forest; in addition, the local rains were too heavy, the soil minerals too poor to produce an outstanding crop. But coffee bushes were planted, primarily along the northern slopes of the mountains. Unlike those of the more profitable coffee regions, the forests in Luquillo were never cleared. Instead, farmers felled just enough trees to plant a modest number of bushes. Citrus trees and other crops

Coffee tree
full
of mature
fruit.

Angel Rosa
explaining tree
planting methods to
high-school-aged
Youth Conservation
Corps enrollees.

View
of present-day
Sabana
in the foreground
and Luquillo
in the background.

were often planted alongside the coffee bushes. Although the lower forests were never totally destroyed, the number of acres owned by the Spanish government shrank as the government granted land to farmers working their way up the mountainside. In 1860, the Crown possessed some 19,400 acres in the Luquillo Mountains; by 1880, slightly more than 15,300 acres; in 1898, when the United States gained Puerto Rico following the Spanish-American War, 12,443 acres.

Before long, the encroachment stopped. A year after the Spanish-American War, the brutal San Ciriaco Hurricane leveled virtually every coffee bush on the island, gravely wounding the industry. As a result of the war, the island lost its lucrative European market, and it never gained much of a foothold in the stateside American coffee market. In addition, local coffee, grown on relatively small farms using manual methods — quality over quantity — couldn't compete with the cheaper, mass-produced coffees of Colombia and Brazil. Puerto Rico's coffee heyday was over.

❧ Road 988 starts at the Catalina Field Office and hugs the northern boundary of the forest until it reaches the community of Sabana in the heart of the former coffee farms. The road provides as lush a view of tropical vegetation as one can get from the inside of a car, with towering tree ferns, lianas dripping from trees, and streams cascading over rocks. Along the way, 988 passes Puente Roto (broken bridge), a popular swimming hole along the Río Mameyes. It intersects with an old lumber road which leads to several forest trails and the Bisley Watershed Project. It passes the Sabana Work Center, a collection of concrete buildings that once served as the Forest Service field office and was originally a center for the Civilian Conservation Corps in the 1930s.

It crosses a bridge and enters Sabana at the northeast corner of the forest.

Sabana is the only community of any size found along the edge of the Caribbean National Forest. It resembles a town in miniature, pocketed in a small savanna (sabana) that lies between the foothills and the upper reaches of the mountains. Unbroken greenery encircles the community, giving it a perpetually shady look and damp feel. There are no far-flung vistas here, only the immediate view of a low-lying, deep-green ridge to the south. Three paved streets, two of which fork from the third, comprise the "downtown" area. Houses huddle close together, spaced by small yards. Elegant concrete homes exist alongside modest concrete homes, a few small wooden homes and a shedlike home or two built out of a patchwork of materials. All homes, regardless of their occupants' economic status, are trimmed with colorful vegetation — impatiens in cracker tins, orchids on tree stumps, ginger, crotons, African tulip trees.

As of the last time I asked, some 900 families live in Sabana and along nearby roads. The community has one school, with classes up to the ninth grade; one Catholic church; a dozen Protestant churches, most of them Pentecostal; two bars; three small stores; one small community center; and a large colmado. A colmado is a local grocery store, where traditional foods — piles of wizened tubers, large bags of rice and flour, bananas hanging from rafters — are juxtaposed with contemporary frozen foods, soft drinks, snacks in shiny bags and an abundance of canned foods. Residents also speak of three dairy farms on the outskirts of town, one pig farm guarded by unleashed dobermans, and a woodworking shop, closed more often than open, that is owned by stateside Americans who live private lives on a nearby farm. Most residents make their living by working with the Forest Service or driving down the mountain to jobs in the north-coast town of Luquillo. U.S. Social Security or food stamps help many get by while tiny backyard gardens contribute to family food supplies. All in all, Sabana seems a sleepy community. By day, lizards sun on porches; in the late afternoon, birds flit among the trees; at night, thousands of tiny tree frogs belt out their two-toned chants. On weekends, families pile into cars and visit the river pools at Puente Roto or Charco La Pila in El Verde. Many families attend church. "Those who don't go to one of the churches go to the bars," one resident jokes. To the outsider, Sabana retains a sense of yesteryear, a feeling that time has slowed down. Yet to older residents who have lived a lifetime in the community, the changes have been vast.

"At the time I was born," Angel Rosa told me, "there were around eight or ten families in this area. There were paths but no roads. Horses, mules, donkeys and oxen pulling carts got the people to Fajardo or to Luquillo. Luquillo was the closest town — it took two hours to get there on foot. People usually went on Wednesdays and Saturdays. Those were market days. There was no plaza in Luquillo then, not even a market plaza. People sold their crops, bananas usually, in stores and bought rice, beans, sugar, butter, bacalao [salted codfish]. There were no bars, either. Men could get drinks at the stores. The movie theater didn't come until much later, and no one bothered with it. Then we returned home. It wasn't much of a town. Fajardo was bigger, with a small plaza, and occasionally we went there."

Angel Rosa Torres, the man who sat out Hurricane Hugo in a ground-floor bathroom, was initially described to me as "Angelito", a retired forester who went to school for one day and refused to return because it taught him nothing he needed to know. He probably knows more about the Caribbean National Forest than just about anyone and is an authority whom Ph.D. botanists consult when they are stumped about certain species. I first went to meet him with forester Jerry Bauer one evening ten years ago when I was writing an article on one of the forest trails for a local newspaper. Rosa's house is of prefabricated wood, set on stilts on a triangular piece of property at the fork of two of Sabana's streets. Though it wasn't much past 7:00, Sabana was cloaked in a blackness I don't see in the San Juan metropolitan area. The shutters of Rosa's house were bolted: he had gone to bed for the night.

I did meet Rosa several years later, when Bauer and I came, carrying notebooks and tape recorder, on a previously arranged visit during the day. We were curious to know more about the people who had lived and farmed on the land which would eventually become part of the Caribbean National Forest. They were the last of generations of farmers who had shared an intimacy with the forest, depending on it for their very survival.

Throughout much of the interview Rosa seemed serious to the point of being nervous. He was dressed in a short-sleeved shirt over a sleeveless teeshirt, dark green polyester pants and black fabric scuffs. His thinning gray hair was neatly combed around tanned skin, and he wore thick, amber-framed glasses. After we arrived, he carefully placed three mismatched chairs on the concrete floor underneath the house, and the floor was transformed into an open-air drawing room. Sitting upright, he listened to our questions with great concentration; at times our accents in Spanish seemed to confuse him. When we off-handedly asked his age, he bolted out of his chair, climbed the stairs to his house and returned with a certificate which stated the year of his birth as 1906. When a neighbor strolled by and stood next to Rosa's fence, obviously interested in participating in our conversation, Rosa refused to take notice. Later in the interview we asked about the type of saw he had used in the forest. He again sprang from his chair and retrieved a six-foot-long two-man saw from the side of a shed and proceeded to demonstrate how lumber was once cut.

For a second interview several months later, Rosa was not so formal. He led us to a shed in the back of his property. The shed was of wood, with an earthen floor, zinc roof and timber posts. A red plaid hammock was strung up next to a rough wooden table. Pods of pigeon peas (gandules) hung from the walls, and a hard hat, a knapsack, loose burlap, wire, cans, cups, a hoe, a saw, mosquito spray, boots and plastic sandals cluttered the room. It seemed an ideal place to putter, and I was sorry when I learned it had been destroyed by Hurricane Hugo shortly afterwards. Behind the shed, on the widest wedge of his triangular property, Rosa had planted a garden of bananas, pigeon pea bushes, tubers and a variety of plants and flowers. A spreading rose-apple tree (pomarrosa) next to the shed was dropping magenta pom-pom flowers.

Wearing a teeshirt without a shirt, Rosa made himself comfortable, sitting in the hammock with his feet touching the ground. Instead of waiting for our questions, he immediately presented us with one of his own: "Why," he asked Bauer, "do you call me Angelito? You make me seem like the little kid of the family, and here my teeth are falling out!" Bauer mumbled something about merely repeating what others called him.

During our interviews, we learned much about the Sabana of Rosa's childhood. "Everything below Sabana was planted in sugar cane, and two or three hundred oxen were used in harvesting the cane. In the mountains, in places like Cocal and Río Chiquito, there was no cane. Some people had their own little farms to work. They planted tubers like yautía, malanga, and yuca, and other food crops, and coffee. [Tubers are local root plants; yuca was the tuber the Arawak Indians made into cassava, a staple of their diet.] The ones who didn't have their own farms lived together with those who did. The bigger farms had approximately 200 acres, with maybe 150 in coffee and bananas. The land around Sabana was also planted in oranges, also some in grapefruit."

Rosa mentioned three farms that were located in the area of Sabana. "La Finca Rosario, where my family lived with about four other families, had some 300 to 400 acres. It was owned by Diego Saldondo, who died around 50 years ago. He lived in Fajardo." On a different visit to Sabana, another retired forester, Manuel Corsino, told us an interesting story about Sr. Saldondo. It seems he bought his entire farm for the modest sum of five dollars. Later, he sold one palo colorado tree on the property for the same amount.

"La Finca Perla," Rosa continued, "was owned by an American, Mr. McPhee, who also lived in town." After the Spanish-American War and the change of island sovereignty, U.S. Americans became the newest wave of immigrants to the island. "Coffee, oranges and grapefruits grew there. When I was around

12, Mr. McPhee left, leaving Juan Cardona in charge of the farm. Mr. McPhee was fairly old and never returned. His wife was from here, and his children still live in the area. La Finca Bisley was about the same size as La Rosario. Bisley had bananas, coffee, a couple of acres of cacao. The cacao was for personal use, to grind, mix with water, boil and add sugar, like hot chocolate. I don't remember much about the three or four families that lived there except that they were always picking coffee. Three families lived near Palo de Pollo, a small hill covered with oranges. That was many years ago. It's hard for an old man to remember," he joked, then laughed. In fact, his memory was very sharp.

"People harvested coffee for one month only. They picked it by hand and put it in a sack." He went to get an old burlap sack, tied it to his waist and around his back and demonstrated how people picked as they walked. "They were paid by the can, 25-pound lard cans. Pickers got one-third of their harvest, which they'd sell or use. Once the beans were picked, they were put into the sun to dry. Then the beans were pounded in a mortar to get rid of the husks, put into hundred-pound sacks and transported to town. At other times of the year, these people worked on other farms, or made charcoal, or maybe panned for gold."

Before electricity came to the Sabana area in the late 1940s, meals were cooked over charcoal or wood. Charcoal was preferred, for it yields more heat over a longer period of time than the same amount of wood. Actually, charcoal begins as wood. The wood is heated in the absence of air, and the result is a residue of almost pure carbon. Charcoal making was a major forest industry, one involving an astounding amount of time and effort, Rosa explained to me in a later interview. First, you gather up pieces of wood suitable for charcoal, such as guamá or guaba, common coffee shade trees, pomarrosa or moca. Chop the pieces into one- to three-foot lengths. Then stack them so they form a low tepee. Cover the wood tepee with grass or bits of branches, leaving a stick in the center. Next, take the stick out of the center and fill the center with previously-made charcoal that has been lit. Light the tepee as well and place dirt around the bottom and halfway up the sides of the tepee. At this point, you should build a tentlike rain shelter out of palm fonds if one isn't available. You'll be here for awhile: the tepee smolders for two to three days. While it is smoldering, occasionally pile on more

HARVESTING COFFEE

dirt. When the smoldering is finally complete, douse the tepee with water and move away the dirt. Pull out the pieces of wood, which — voilá! — are now charcoal. Stuff the freshly-made charcoal into sacks, and lug the sacks, two in front and two in back on a stick you hoist onto your shoulder, down the mountainside to market. Your compensation — some 10 cents a sack when Rosa was a boy. Charcoal making was tedious and poor-paying work, ranking down there with mining for copper on the steep slopes of La Mina Peak, yet for centuries women needed charcoal to cook and men needed the small change charcoal fetched in order to survive. Rosa's brother still makes charcoal, but he makes it for ten dollars a sack.

During the first half of this century, people who lived in the mountains continued to make use of the forest's resources in much the same way as the Tainos had. Both Rosa and his neighbor, Lucrecia Vázquez, described the houses that were common up until the end of World War II. Of sierra palm fronds, they were so well thatched that heavy downpours didn't penetrate them. Fronds were sewn together with needles made from dense ausubo wood and thread from fibrous sea hibiscus bark. Tree fern trunks made long-lasting posts, and wood or royal palm was often used for walls. Some floors were earthen, but more often the homes were set on stilts, and the floors, reached by three or four steps at the doorway, were also made of palm planks. In the early decades, people lit their homes with candles; consequently, many houses burned down. Today, such homes have vanished from the island.

In his doctoral dissertation, Wadsworth mentions the common furniture found in these homes — chairs, rocking chairs, benches, empty boxes, tables, beds, cots, hammocks, wooden sleeping platforms. "Some houses had one room for the old folks," Rosa recalled, "but not more than two rooms. Children slept on the floor, using old sacks stuffed with banana leaves for a bed and pillow." The versatile sacks, originally used to transport coffee beans and haul charcoal, were also made into children's clothes. "In the morning we rolled up the beds and put them away or put them in the sun. When it was cold at night, we put on an extra blanket."

In one of the more curious household uses of wood, it could make or break a courtship, Rosa explained. After a boy professed his love for a girl to the girl's father, he would nervously wait for his next visit to the girl's house. If a stake was placed in the ground close to her house when he returned, the boy could come in and continue his courtship, but if the stake stood far from the house, the boy might as well keep walking and forget about the girl.

"My family was different from those who didn't have their own land," Rosa continued. "We had three acres. Others didn't have full-time work; my father did. He was a lumber foreman for Saldondo." Early loggers felled trees with axes, hitching large pieces of trunk to yokes and hauling them down the mountain with the help of oxen. Later, they used the sort of two-man saws Rosa had shown us, and yet later, in 1920, a stream-powered sawmill was set up in Sabana. It ran for 15 years. Strong, termite-proof woods like ausubo, moca and granadillo were used for the structures of homes. "The ausubo has a fruit that is good to eat," Rosa added.

Rosa actually had more than one day of schooling. "My parents took me out after three days, to help with the lumber. I didn't feel bad,

I didn't have the capacity. I was the oldest. All my brothers and sisters went to school. But I was content, earning some 30 cents a day pulling lumber out with donkeys." Some of his best memories from that time related to pay day, modest though it was. When he was older, he, his father and brother worked hard, taking out trees, planting plantains and bananas, from sun-up to sun-down. "For 50 cents a day." Rosa laughed.

"Different from today," Bauer commented.

"'Chacho [boy oh boy], a huge difference. In those days, workers started very young, around eight. Today people are 18 and they still don't work! If a person couldn't do one thing, he did something else, but he worked. Boys and girls. They fetched wood and water, helped in the house, went looking for a stray cow. If they didn't work..." Rosa slapped at the air several times. Those were good times for him. "When I was 15, 18, I was content and happy. It was tremendous. There were no pressures, and I was fit as a bell." He also felt it was, in many ways, a better time for the region. "There was a lot of shrewdness then, little money but a lot of honor. People had more respect for everyone, they couldn't rob."

He returned to talking about his family. "My parents were really something, strong people. My father worked in the mountains all his life. He had ten children, through two unions. When I was around 14 or 15, he died. He was 40 or 50, I'm not sure exactly. Of natural causes. My mother died when I was in my thirties." At the time we spoke, Rosa had a brother in Sabana, another nearby, one in the States, two sisters in the States, others... He paused to calculate with his fingers. "Two have died, four are here, several up there — Philadelphia, Chicago, the Bronx." He has never

gone to those places, and he never will. "I'm not a bird," he pointed out.

We asked Rosa about a routine day during those times. "A routine day? Let's see. We'd get going by 6:00, have black coffee and a sorruyo." He laughed to remember it. "Flour wrapped in a banana leaf and cooked on a little fogón which was heated with wood or charcoal. We could use it inside or out of the house. Or we had a sweet potato. Then it was on to cutting wood, burning charcoal, bringing wood down the mountain. Lunch was around 11:00. The men either took their own, usually a fried arepa or guanime, or children brought it up the mountain. Then we worked until 6:00. Afterwards, we'd wash up in the stream — most homes were next to a stream — using a cream-colored soap. Then we ate, rice, beans, yautía, plantains, squash, sancocho [a tuber stew], whatever you wanted. Meat, chicken or pig, maybe once or twice a week. My family usually had two pigs, one to fatten and one to kill and eat, and usually four to six horses. Most families had pigs, goats, cows, horses, chickens, cats. After dinner there was no dessert, only coffee, perhaps with sugar and milk when the cows were giving milk. We also ate oranges, grapefruits, and we made caimito into a conserve. Though many had to go barefoot back then, people didn't go hungry. By 7:00 we were in bed."

On special days the routine changed. "Three Kings Day [January 6] was a big fiesta. People swam, drank rum, ate lechón [pig roasted on a spit] and sweet rice, invited a few neighbors into the house to dance. They played guitars and cuatros [five-double-stringed instruments], playing traditional music, aguinaldos..." He sang a few notes, "a lo lei lo lei lo lai," then laughed. "They still sing those songs. And 'chacho, the parrandas [impromptu parties]. Boys would go partying from house to house, even to farms near Fajardo. Easter week was very sacred. People didn't work, they cut their wood earlier. They stayed home, contemplating. We played a game with a stick bat and a paper ball. We didn't go to church, there was no church here. The Catholic church was in town. People went to the church in town to marry. On horseback." He laughed.

"And you never did this?" Bauer asked.

Rosa recoiled. "No! I had girlfriends, but it didn't suit me to marry. My parents actually never married, like many others. There was no pressure to marry, except for the names. I took my mother's last name, Rosa, then my father's, Torres." Conventionally, the father's name is used first, followed by the mother's.

"You also went to town when someone died," he continued. "You could only bury in the cemetery. The deceased was put in a wooden coffin and a wake was held at night. They would announce the burial in the neighborhood. Many people were needed to help carry the coffin to town." He also remembered his first trip to the big city. "When I was 12 or 14, I went to San Juan for the first time. My mother had to go to the doctor. A boy doesn't know what's going on. It was no big thing. We took a motor car, and the road was rocky."

Other people in Sabana also remember the old days. The night we found Rosa asleep at 7:00, still faithful to the routines of his youth, we crossed the road and spoke to Manuel Vázquez, another retired forester, and his wife, Lucrecia. They had spoken to me on a different occasion about Luquillo's hurricanes. Both of them grew up on the other side of the mountains, near the town of Naguabo.

Vázquez started to work as a laborer in the forest; eventually the couple settled in Sabana and opened a bar while Vázquez continued working as a forester. After talking for a few minutes, Vázquez offered us a drink at the bar. A wooden structure, it was set behind a legume tree laden with flowers known as poorman's orchids. Inside, a bare light bulb dangled over a formica counter, religious pictures were hung on the wall, and a juke box shared a side room with a pool table. The music from the juke box drowned out the din of nearby tree frogs.

Sra. Vázquez was tending the counter. She began to talk of the old days, around the time of World War II, when roads were not paved and residents walking on them had to slip off their shoes, wade through mud, and clean their feet in buckets of water before entering their homes. Oil lamps in the houses left sooty films on faces, and ashes from cooking fires were scattered by cats seeking warmth. Work hours were long, and pay rarely topped $30 a month, often received as notes to take to the general store and exchange for supplies. Shy farmers hid in the forest when strangers passed.

Although people didn't go hungry during the first half of the century, poverty in the region was grim. In his dissertation, Wadsworth summarized a 1941 study of 115 families living in the Luquillo Mountains. The families were large, with an average 6.7 members. Family heads had an average 1.6 years of schooling. Fifty percent of the population was illiterate, 30 percent of the children had no schooling. Almost half the homes had no latrines, more than half used water from streams for cooking, drinking and bathing. The average plot of land was 3.5 acres. The annual value of crops from farms totaled $35, but two-thirds of the crops were eaten by the families and never reached market. The net annual farm income was $153.

Sra. Vázquez felt there had been un-dreamed-of progress since that time, due in large part to the vision of the island's first elected governor, Luis Muñoz Marín. Gone are the thatch homes, the muddy roads, the shy farmers. And yet, Sra. Vázquez reflected, there were certain disagreeable aspects to the progress. Young men didn't appreciate the sharp increase in wages, and young women preferred canned food to preparing their own fresh tubers and plantains.

Bauer and I also spoke with Manuel Corsino and his wife. Corsino, 69 years old at the time, is another retired forester. He too has lived through the undreamed-of progress mentioned by Sra. Vázquez. When in his mid-teens, he began to work in the forest, earning 50 cents a day. Now he has his own home, a small sturdy concrete structure with a spa-cious porch decorated with pots filled with orchids and other flowering plants. A tall Nor-folk pine stands in the front yard. After Corsino seated Bauer and me on the porch, Sra. Corsino brought us tall glasses of home-made passion fruit juice. She remained with us, adding her comments and corrections to what Corsino said, in spite of his admonitions to keep quiet and go away. He did not want to share his moment in the limelight.

"Downtown" Sabana didn't exist until the 1930s, according to Corsino, when a road was built to link the area with Luquillo. "Before that, people lived in houses apart from each other. Most didn't have land, they lived on oth-ers' land. Early homes were of thatch, zinc and/or wood. One neighborhood of zinc homes in the community was called Pueblito de las Viudas because it was made up mostly

of widows." That, at least, was the version Corsino told in my presence. I later heard that these women were not so much widows as single women who entertained male visitors at night.

Homes began to improve in the 1930s, when the Puerto Rico Authority financed the construction of 20-by-20-foot concrete houses with outdoor wood kitchens for cooking with wood or charcoal. Each concrete home had an acre of land, and there were communal areas for growing chickens, pigs and subsist-ence crops and for storing harvests. Corsino's memory was also good. "People could buy these homes for $1.42 a month the first year, $2 a month the second, $3 a month the third, and so on. There was also a second project, houses of wood and zinc with six to seven acres of land. Concrete houses are better, though, because they provide more security in a storm or earthquake." The Corsinos still live in their concrete house, now enlarged to include an indoor kitchen. Plumbing and elec-tricity reached Sabana in the late '40s, and telephones are a relatively recent addition to the community.

But what about the coffee, which had been so instrumental in opening up the lower slopes of the Luquillo Mountains and in es-tablishing the community of Sabana? "San Felipe and San Ciprian helped bring the end of coffee," Rosa told us. Occurring in 1928 and 1932, those back-to-back hurricanes reduced farms in the Luquillo Mountains to ruin. "Cof-fee wasn't planted again after those two. It was too hard for a man of 40 or 50 to start over." Those who did remain on the land concen-trated on lumber and subsistence crops. Wad-sworth listed the chief crops in the Luquillo Mountains in 1940 in their descending order of importance — sweet potatoes, beans, rice, corn, coffee, tobacco, yautía and bananas. By 1950, coffee had slipped from fifth to eighth place. Many farmers chose not to stay on the land. "When Mr. McPhee died, he gave his farm to the children," Rosa remembered. "They sold it to the government. The three families who lived near Palo de Pollo stayed until the hurricanes. Then they sold to the government. We sold our three acres to the government."

Beginning in the 1930s, the Federal Government bought abandoned farms from Sabana to El Verde and added them to the national forest acreage. A few farmers continued to work on national forest land. Corsino told us of a family by the name of Pérez who lived next to the Río Mameyes until 1956. Theirs may have been the house my brother and I had tried unsuccessfully to find, al-

though when I later spoke of this to Frank Wadsworth, he thought that house was the vacation home of a Francis Reed. He also felt the ruin still existed. Eventually, crop cultivation stopped, and ferns, sierra palms and pioneering Cecropia trees quickly moved in.

Today, those who venture into the lower forest slopes can still spot vestiges of the farming decades — oranges, sweet lemons, grapefruits, passion fruit, ginger, avocados, pigeon peas, sweet potatoes, ñame, malanga, yautía, yuca, bananas. And coffee. But this period has ended, and, given the increasing desire of the public to preserve the national forest and the eagerness of developers to build resort and residential tracts along the foothills and coastal plains, it is doubtful people who live in the area will ever again eke out modest livings by making use of the forest's resources.

CHAPTER 11
THOSE RARELY SEEN

In 1984 Carlos Rivera, biological technician at the time, was working in the Caribbean National Forest, in the northwestern part known as El Verde. Part of his job was to make periodic field trips into the forest, along with another technician, in order to measure plants and trees growing in special study plots. These plots were established half a century ago in several distinct areas of the forest, and every five years each plot is revisited to check on its growth. Technicians note the height of trees, their trunk diameters, whether or not they are flowering, and other features. Any new trees that are found within the plot are in turn measured and duly noted. Eventually the new trees receive a dab of paint around the height where the trunk will be measured in future visits and a metal tag with an identifying number that includes the year of the tree's discovery.

When Rivera reached one of the plots in the area known as Colorado Valley, he noticed a young tree that he hadn't seen before. Not only had he not seen it in the plot, but he didn't recognize it as any known tree in the forest. Rivera had been working in Luquillo for a decade, and he knew its plants and trees well. His hand could fit around the slender trunk, and the leaves were of small size, glossy, dark green and elliptical. On further investigation, he noticed two more young trees of the same type near the study plot. He collected several leaf specimens and took them to Caribbean botanist Roy Woodbury. Rivera realized he could be the discoverer of a new tree species.

In San Juan, Woodbury examined the leaves, compared them to other leaves stored at the University of Puerto Rico's herbarium, and sent a specimen up to botanist Richard Howard of Arnold Arboretum in Massachusetts for a confirming opinion. The tree was not a new species, it turned out, but one thought to be extinct. Rivera had rediscovered *Styrax portoricensis*, known locally as palo de jazmín or jasmine wood, a tree that can grow up to 65 feet high. This tree is endemic to Puerto Rico, that is, it grows naturally here and nowhere else, and it is the island's only known member of the storax family, a far-flung group of shrubs and trees found in both old and new world tropics and subtropics. With their tendency to spread and their dangling white flowers, many of these trees are planted as ornamentals. Several Mediterranean species are also cultivated for their aromatic resins, and in fact the name "Styrax" itself comes from an ancient Greek word for a fragrant resin used as incense and medicine, and for the plant from which it was obtained. (This may have given rise to S. portoricensis's local name, although no description of the tree

I have seen mentions a jasminelike fragrance.) In 1885 a German botanist, Paul Sintenis, collected the first specimens of S. portoricensis in the eastern mountains of Puerto Rico. In 1935 forest researchers Claud Horn and Leslie Holdridge made a second collection somewhere in the Luquillo Mountains. A third collection, of the fruits, occurred in the El Verde area of the forest in 1954. A quarter century later, no exact localities of the tree were known.

For his efforts, Rivera received an American Horticultural Society Wildflower Rediscovery Award, which he displays along with a number of photographs and clippings in his office. Rivera, now a botanist with the Forest Service's International Institute of Tropical Forestry, guesses that there is an adult S. portoricensis somewhere in the vicinity of the three young trees, but, as he pointed out when I visited him, it is difficult if not impossible for foresters and scientists to cover every inch of the forest, even in a limited area. In 1989 Hurricane Hugo stormed through the forest, and foresters feared the worst for the slender palo de jazmín trees. Since then, Rivera has been trying to revisit the site, but the hurricane wiped out virtually all paths to the various study plots. New paths have been made, but he is not yet familiar with the one to that particular site. The current biological technician, Juan Ramirez, has been there and says he saw the tree in the plot, identifiable by its metal tag. Although bent by the hurricane, it was alive and flowering, a good sign. The fate of the neighboring two trees remains uncertain. Thus, for the moment, the entire verified worldwide population of Styrax portoricensis consists of one tree in the Colorado Valley of the El Verde region of the Caribbean National Forest.

❦ Though the Styrax is an extreme example, it is by no means the only rarely seen species in the Luquillo forest. Basically, a rare species is one that is uncommon, that occurs in small numbers, often in limited or specialized habitats. A rare species may be uncommon naturally, or it may have become uncommon through human actions, but its small numbers make its existence more precarious than that of more common species. Specific terms define various degrees of rareness. If a species is uncommon and likely to find its existence in jeopardy in the foreseeable future, it is considered threatened. If its existence is in jeopardy right now, it is considered endangered. Endangered species are those in immediate danger of extinction, unlikely to survive without special care. The U.S. Fish and Wildlife Service maintains a Federal list of both endangered and threatened species, providing these plants and animals with special, legal protection in the hopes of keeping them from becoming extinct.

When botanists Elbert Little and Roy Woodbury calculated 225 native tree species in the Caribbean National Forest, they classified 88, or slightly more than one-third, as rare or endangered, a number greater than in any other national forest. This is true of Puerto Rico in general: the island has a whopping 537 native tree species, yet only half are considered common, and many are categorized as rare or endangered. Of approximately 920 plant and animal species currently found on the Federal Endangered Species list for the United States and its territories, 71, or some 13 percent, are harbored in Puerto Rico (13 in the Caribbean National Forest). The Puerto Rican government, through the Natural Heritage Program of the Department of Natural and Environmental Resources, has a separate critical species list, which includes those on the Federal list as well as other locally designated plants and animals, ranging from species that are endangered to threatened to just plain rare but in need of a watchful eye. Some 585 plants and 42 animals are on this list. Of them, 93 of the plants and 16 of the animals are found in the Caribbean National Forest.

"It is one of the ironies of tropical rain forests," state Adrian Forsyth and Ken Miyata in their book, *Tropical Nature*, "that common species are rare and rare species are common." In temperate forests thousands of acres can be made up of a handful of species while in the tropics a handful of acres can claim thousands of species. Most ecologists agree that a large number of species can occur in a small habitat if that habitat has a rich resource base from which to nourish its population or if a species is so specialized in its needs — for example a bird that only feeds on the seeds of one type of tree — that it doesn't compete with other species. Ecologists have suggested that the great stability of tropical forests — little change in seasons and length of days along with continual warm, wet weather, eon after eon — has something to do with its incredible diversity.

But Forsyth and Miyata point out recent evidence suggesting that the tropics may not be such a model of stability after all. The temperature and moisture fluctuations that occurred between ice ages in the last two million years affected tropical forests as well as temperate ones. Though the fluctuations were not as great in the tropics, it is possible they were more disastrous to the tropical community, which was unaccustomed to any sort of change. The weather changes, occurring over hundreds of thousands of years, caused existing forests to shrink and expand and shrink

again. When the forests shrank, the species within them often became isolated from each other. If they remained isolated for tens of thousands of years, individual species could begin to change, adapting to the conditions of their new environment or drifting apart genetically, until they became distinct, separate species.

Scientists tend to consider species to be separate when they can no longer interbreed. This process, in which populations become geographically separated from each other until there is no genetic connection between them, is known as geographic speciation. Islands are the most obvious examples of geographic speciation. When sea levels were low within the Caribbean, plants and animals were able to make their way north from South America and east from Central America. When sea levels were high, as they are now, the islands became physically isolated from each other, and species took distinct turns. Being relatively small and endowed with an abundance of the tremendous diversity of tropical America, the islands didn't offer species a lot of room for expansion. Island species could not heed the call to "Go West", or north or south or east, for that matter. Many species had to remain small and specialized in order to survive. This in turn has made them acutely susceptible to even minor environmental changes. Of all the species that have become extinct in the world in the last centuries, an extremely high number existed on islands.

As the largest chunk of original forest remaining in Puerto Rico, the Caribbean National Forest shelters dozens of small, specialized populations, some of which have always lived here and others which gravitated here after their preferred habitats were destroyed. In the long-range management plan prepared

*Biologist
Wayne Arendt,
specialist in the
pearly-eyed
thrasher.*

Flower of the rare Tabebuia rigida *in dwarf forest.*

Endangered Puerto Rican parrots.

for El Yunque in the 1980s, the Forest Service presented its own list of rare flora and fauna — here they are referred to as sensitive species — which need to be monitored. The flora list contains 32 species — ten plants and 22 trees. Almost half of them are endemic to the Luquillo Mountains, and 26 exist in limited spaces. (By 1994, the number had increased to 38 species.)

Eight of the flora species have been designated by U.S. Fish and Wildlife as endangered. All exist in limited spaces. One of these is an orchid, *Lepanthes eltoroensis*, which is found only on El Toro Peak. L. eltoroensis is a good example of the precariousness of rare species: if a communications tower is ever built on El Toro Peak, the orchid becomes an historical footnote.

The other seven endangered species are trees, one each from the canella, myrtle, holly, verbena and storax families, and two from the tea family. The styrax representative is the species rediscovered by botanist Carlos Rivera, *Styrax portoricensis*. The canella species, *Pleodendron macranthum*, locally known as chupacallos, has been dubbed one of the rarest trees in Puerto Rico by the authors of *Trees of Puerto Rico and the Virgin Islands*. It was discovered by a French botanist, August Plée, while he was collecting plants in Puerto Rico in 1822. By the end of the century, the tree was determined to be sufficiently distinctive to be placed in its own genus. "Pleodendron" means tree of Plée, in honor of the tree's discoverer; "macranthum" refers to the tree's large yellowish-white flowers. It now can be found — very rarely — in the lower Luquillo forest and the limestone region of north-central Puerto Rico. On the other hand, the myrtle tree, *Eugenia haematocarpa*, or uvillo, forms part of a genus that has some 20 spe-

cies in Puerto Rico alone. This specific species, found only in the Luquillo Mountains, wasn't even collected until 1939 and wasn't named until 1963.

The verbenaceae representative, *Callicarpa ampla*, is a shrub or small tree once found throughout the wet mountain forests of Puerto Rico. It was apparently always uncommon. Noticeable for its many delicate white flowers and its fruit drupes that change in color from white to pink to pale purple when ripe, the tree has accumulated two common names, capá rosa (which means pink West Indian 'oak') and péndula cimarrona (wild pendent).

The history of capá rosa is typical of many of the forest's rarely seen trees. According to a Department of Natural Resources status report published in the 1970s, capá rosa was first cited by someone named Schauer in 1847, described from specimens collected by one Wydler in Puerto Rico in 1827. Since then, the tree has only been collected seven times, six of them in lower mountain forests of Puerto Rico and once on St. Thomas. The tree was never seen on St. Thomas again, which may mean it has been exterminated or that it was mistakenly ascribed to the smaller island. In the 1880s Sintenis collected specimens in Puerto Rico's mountain regions of Cayey, Barranquitas, Utuado and Adjuntas. These areas were soon planted in coffee and other agricultural products, and the species has not been found there in recent decades. A couple of trees were found in Luquillo in 1883 by Eggers, in 1940 by Holdridge, and in the 1950s and 1960s by Woodbury. Of them, one was destroyed in a landslide. A local forester brought leaf samples of a capá rosa tree to Woodbury from within a forestry plantation on the southern side of the forest.

The status report continues: "With a single, poorly defined locality for this species after a hundred years of intense botanical exploration in Puerto Rico, the species certainly qualifies to be placed in the category of rare. Rareness is compounded by the low density in which it has been found, for only single trees have been reported. Rareness and low density make this species particularly vulnerable to destruction, a set of circumstances that demand special protections coupled with a more intense effort to localize new localities."

The tree's numbers have increased in recent decades, perhaps because there have been more intense efforts to locate them. A 1993 U.S. Fish and Wildlife Draft Recovery Plan for five of the endangered trees found in Luquillo states that 14 capá rosa trees have now been located within the upper palo colorado region of the forest.

❦ When it comes to animals, the larger mammalian varieties are more than rare in the Luquillo Mountains: they are, in fact, nonexistent. Jaguars, tapirs and other large animals of South and Central American forests are not here primarily because it was not possible for them to get here. Even when the oceans were at their lowest, water still separated the islands. Land mammals cannot swim great distances, and most of them are too large to be swept along by winds, like birds, or carried along by water, like seeds. Fossils up to a million years old show that such small ground

/ PUERTO RICAN PARROTS

mammals as sloths, rats (a different species from today's introduced roof rat), moles, shrews and hedgehogs once inhabited the Luquillo Mountains, but these species were extinct by the time Columbus discovered the New World. Today only a handful of bat species remain of El Yunque's native mammal population. Forest animals are small, ranging in size from foot-long birds to inch-long frogs to barely visible ants.

The paucity of island animal species is not limited to mammals. In an article on the fauna of island ecosystems, biologist Robert Waide compares the fauna of Puerto Rico with that of mainland tropical regions, and the differences are significant. Costa Rica has 136 mammal species (63 of them bats) while Puerto Rico has a mere 15 (11 bats and 4 nonnative mammals such as the mongoose). Guyana has 464 bird species (21 migrants); Puerto Rico, 66 (32 migrants). Guyana claims 93 reptiles to Puerto Rico's 13, 85 termite species to Puerto Rico's 4, and 96 ant species to Puerto Rico's 22. Costa Rica has 45 amphibian species; Puerto Rico, 14. Brazil has 550 butterfly species; Puerto Rico, 18. And so on. In comparing a typical food chain in a mainland forest with one in El Yunque, Waide notes an absence of mammals in the latter. On the mainland, eagles feed on boas, which feed on raccoonlike coati, which feed on insects, which feed on plants; in El Yunque, lizards and spiders have replaced coati in the chain.

The Forest Service's 1980s list of sensitive fauna consists of ten species. Five of them (one falcon, two hawks, one parrot and a snake) have been officially designated as endangered by U.S. Fish and Wildlife, and five (one bat, one warbler and three tree frogs) are categorized as needing to be watched. The newly released 1994 list includes two more tree frogs and a crow that is extinct in Puerto Rico but still exists on two neighboring islands.

Of the four bat species found in El Yunque, the red fruit bat is on the sensitive species list. Also known as the red fig-eating bat, or *Stenoderma rufum*, it is a small furry creature with big wings, a white crescent below the ears and a white spot on the shoulders. Though modest in appearance and size, the red fruit bat claims a baroque tale of discovery. Mammalogists J.R. Tamsitt and Darío Valdivieso, who wrote a chapter on bats for the El Verde tropical rain forest project, sum up its history: In 1813 one E. Geoffroy St. Hilaire, who was doing work on Egyptian mammals, described the S. rufum bat. No locality was given. This perplexed many mammalogists, who looked at St. Hilaire's lone specimen and regarded the species as New World because of its resemblance to other New World species. For decades its existence remained an enigma, and some nineteenth-century mammalogists intimidated that S. rufum was nothing more than a taxonomic artifact, an error in the classification process. Finally, in 1916, a man named Anthony found fossil skull remains of S. rufum in caves near the mountain town of Morovis, Puerto Rico. The red fruit bat now had, or at least once had, a home: Anthony surmised that the bat had become extinct in Puerto Rico but possibly survived on adjacent islands.

In 1957 three live red fruit bats were found on the nearby island of St. John. This encouraged Tamsitt and Valdivieso to search with greater vigor for the bat in Puerto Rico. Stretching a mist net across a fast-moving stream in the El Verde section of the forest, they finally caught their first red fruit bat on July 3, 1965. Subsequently, they caught or saw several others. After a century and a half of doubts, a population, albeit small, of red fruit bats was alive and well in the Luquillo Mountains.

The warbler of the Forest Service's sensitive species list was not even discovered until 1971. While working with the endangered Puerto Rican parrot in the Luquillo Mountains, Cameron and Kay Kepler came upon this small black and white warbler tucked away in dwarf forest thicket. It had been 45 years since the last discovery of a new bird species in the Caribbean. "One immediately wonders (and we have been asked by many colleagues) how an avian species could have escaped detection on an island as densely populated, deforested, and repeatedly studied by ornithologists as Puerto Rico," write Cameron Kepler and Kenneth Parkes in an article related to the discovery published in *The Auk* magazine (1972). They go on to cite several explanations. Perhaps the most important relates to the bird's habitat. Known as the elfin woods warbler, or *Dendroica angelae* (angelae in honor of its co-discoverer, Angela Kay Kepler), this is the only bird in the Luquillo Mountains that lives exclusively within the dwarf forest. (Oddly enough, it was later found in two other places, one of them being the Maricao forest in the island's western mountains, at a lower altitude and within a more diverse vegetation. This indicates it was probably more widely found at one time and severed from other populations when forests were cleared for agriculture.) Dwarf forest is a short and shadowy tangle of all sorts of vegetation, very difficult to penetrate, so the warbler remains hidden from most bird watchers' eyes. In addition, its rather inconspicuous appearance — black and white or greenish plumage with a black crown and a partial white eye ring — enables it to blend into its surroundings, and the adult looks similar to the black and white warbler, a migrant forest visitor. It is an uncommon bird — Kepler and Parkes roughly estimated fewer than 300 pairs comprising the total population — and its calls resemble those of the very common bananaquit. The Keplers had lived and worked in the forest for more than a year before they were aware of the bird's existence.

The three Eleutherodactylus tree frog species of the 1980s Forest Service list, known locally as coquís, are good examples of species which have their own small space. *E. karlschmidti* (scientifically named for Karl P. Schmidt, one of the first herpetologists to visit Puerto Rico, and commonly named the web-footed coquí because it is the only species in Puerto Rico that has webs between its toes) is a semi-aquatic frog that prefers rocks and boulders along mountain streams. *E. eneidae*, the mottled coquí, haunts mud banks and mossy trunks along mountain roads and trails. *E. unicolor*, the burrow coquí, tunnels under moss, rocks and roots on dwarf forest peaks. These frogs seem to know what they like, and what they like is very select. In large part because of their specialized habitats, they are few in number, and there have been several concerned reports that their numbers are declining.

In summary, many of the sensitive species — the red fruit bat, the burrow coquí, the El Toro Peak orchid and Styrax portoricensis — are rare endemics, species that are native to and found only in a particular region, confined to specialized habitats. On the other hand, other species — the Puerto Rican boa and Puerto Rican parrot, as examples — were known to have been common at one time and were brought to their current state by human actions. Of the five Federally endangered animal species found in Luquillo, four of them — the boa, the parrot, the broad-winged hawk and the sharp-shinned hawk — exist only in Puerto Rico; the fifth, the peregrine falcon, is a winter visitor.

The Puerto Rican boa, *Epicrates inornatus*, provides an interesting example of the complexities involved in identifying endangered species. Although the Puerto Rican boa is found only in Puerto Rico, the other Greater Antilles islands have their own boa species, indicating the snake probably made its way along the Caribbean archipelago, most likely from Central America, at some distant time in the past. The largest native snake on the island, this rather plain brown creature grows up to seven feet long. It is found primarily in the island's foothills, on the ground or coiling up tree trunks or near the entrances to caves, but it is not found often, for it is a shy, nocturnal creature. It is a constrictor, coiling around and crushing its prey — bats, rats, mice, birds and the occasional chicken. Though it hisses and bites when cornered, its bite is not poisonous. Perhaps because of its menacing size, the boa has become the subject of several superstitions. One of the more bizarre has it that the boa inserts its tail in the mouth of a crying infant to calm him while it sucks the (human) mother's milk. "Absurd," writes herpetologist Juan Rivero, yet the superstition apparently endures in Puerto Rico and several other countries.

Once common throughout the lower elevations of Puerto Rico, the boa has become scarce in the last hundred years. Centuries ago, the mongoose was brought in to control rats in cane fields; unfortunately, it proved more effective on native birds and reptiles, including the boa, than on rats. Rats, which came along for the ride on early ships bound for the New World, also feed on young boas that are not yet large enough to feed on the rats. Humans have proved even more dangerous to the boa. Residents have captured some to sell as pets and killed others to extract their oil, considered useful for a variety of ills. Rivero explains how the oil is obtained: the hunter stretches the living snake between two stakes, dissects it, removes the oil (probably from fat deposits) and releases the snake in the somewhat naive hope it will recover. Biologists feared the boa was approaching extinction and made a concerted effort to get it onto the Federal Endangered Species list. Once on the list, the boa has been showing itself fairly commonly, on the lower slopes of El Yunque but primarily in the karst region from north-central to northwest Puerto Rico, and it is thought that its shy ways made it seem scarcer than it is. But until scientists are satisfied that it is, in fact, fairly common, it remains officially endangered.

Somewhat ironically, the best-known and most painstakingly protected endangered species in the Luquillo Mountains — the Puerto Rican parrot — is not originally from these mountains. At one time it had a vast population that inhabited every niche of lowland Puerto Rico. Its dramatic decline is well documented in a book by biologists Noel Snyder, James Wiley and Cameron Kepler. *The Parrots of Luquillo: Natural History and Conservation of the Puerto Rican Parrot* (1987),

tells a tale typical of many species made rare by humans.

In the late-1960s, less than two dozen Puerto Rican parrots inhabited the upper valleys of the Luquillo Mountains. They were all that was left of the species *Amazona vittata*, a foot-long, predominantly green bird. Not only was this tiny colony the last of the species, it was also the last of four parrot species once native to the U.S. and its territories. It seemed Americans would soon be doomed to visiting zoos and pet shops if they wanted to see live parrots or parakeets.

Twenty-two individuals. They were the remnants of a population that may have topped a million when Columbus first approached the island. Found primarily in lowland forests, parrots darkened the sky as their huge bands flew in search of food. Most scientists believe the birds' ancestors originated on the mainland of Central America and island-hopped to Puerto Rico, either along a northern route from the Yucatán Peninsula to Cuba or a more southerly one from the Honduran-Nicaraguan bulge to Jamaica, at a time during the last ice age when sea levels were hundreds of feet lower than they are today. Tainos were quite familiar with the birds, which they called iguaca. They showed the conquistadors how to catch them; in one method Indians made smoldering pots out of gourds and wet leaves in order to smoke the birds temporarily senseless, at which time they would take a few feathers. Feathers were used as decorative ornaments; Indians also kept the birds as pets, and they ate them.

Although parrots began to decline after the arrival of Spaniards, they remained in great numbers until the 1800s, when agriculture spread over much of the island. Lowland forests were destroyed, and the parrots, forced to feed on crops, became fair game for farmers' slings and guns. Slaughter by farmers continued into the early years of this century. Periodic hurricanes wiped out large numbers, and the parrots could no longer rebuild their populations as they had in the past. Poor country residents collected young parrots to sell as pets: one parrot would fetch up to two dollars, a princely sum to the farmers. By the 1920s the birds' original lowland habitat was reduced to isolated nooks in the karst country of northwestern Puerto Rico. There, erosion has sculpted the region's porous limestone into vast cave networks, rugged conelike hills and crater-shaped sinkholes, good hideouts for any animal. Yet after Hurricane San Felipe in 1928, no parrots could be found in the karst region. By the late 1930s a census estimated some 2,000 remaining birds, all in the Luquillo Mountains. Though not traditional parrot country, the Caribbean National Forest became the birds' last hope on a densely populated island.

Yet even within the protective boundaries of the forest, the birds continued to decline. In 1959 José Rodríguez-Vidal published a study of the parrots, in which he counted some 200 individuals; in 1966 Victor Márquez sighted 70 birds in a single flock; at the end of the decade when the Keplers came to the forest, they found no flocks at all. A number of factors contributed to the startling decline. Several of them, so easy to list in retrospect, took a tremendous amount of time and analysis to understand. Back in the 1930s workers disturbed habitats while constructing trails and building a road through the forest. Local residents continued to hunt parrots to sell as pets, often destroying nests as they did so, confident at the time that more birds could be found just over the next hill. Loggers re-

moved trees for fuelwood, timber and posts. Foresters cleared out old, decaying, cavity-riddled trunks; these trunks, biologists eventually learned, were favorite parrot nesting sites. To make matters worse, competition developed over who would use the limited remaining cavities: bees needed them to make their honey, and pearly-eyed thrashers took over the parrot nests that appealed to them. Predators such as red-tailed hawks, Puerto Rican boas and stray cats stalked the parrots, and warble fly maggots lodged in the skin of chicks. Hurricanes also took their toll. In the 1960s, military testing activities — a dab of defoliant here, a helicopter-supported maneuver there — may, or may not, have affected the birds, and a radiation experiment in El Verde was close to a popular parrot habitat.

"The wonder," the authors of *The Parrots of Luquillo* wrote in summary, "is not that the parrots rapidly declined, but that a small population managed to survive to the present."

It would take hundreds of thousands of dollars and dozens of biologists working thousands of hours before the parrots would begin to inch away from near-extinction. By the end of 1968 Frank Wadsworth, then director of the Institute of Tropical Forestry in San Juan, and Ray Erickson, assistant director in charge of endangered wildlife research at the Patuxent Wildlife Research Center in Maryland, received commitments from the U.S. Fish and Wildlife Service, the U.S. Forest Service and the World Wildlife Fund (and later from Puerto Rico's Department of Natural Resources), to establish the current research and conservation program to study the parrot and its natural enemies. Yet even after the program was set up, the parrot's numbers continued to slip, and by the mid-1970s biologists estimated a mere baker's dozen parrots in the wild. The Puerto Rican parrot was listed as one of the ten most endangered birds in the world.

Authors Snyder, Wiley and Kepler directed the project in three separate periods from 1968 to 1987. Their book is a polished, meticulous account of virtually everything related to the Puerto Rican parrot. Parts of the book, especially those describing the bird's origins, history and habitat, make interesting reading for anyone, while other sections are obviously geared to biologists. A primary objective of the book, and the project itself, is to be an information source for those working with other parrots in the Caribbean. Of the more than six macaw, eight parakeet and 12 parrot species that once inhabited the Caribbean, nine parrot and three parakeet (no macaw) species still survive. None is as critically endangered as the Puerto Rican bird, but all are declining in numbers, and the authors hope that the material collected about the Puerto Rican parrot can be adapted to species on islands lacking the economic resources to produce such in-depth studies.

Early into the program it was decided to maintain the Puerto Rican parrot both in the wild and in captivity. The captive birds reside at the Luquillo aviary, a large hurricane-proof reinforced-concrete two-story building tucked away on the upper slopes of the mountains. Several cars are usually parked on a lawn in front of the building, and a high cyclone fence surrounds the grounds. Originally meant to be a military barracks, the building was donated to the project by the Forest Service and converted into an aviary in 1973. The authors explain the decision to establish a captive community: "By 1971 we could account for only 16 birds in the wild and trends suggested that extinction could come within a decade. Causes

of the decline were still not well understood, and it appeared that the only reasonable hope for the species was to begin captive breeding immediately." Yet they also realized that the only hope for long-term survival was to maintain a wild population and to balance it carefully with the captive one.

As the conservation program got underway, biologists tackled the bird's problems one by one. Pearly-eyed thrashers ranked as the parrots' number one enemy. Innocuous-looking birds with a brown body and white underside, thrashers inexplicably increased and became a problem in the forest in recent decades. Unlike most thrashers, this species commonly nests in tree cavities, and the aggressive birds would swoop down on unguarded parrot nests, commandeering them and knocking out parrot eggs and chicks in the process. Biologists searched for a solution to this problem, and the thrashers became the second most studied bird in the forest. It turned out that parrots like deep nests, using holes up to 18 feet deep, while thrashers use shallow nests. The biologists became architects, designing deep, S-shaped tube nests which they decorated with epiphytes and tacked onto trees in remote parrot-breeding areas of the forest. Nearby, they placed shallow nests for the thrashers. Both parrots and thrashers took to their artificial nests, and the thrasher problem was effectively eliminated. In an inspiring turn-around, the spunky little thrashers have even helped the parrots by defending the area from other predators.

Some of the most innovative techniques used in the parrot project relate to breeding, and the book's chapter on the captive breeding program has all the tension of a good thriller. Crisis — Puerto Rican parrot mysteriously dies in quarantine. This happened when the bird was en route to the Patuxent Center in Maryland to become part of a new parrot breeding program; as a result, it was decided to establish breeding facilities at the Luquillo aviary. Crisis — two birds paired for breeding live together happily but sterilely for three years. Male and female parrots look alike; consternated scientists eventually realized these two birds were female. Crisis — two pinch-hitting Hispaniolan parrots die after undergoing laparoscopy. Hispaniolan parrots, found on the neighboring island, are more abundant than their Puerto Rican relatives and have been used as surrogates in a number of ways in the parrot program. Laparoscopies, to determine the birds' sex, were (perhaps needless to say) not performed on the Puerto Rican parrots after the deaths of the Hispaniolans. Eventually, a safe method of analyzing steroids from bird feces to determine sex was applied. Crisis —priceless parrot egg must be taken from its nest along a steep, slick, root-strewn path to the aviary. In the early stages of the program, especially when the thrashers were a problem, parrot eggs were often taken to the aviary for safekeeping and substituted in the nest with plaster of Paris eggs. Tiny access doors and foam-lined carrying cases helped but did little to relieve the transporter's sweaty palms and pounding heart. Crisis — a power outage at the aviary renders the incubators useless as the first two captive chicks are born. Wind and rain storms wreak havoc on the above-ground power lines in the forest, and outages are numerous and lengthy. An emergency generator was bought after the first breeding season, but it too has had its moments of failure. The first two chicks did survive.

When writing *The Parrots of Luquillo*, the authors were cautiously optimistic about the bird's future. One caution related to the question of genes in a species that has been reduced to so few individuals. I visited a parrot blind with Jim Wiley in the mid-1980s, and he expressed optimism: "The parrot's high fertility and hatching rates are good signs that there are no adverse effects of inbreeding", he explained, adding that the tendency for a species' population to "bottleneck" when it first arrives on an island may help it adapt to a low gene pool. Two years later, the parrot's fertility rate dropped; a year later it rose. In the epilogue to the book, the authors also expressed caution that, in spite of resolving the birds' major problems, the parrot community had not increased as much as they had hoped it would, and mating pairs remained relatively few. Why? Do the birds sense they are closely related to their potential mates? Or are there not enough experienced breeders to show the others how it's done? Or is there something lacking in the bird's diet high in the Luquillo Mountains, where Puerto Rican parrots fled only after their natural habitats were destroyed?

Two years after the book was published, in 1989, Hurricane Hugo passed over the Luquillo Mountains. Parrot watchers could do little more than pray while furious winds and driving rain slashed through the forest. Afterwards, they ventured out to assess the damage. Many trees within the bird's habitat had fallen or were severely broken by the sustained winds, clocked at 150 miles per hour. Although all 53 parrots in the aviary at the time survived, of the 45 to 47 parrots that were known to exist in the wild prior to Hugo, only some 22 could be found.

After the hurricane, a small miracle occurred. The parrots' breeding seems to have taken off. From 1991 to 1993, six parrot pairs nested in the wild each year, the highest number since Rodríguez-Vidal studied the parrots back in the 1950s, and parrots are beginning to nest at lower elevations and in the cavities of trees other than the preferred palo colorado. Eleven chicks were hatched in the wild in 1992, 13 in 1993 (along with 9 hatched in captivity), and 13 again in 1994 (along with 7 hatched in captivity). At the end of the 1993 breeding season, the total wild population was 41 birds, or more than 90 percent of the pre-Hugo population. Some biologists attribute this increase to certain positive effects of the hurricane, but Francisco Vilella and Ana Arnizaut, currently working with the parrot recovery program, feel there may also be other factors. These factors could include a more resilient bird population, the availability of improved natural cavities (improved upon by parrot program staff), and the effectiveness of the nest management program in such aspects as better camouflaging nest observation blinds. In April of 1993, ten parrots from the Luquillo aviary were transferred to an aviary within the Río Abajo Commonwealth Forest to begin a second parrot population. Río Abajo is located in the limestone-rich karst hills of north-central Puerto Rico, the last known natural habitat of the Puerto Rican parrot.

Has it been worth it, all the years of research, the money spent, the occasional bickering and agonizing over the best course to follow? The question came to mind when I visited the parrot blind with Wiley and watched a parrot step out of her nest into the dim morning light. Though somewhat drab compared to some of her more colorful Caribbean cousins, she nevertheless displayed a set of feathers that are the quintessence of tropical forest green. And there she was, a bird predicted to be extinct by then, preening herself and squawking good morning to another day. I thought of another member of the Luquillo forest community, the white-necked crow (*Corvus leucognaphalus*), that has become extinct in Puerto Rico although it still exists in Jamaica and the Dominican Republic. A large black bird whose neck is ringed with a scarcely detectable touch of white, the white-necked crow was once common in island forests. It, too, sought final refuge in the Luquillo Mountains. In 1963 two crows were spotted high in the forest. None were ever seen again.

Monies have been spent on less noble intentions. It seemed worth it to me.

CHAPTER 12
CREATURES OF THE JUNGLE

"The jaguar kills you with a bite to the head, but only in exceptional circumstances. Two vipers, the fer-de-lance (up to seven and a half feet long) and the bushmaster (up to twelve feet, the largest in the world), only kill you if you step on them. The anaconda is known to tighten its grip only when you breathe out; the electric eel can only deliver its 640 volts before its breakfast; the piranha only rips you to bits if you are already bleeding, and the Giant catfish merely has a penchant for taking your feet off at the ankle as you do the crawl."

Perhaps Redmond O'Hanlon unearthed more than one would want to know about the terrifying creatures of the jungle, yet he still ventured into the Amazon, making it back alive and in enough of one piece to describe such animals in his book, *In Trouble Again: A Journey between the Orinoco and the Amazon* (1988). For most people, tropical jungles conjure up similarly horrifying images — of swarming insects, night-preying birds, ferocious beasts. These same people inquire, with trepidation, about the animals lurking in the Luquillo Mountains, and they find the answer somewhat hard to believe.

For in fact there are no dangerous animals in the Luquillo Mountains. Bilharzia offers perhaps the greatest concern, at least to those who like to bathe in the mountain streams. Bilharzia is a parasitic disease which is common in slow-moving tropical fresh water in both hemispheres. It is caused by schistosomes, or "blood worms", parasitic flatworms that infest the blood of humans and other mammals in a cycle that moves from blood vessels to the intestine and bodily feces; to water and a host known as the Biomphalaria snail; to water again and the skin of a mammal; through tissues and back to the blood vessels. The disease attacks humans in the abdominal area; though it rarely kills, it damages the liver and causes an illness that can last for decades. Treating the disease requires early diagnosis and persistence. Much has been done to eradicate the snail on the island, but it does still exist. Years ago, when I asked an expert on bilharzia about swimming in streams, he advised me to stick to the ocean. However, two important criteria for furthering the worm's life cycle — slow-moving water and egg-carrying cattle or human feces — are absent in the swift, pristine streams of the upper Luquillo Mountains. Many forest visitors (including myself) bathe in those pools that lie far above mammalian gatherings.

As for beasts, the squirrel-like mongoose, brought to the island by Europeans to combat a rat problem, counts among the largest animals, and the six-foot-long Puerto Rican boa, rarely seen and non-poisonous, is frightening in appearance only. Only one island snake, *Alsophis portoricensis*, is mildly poisonous, and to get bitten you almost have to stick your hand in the snake's mouth. Painful but non-life-threatening scorpions, tarantulas and centipedes tend to keep to themselves in the hidden niches of the forests. For the casual hiker, and even the scientist poking about in the underbrush, plants offer far greater opportunities for pain. I seem to have come in contact with all of the infamous ones, from carrasco, a shrub of the sumac family, to a local stinging nettle called ortiga, whose spikelike hairs bring intense pain to the hand that touches them. One unidentified culprit bestows upon the susceptible hiker, a day or two after the outing, painful and long-lasting hives around the crotch and ankles. But poisonous plants are rarely encountered by those who stay on trails. One scientist declared that the biggest hazard in the forest lay in its slippery rocks, and he is probably right.

Yet it would be naive to think that the animal kingdom in the Luquillo Mountains is a model of peaceful coexistence. Dangers lurk everywhere — for the animals themselves. Hawks swoop down on birds, birds feast on lizards, lizards ensnare insects, larger insects devour smaller insects. The headlines of a *Luquillo Mountain Tattler* would read something like this: "Dozens of Maggots Burrow under Skin of Newborn Parrot"; "Boa Swallows Bat Whole in Dead of Night"; "Unidentified Rats Demolish Nest in Palo Colorado Tree near La Mina Peak"; "'Who Stole My Eggs?' Wails Berift Coquí Mom"; "Spider Web Traps Insects for Record Meal".

I recently spoke with Bob Waide, a zoologist who heads the Terrestrial Ecology Division of the University of Puerto Rico, originally part of the former Center for Energy and Environmental Research (CEER), now funded by the university and the National Science Foundation's Long Term Ecological Research (LTER) grant. The CEER building is located in the traffic-congested heart of San Juan's sprawling Medical Center complex. It is the only building in the complex topped by a windmill, Waide told me, but the windmill is too small to help when one is adrift in a sea of cars and parking lots and old buildings and new highrises. I arrive more than a half-hour late. Waide is a friendly, middle-aged, boyish-faced man who sports a beard and glasses. One look at his office tells visitors he is a busy person who is not concerned with having a place for everything and everything in its place. Books and papers are piled, at all angles, on desk and tables. We retreat to an unadorned room on the ground floor where we can talk without interruption.

Waide adds several gruesome examples of the less-than-gentle behavior within the rain forest. Here is one: "The tailless whip scorpion of the genus Phrynus can get six to seven inches in diameter. It looks like a robust daddy long legs, whose legs end in paddles with spines. It can impale lizards on the spines, then inject enzymes into the lizard, sucking out the juice and leaving an empty bag of bones." And another: "An observer of centipedes watched one eating a bufo frog. The centipede had paralyzed the toad with its venom and was attached to its belly, feeding on its stomach. The toad was still alive." Before long, the story goes, the centipede came in contact with the toad's venom, stored in glands on the toad's back, and when last seen it was staggering away from the toad. Both animals seem to have fared poorly in that particular struggle. Though Waide knows of no serious incidents, he imagines the centipede packs a painful sting for humans. One of the curious aspects of the fauna in the Luquillo Mountains, Waide explains, is the high degree of predation on the same food level. "Big lizards eat small frogs or other lizards. Coquís eat the eggs of other coquís. Big tarantulas eat small frogs, big frogs eat small tarantulas. In other words, if you're a certain size, you can beat up on anyone." On the mainland, animals have a lot more species to choose from; here the differences fall into size classes of the same species.

This rather gruesome behavior is not the only reality of the rain forest to remain hidden from most visitors' view: many of the more curious creatures of the jungle are also rarely spotted by the casual observer. Yet there are enough curious creatures to fill a decent sideshow.

"Ladies and gentlemen," the barker begins, "step right up, step right up to one of the most amazing shows on earth! In this corner we have the greatest camouflaging act of all times — the walkingstick!" You look at a branch with numerous twigs jutting out. The branch is a mottled tan color, and you look at it for a moment, wondering what the fuss is about. Suddenly, one of the twigs starts to inch away from the others, making its way up the branch. When it moves, you notice the twig has the shape of a grasshopper, a grasshopper that has been assembled with pick-up sticks. It is actually a phasmatid, a primarily tropical insect that feeds on plants and has developed an ingenious camouflage to protect it against insect-eating animals.

"And over here, folks, we have the truly amazing two-headed snake!" What's more, this animal is not a snake at all but a lizard, an Amphisbaenid, a limbless, wormlike lizard which has adapted its body to suit its underground existence. Its body is elongated and uniform in diameter, etched with hundreds of annuli or ringlike sections; its tail is stumped; it has no ear openings and merely indistinct, scale-covered spots for eyes. Consequently, one can hardly tell this lizard's front from its back, which gives rise to its nickname. One of its favorite foods is the earthworm; having only vestigial eyes, it probably tracks the worms down by listening for them as they squirm through the soil.

"And just look at its companion, the four-legged snake!" This is also a lizard, the Puerto Rican galliwasp of the family Diploglossus, a shiny dark-brown snake-shaped creature with four tiny legs placed almost as an afterthought along the body. It is partial to deep forest environments.

"And, folks, pity this creature, the pitiful blind snake!" Although this is in fact a snake, of the genus Typhlops, it resembles the Amphisbaenid lizard in several ways. Like the lizard, it has forfeited eyes and ears in order to specialize in a subterranean existence. It is often found in the nests of ants and termites, where it ungraciously eats its hosts.

"And raise your eyes to the ceiling, for a look at the world's most incredible acrobat!" The acrobat is a gecko, a small member of the lizard family. It makes its way across the ceiling, unconcerned that it is defying all laws of gravity. To perform such a feat, hairlike projections on its toe pads press into tiny irregularities in the ceiling. In times of trouble, when, for example, escaping an enemy, the gecko has another clever trick up its sleeve — like many lizards, it sheds its tail, leaving it to wriggle on the ground, and later regenerates another. Because of these seemingly

Neysha Bauer
sporting
two coquí frogs.

supernatural feats, geckos have spawned several superstitions — they are poisonous, they poison the food over which they walk, they cause leprosy by running over the face of a sleeper — none of which have any basis in scientific fact.

"And in this corner, we have the strongest creatures on earth — the world-famous river shrimp, able to push against raging waterfalls as they make their way up sheer cliffs!"

back, the height of the cliffs must seem insurmountable to such miniature creatures, but, undaunted, they keep coming, one after another after another. Watching them, one can't help but feel inspired.

🌿 A study of rain forest in the section of the Luquillo Mountains known as El Verde, undertaken in the 1960s to analyze the effects of radiation on a tropical forest community, amassed an incredible amount of informa-

Top left:
Coquí frog on bromeliad.
Bottom left:
Large forest spider.

Top right:
Small snake, Alsophis portoricensis.
Bottom right:
Puerto Rican tody.

Well, not exactly. River shrimp, which spend part of their youth in coastal estuaries, eventually swim upriver in search of a suitable pool in which to live out their lives. If they encounter an obstacle, like a waterfall, they leave the water and climb the rocks, staying near enough to the spray so their gills don't dessicate. I've seen a caravan of these shrimp make their way up a waterfall cliff. The rocks are slick, the water sometimes flicks them

tion about the local plants and animals. In the introduction to the animal section in the project book, director Howard Odum and fellow scientists George Drewry and Elizabeth McMahan make several interesting comments about the animals in this one small, intimately studied piece of tropical rain forest. The rank abandon of rain forest vegetation does not extend to the animal community: the mass of animals per square meter of tropical rain forest is possibly one-tenth that found in a tropical savannah or coral reef. Though the total mass is small, no greater than that found in temperate forests, the numbers of species are large, with many species of similar animals separated by geographic factors such as altitude. In addition, most animals tend to be quite small, "dispersed like gems through the great mass of greenery".

Many of these gems lie below the great mass of greenery. Odum calculated that half of the animal biomass, the estimated total mass/weight of the animal kingdom, is found within or below ground leaf litter in tabonuco forest, the type of forest found in El Verde. Animals that live off plants, the herbivores — which tend to be the smaller, harder-to-spot species — were found to have a biomass fifteen times greater that that of animals that live off other animals, the carnivores. Oddly enough, lowly earthworms, when counted as a group, ranked as the forest heavyweights, amassing one-third of the total weight of all animals. In addition to earthworms, the ground provides a home for a wide variety of species, from the previously described two-headed snake, four-legged snake and blind snake to threadlike parasitic microscopic nematodes, commonly known as eelworms, and immense ant colonies. Some ant species prefer the lower regions of trees and tree trunks, and even more prefer the forest canopy, but the greatest numbers of ant species and colonies exist in soil, leaf litter and rotting wood at ground level.

Some ground-level inhabitants are creatures that are neither animals nor plants, members instead of three newly recognized kingdoms encompassing bacteria and algae, protozoa, fungi, slime molds and the like. The El Verde study found that hundreds of species of fungi and bacteria lie on the damp, dark rain forest floor. Some of them emit a dull glow at night. The fungi in Luquillo are so prodigious they make short work of any wastes that land on the ground. Lowly slime molds can also be found throughout the forest, although they are not so extensive as the fungi. This is because torrential rains often wash their spores away, the forest's many insects eat the spores, and the high humidity encourages fungi over molds.

Termites, the bane of those with wood homes and furniture, have established immense colonies within the forest. Here they are members in good standing of the local community. They work as pruners, ridding trees of their dead branches, and they run marvelous wood decomposition factories. Two types of termites were found to be common in the El Verde study — *Parvitermes discolor* and *Nasutitermes costalis*. The latter build mound nests which can house up to hundreds of thousands of termites. Like their fellow invertebrates, ants and bees, termites live in a highly specialized caste system. For N. costalis the system includes a reproductive pair, soldiers known as nasutes, large and small workers which make up more than half the residents, and the eggs and young of all types.

Elizabeth McMahan describes N. costalis nests in some detail. Along the coast they resemble bulbous papier-maché-like growths up to two feet long on tree branches, but in the mountains they almost always lie on the forest floor. The papier-maché appearance comes from wood carton, a material that is passed from the alimentary canal of the termite and mixed with soil particles. The nest interior resembles a large stiff sponge with interconnecting chambers and galleries surrounding a royal cell near the lower central area. The worker termites continually repair and expand their nests, applying quick-drying anal and salivary secretions to unwanted holes and making new holes for additional chambers, usually in the upper areas of the mound. Often the lower portion of the mound is left uninhabited and unrepaired.

Food and drink must constantly be brought in to feed the N. costalis colony's large population. To do this, the termites build extensive networks of tunnels that extend under litter, through soil and as much as 50 feet, or even higher, up forest trees. The worker termites that use the tunnels learn to move through them quite quickly in order to get food back to the nest without delay. The tunnels, made of the same wood carton as the mounds, are hard and of a fairly uniform eight millimeters in width, a mere fraction of an inch. Though the tunnels spiral up the trunks of living trees — it is estimated that one-tenth of the trees in the study area have tunnels — N. costalis only feeds on dead branches and other decaying wood. Apparently the wood cannot be too badly decomposed, which is why the termites prefer dead wood in trees over that found on the ground. They dine on dozens of tree species in the forest but in the study area are partial to the predominant tabonuco as well as a large mountain tree known as motillo, and varital, a small tree of the Spurge family. Other termite species and even ants have been known to use the N. costalis tunnels.

Termite nests are scattered fairly uniformly throughout the

COQUI

forest. What Waide finds interesting about termites is their static nature. McMahan, who has studied them for more than 30 years, has found that their communities remain the same size: when some die, an equal number replace them, but the communities themselves neither increase nor decrease. With the tremendous amount of dead wood produced after Hurricane Hugo, scientists wondered if the communities would remain static. They have.

Nowhere is the tendency toward numerous species more apparent than in the world of insects (of which termites form a part). Over a span of five years, George Drewry and coworkers combed the El Verde study areas, capturing those tiny creatures most people avoid. They used their hands, light traps, sticky traps and berlese funnels, in which insects, avoiding a light at the top of the funnel, fall into an alcohol solution. In one above-and-beyond-the-call-of-duty study, men (no women) took turns sitting in a circle in the middle of the forest for 24-hour periods. During nighttime hours, small hurricane lanterns they had taken with them gave off a dim reddish glow. Each participant stripped to the waist and captured mosquitoes landing on the front of his body and the back of the person in front of him, placing them in glass tubes stopped with cotton plugs. Results of this study showed that mosquitoes did most of their biting at dawn and dusk, a pattern which, by the way, is also true of Old World forests.

As a result of the many studies, 1,200

different species of insects were collected in El Verde. The insects range from herbivores and predators to parasites, pollinators and decomposers. Though most tend to be smaller than their temperate counterparts, the sheer numbers of individuals and species greatly affect the tropical forest ecosystem. Unfortunately, this tendency to large numbers is not true of butterflies, perhaps the most popular of insects. Butterflies encompass relatively few species in Luquillo (and Puerto Rico in general), and those that are here tend to be dull in color. For reasons not yet understood, Hurricane Hugo in 1989 caused large outbreaks of moth-producing caterpillers in the forest.

Sit in El Yunque any evening and you will discover yet another creature of the Luquillo Mountains. Out of the black, wet world come the two-toned chants of hundreds of unseen forest inhabitants. The second tone the chant is higher and more accented than the first, producing a loud "koKEE" sound. "KoKEE, koKEE, koKEE, koKEE" reverberates through the forest. To those who hear the sound for the first time, it is a cacophonous din; to those who live on the island, it becomes a sort of lullaby. Though loud, the chant is made by animals which aren't more than a couple inches long. Known onomatopoetically as coquís, they are tree frogs, tiny E.T.-like creatures with large bulging eyes, earthy coloring, webless toes and disks or pads on the tips of their fingers and toes. They are shy creatures, and if they sense humans approaching, they stop singing. Their cute appearance and distinctive call have made coquís one of the most beloved of island fauna. Figurines, ashtrays, pins, postcards and fabrics bear the stamp of the frogs, and their chants can be heard in commercials, country music, even telephone answering messages. Adding to

their popularity is the legend that coquís transported off the island never sing again. There are tree frogs in the Virgin Islands which produce a similar chant, and I once read that members of a small community of coquís in Florida did in fact sing, but there is no movement afoot to debunk the legend.

Before the 1960s, biologists believed that *Eleutherodactylus portoricensis* was the only local coquí species (of more than a dozen) that made the distinctive "koKEE" sound, yet the sound is actually made by two different frogs. E. portoricensis is restricted to the mountains, while the newly named *Eleutherodactylus coquí* is found both in lowlands and highlands. Both are tan colored, but E. coquí is larger, with a darker abdomen and a slower, more deliberate chant. The chant, performed by male frogs, serves not only to attract prospective mates but also to keep rival males away from the frog's reproductive territory.

E. coquí has been an important protagonist in the annals of frog reproductive research. In his 1978 book on amphibians and reptiles in Puerto Rico, University of Puerto Rico herpetologist Juan Rivero mentions an 1871 study, conducted in the west-coast city of Mayagüez. In this study, E. coquí (thought at the time to be E. portoricensis) was apparently the first frog in which biologists observed direct development: the frog lays eggs which hatch directly into miniature frogs, bypassing the tadpole stage. Direct development, which enables frogs to eliminate their ties with the aquatic environment, is now known to occur in many frog species.

Waide mentions a study published in *Science* magazine more than a century later that gives this frog yet another distinction: E. coquí became the first frog for which internal fertilization was demonstrated in an experiment. "Usually the female lays eggs and the male comes along and fertilizes them. With the coquí, the male actually fertilizes the female, the female lays the eggs, and the male then guards the eggs."

Though only two coquí species vocalize the "koKEE" chant, all 17 Eleutherodactylus frogs found on the island are commonly known as coquís. Though many local residents consider such frogs unique to Puerto Rico, the Eleutherodactylus genus actually encompasses more than 200 species, found primarily in the Caribbean and Central America. As already indicated, the genus is known for its great variety of reproductive methods; one newly discovered species in Puerto Rico *(E. jasperi)* bears its young alive rather than through eggs. Scientists imagine that these adaptations (bearing froglets directly through eggs, fertilizing internally, bearing the young alive) have come about to ensure Eleutherodactylus frogs success in their terrestrial environment.

In his book, Rivero describes Puerto Rico's tree frog species, 12 of which are found in the Luquillo Mountains. All are restricted to this island and perhaps a neighboring island or two. Some of them frequent lowland areas (and most of these live in trees) while others frequent the highlands (and most of these live on the ground, though they are still commonly referred to as tree frogs). Rivero seems quite taken with the inch-long *E. wightmanae*, an elusive species common to El Yunque, considering it "one of the prettiest Puerto Rican frogs, and its voice one of the most melodious, consisting of three to ten high pitched whistles."

Another inch-long frog, *E. locustus*, exists in two separate highland locations, one in El Yunque and the other in the island's southeastern Cayey mountains, unaware of the enigma its separate populations present. Lowland Eleutherodactylus frogs often venture into the highlands, but highland frogs never descend to the lowlands. How, then, did these two populations come about? Rivero mentions the following theory: During the Ice Age, lower temperatures occurred at lower elevations on the island, and the seas were lower, in turn making the mountainous region larger. Montane flora and fauna had more room to move about, and highland coquís were able to establish themselves at suitable elevations all along Puerto Rico's mountains. However, after the Ice Age the north-south Loíza river valley became too pronounced, and lowland conditions became too warm for most montane flora and fauna to descend into the valley and cross over into the central and western mountains. It is thought that after the Ice Age, E. locustus may have evolved from another frog, E. cochranae, to which it is closely related. This would explain why E. locustus is not found west of the Loíza River. It is also thought that the frog evolved before the formation of the Gurabo river valley, which separates the Luquillo Mountains from the southeastern mountains. E. locustus would thus have had time to establish its two mountain populations before the Gurabo valley impeded further travels. In his book Rivero suggests the two populations should now be considered separate species.

Cold-blooded vertebrates seem to find El Yunque to their liking. Odum and his fellow scientists were impressed with the large numbers of tree frogs and Anolis lizards found in the forest. Based on studies made at two plots in El Verde, they estimated 400 male E. portoricensis per acre (this study was done shortly before the discovery of the two separate "koKEE" chanting species, so they were actually referring to the two species). Assuming a one-to-one ratio between male and female, this meant 800 males and females per acre. They also estimated 800 *Anolis gundlachi*, the forest's most common anole, per acre. This is an exceptionally high number; most temperate regions rarely have more than 100 anoles in the same area. The scientists thought the large number of frogs and lizards might have to do with the paucity of larger animals and the relatively small variety of birds in the forest.

Waide agrees. "Islands are different for the simple reason they are separated from the mainland by water. Mainland tropical forests have more mammals and birds while here the most common species and principal players in the food web are lizards and frogs." As part of the Long Term Ecological Research project, Waide and other scientists have worked together on a book titled *Food Web of a Tropical Rain Forest*, scheduled to be published in 1996. The book's 12 chapters look at the breakdown of the Luquillo forest food chain — plants, soil microorganisms, termites, litter arthropods, terrestrial invertebrates, spiders, frogs, anoles, other reptiles, birds, mammals, and stream fauna. Waide cites more recent estimates of up to 20,000 lizards and 20,000 frogs per hectare of land in El Yunque (roughly 2.5 acres), or two per square meter. Taking this a step further, he estimates that the lizards and frogs on a hectare of land eat 800,000 insects in one day; calculate a bit more and you discover that 22 and a half billion insects become someone's meal every day in the forest. Not only does this indicate an incredible supply of insects in the forest; it also may explain in part why mosquitoes are not as bothersome here as in many other tropical forests. A curious aspect

of the food web is its distinct day and night components. Lizards eat primarily during the day (along with birds) while frogs commonly eat at night. Habitat is another component. Many frogs and lizards live in specific areas; though they all eat the same ants, beetles and other insects, they do not compete with each other.

Several years ago two friends and I found ourselves on a flood plain of the Río Mameyes in the remote northeastern part of the forest, next to the 60-foot-long Mameyes Pool. Arching sierra palms and gnarled pterocarpus trees shadow the soggy forest floor. Since I was last there, two makeshift lean-tos had sprung up next to the pool. Saplings and palm fronds formed the walls and roof, and old blankets covered the ground. The remains of a fire marked the entrance of one lean-to. The structures gave us an uneasy feeling, and we didn't stay long. I later learned that such structures are part of a once-common local operation, that of catching river shrimp to feed humans, highest species on the food chain. Night is the best time to catch these tasty animals, when the shrimp come out in search of food; fishermen from nearby communities construct the makeshift lean-tos to provide a warm, dry place to rest when they are not in the water. Though illegal, the structures remain until forest personnel come upon them.

Eight species of river shrimp (along with mullets, eels, one crab species and an algae-eating gobiid fish) inhabit the streams and rivers of the Luquillo Mountains. These shrimp were originally saltwater animals. Over the eons, they adapted to freshwater, evolving claws resembling those on Maine lobsters in the process. Most are several inches long, though the older ones can grow up to a foot in length. Though freshwater animals, these shrimp still need the brackish waters of coastal estuaries in order to survive, and this is proving to be their downfall. Ecologist Miguel Canals once gave me a thumbnail sketch of the shrimp's life cycle: "When the female is ready for ovulation, the male pays a visit to externally fertilize the eggs held on the female. In 15 to 30 days the eggs mature and turn dark. At this point the mother either gets rid of them, letting them float on their own to the sea, or protectively migrates with them to the lowlands." For almost two months the young kick around in the estuary as larvae. Larvae make a tasty dish for estuary fish, and river flooding occasionally sweeps the larvae out to sea (to avoid this, they sink to the estuary floor during floods). Those who survive their time in the estuary form groups to begin the long swim upriver. Now shrimp, they scale boulders and work their way around cascades. Two species of filter feeders, which are shrimp with brush-like claws, have been found as far as 2,700 feet above sea level. Unfortunatly, coastal construction has destroyed many of the estuaries, and dams built along the rivers prove too great an obstacle for the shrimp to surmount. The numbers of shrimp found in streams have greatly decreased in the last decades.

At one time river shrimp were common in farmers' diets. They were a popular accompaniment with rice, served up in a stew with coconut, local condiments, garlic and onion. The day Canals explained the life cycle of shrimp he also introduced me to Alejo Estrada Pinto, head of El Verde's field station, who in turn gave an illustrated talk about traditional methods for catching river shrimp.

"The simplest method uses only the hand and bait placed on the wrist," Estrada Pinto began. He showed how a gloveless hand would reach into an underwater hole and grasp the shrimp's body when it nosed around the bait. Simple, perhaps, if one has no fear of underwater holes. "This next method was used by my grandfather." He looped a vine around a stick, making a small lasso. "Bait can be smoked coconut, corn, cooked sweet potato." A stick on the ground became a shrimp. "When you touch the back side of the shrimp, it rises." He smoothly moved the lasso along the stick body, tightening the vine when it reached the waist; the stick was caught. This is definitely a method that would take a bit of practice. More sophisticated was a nylon mesh net on a hoop —"people originally used burlap sacks, which was all they had" —attached to a long stick pole, with strings to hold the bait over the hoop. The shrimp was swooped out of the water the way a butterfly is swooped out of the air. Lastly, he showed us a wire mesh cylindrical cage with inverted cones on either side. When an unwary shrimp enters a hole in one of the cones to feed on a bit of bait dangling in the center, it is unable to figure out the exit. We spent some time in a nearby stream trying out the last two methods, catching one ten-inch shrimp and a couple of small ones — not a very hearty meal, even when stewed and accompanied by rice.

Some time later forester Jerry Bauer and I hitched a ride with a young man from the forest community of Sabana, and he gave us an update on the state of catching river shrimp. "There are still a lot in the Mameyes [river]. At times fishermen can catch a hundred a night. That's when the shrimp are out. Some use coconut as bait, some use cages, but up there [near the Mameyes Pool] most don't use cages. They'd have to carry them in." He added that Río de La Mina above the Mameyes Pool also has shrimp, "good ones, but it isn't so popular because the men are afraid of the water. It's so cold, and they have to stay in it, at night, remember, for hours. When they go to places like that, they take a lot of rum." He thought that most of the shrimp are eaten locally; a few may reach nearby restaurants.

Actually, anyone trying to sell shrimp caught in the forest would likely get into trouble, for El Yunque has been declared a wildlife reserve, and hunting and fishing are prohibited within its boundaries. Though forest personnel seem tolerant of a bit of traditional shrimp catching for personal use (and would have difficulty stopping it), they would undoubtedly crack down on profiteers. Those who want to sample freshwater shrimp will have to rely on the success of aquaculture.

Although first-time visitors to the forest are grateful for the absence of dangerous animals and relieved over the relative dearth of pesky mosquitoes, they are usually disappointed to find a scarcity of bird calls. There are times during the day when the forest can be strangely quiet. Shouldn't a tropical rain forest be bursting with a riot of squawks, chirps, trills and coos? The most common bird call in El Yunque sounds more like the call of an insect — an ascending buzz that falls into a brief warble. The call belongs to the bananaquit, a small, pert bird with black and white upperparts and an unmistakable yellow breast. Common throughout the Caribbean as well as Central and South America, the bananaquit (*Coereba flaveola*), locally known as reinita, is the only member of the honeycreeper family to be found in this part of the world. Its long, curved bill probes flowers for nectar and insects, and it is also partial to breakfasts served outdoors at any number of West Indian inns.

What is remarkable about this bird is not that it is found just about everywhere on the island and in the Luquillo Mountains, but the numbers that are found. In the 1960s, ornithologists Harry and Judy Recher, working with the El Verde project, made a census of birds found at one site in El Verde and at another atop Mount Britton. Fifteen species were counted, but more than half of the actual birds were bananaquits. One reason scientists give for the great abundance of bananaquits is that they don't have to compete for food with a large number of other bird species. The Luquillo rain forest, which hosts fewer large animals in general than mainland tropical forests, also hosts fewer bird species. Curiously, the number of bird species found in Luquillo is also less than in two other forests in Puerto Rico (Guánica and Maricao), even though its vegetation is richer.

The Rechers counted 39 bird species in the Luquillo Mountains. Included in their list is the red-tailed hawk, Puerto Rican screech owl, Puerto Rican woodpecker, black whiskered vireo, black throated blue warbler, Puerto Rican tanager and Puerto Rican bullfinch. Shortly afterwards, ornithologists Cameron and Kay Kepler discovered the elfin woods warbler to bring the total to 40. Additional species have been spotted in the forest. In his book on birds of Puerto Rico and the Virgin Islands, Herbert Raffaele lists 59 species found in El Yunque; among these, 24 are rare or very rare to the forest.

Of five hummingbird species in Puerto Rico, two are found in Luquillo. Both are known for their bright iridescent green feathers. The Puerto Rican emerald (*Chlorostilbon maugeus*, zumbadorcito), up to four inches long, is the smaller of the two; the green mango (*Anthracothorax viridis*, zumbador verde) grows up to five and a half inches long. According to Raffaele, the green mango is often seen at La Coca Falls.

One of the more abundant and prettier birds in the forest is the Puerto Rican tody (erroneously given the scientific name *Todus mexicanus*), known locally as San Pedrito. Less than five inches long, it has bright green upperparts, a red throat and a white and yellow breast. Raffaele describes the bird's curious method of obtaining food: "When perched, the tody has the peculiar habit of pointing its bill upward and, with rapid, jerky movements of the head, scanning the undersurfaces of the leaves above it for insects. On spying a prey item the tody sallies out, snaps up the morsel, and proceeds to a new perch all in one short, curved arc." It is an untiring eater, averaging 1.8 insects a minute from dawn to dusk.

Waide enjoys explaining a peculiarity in the eating habits of another forest resident, the Puerto Rican lizard cuckoo (*Saurothera vieilloti*, bobo mayor), a gray and cinnamon colored bird with a long black and white tail. The loud ka-ka-ka of the lizard cuckoo is heard more often than the bird itself is seen. It preys on small lizards, thus the name, as well as on large spiders and other insects. Waide has seen the bird extend its tail around the back of a tree branch and wag the tail. An unsuspecting lizard spies the tail on one side of the branch and backs away from the tail, thinking it is moving out of harm's way, only to fall right into the jaws of the cuckoo.

The tody and the lizard cuckoo, and most birds with Puerto Rican in their names, are endemic to Puerto Rico, which means they exist naturally only in Puerto Rico. Almost half the birds found in the forest are winter visitors; some, like the bananaquit, are common to the Caribbean; a few were brought to the island and survived; the rest are endemic. In their report on the avifauna of the Luquillo

Mountains, the Rechers wrote that, with two exceptions, the birds they spotted in the Luquillo Mountains seem to be abundant and well-protected. The two exceptions were the white-necked crow, now extinct in Puerto Rico, and the Puerto Rican parrot.

In the heart of the forest off Road 191 a concrete patio hangs over a valley extending down the mountain. Before Hurricane Hugo, this patio formed part of El Yunque Restaurant. The restaurant was a pleasantly rustic place, with walls painted to look like stones and massive fireplaces at either end. It had a solid mountain lodge feel, but, alas, its zinc roof was no match for Hugo's winds. With the construction of the El Portal Tropical Forest Center at the lower entrance to the forest, El Yunque Restaurant will probably never reopen, but if you can get to its patio, you will look out on orange trees and sierra palms which frame a view of dense vegetation growing at all angles. Fog traveling along the valley often obscures the view. Noises are muted ones — the gurgling of Río de La Mina, the rustling of wind-blown leaves. But at certain times of day, loud buglelike calls disturb the silence. If you are lucky, you might catch a glimpse of the birds that make the calls as they fly to their favorite feeding grounds. A foot long, they have green feathers, heavy hooked beaks, white rings around the eyes, red foreheads and blue edging on the wings. As quickly as they appear, they vanish into the forest again, trailed by their raucous calls. These are Puerto Rican parrots, scientifically known as *Amazona vittata*.

The odds that you will see these birds are slim, for there are less than 50 of them in the wild. Yet ask any Puerto Rican school child, or any Puerto Rican, for that matter, to name animals in El Yunque, and he or she will almost invariably start with "la cotorra de Puerto Rico", the Puerto Rican parrot. This is due in part to the bird's physical appearance — its large size and tropical green color — and to the beloved status of parrots in general. But, as detailed in the previous chapter, it is also due to the bird's dubious distinction as Puerto Rico's best-known endangered species, protagonist in the most ambitious species recovery program on the island.

Early one morning a decade ago, I was fortunate to be able to view one of the parrots with biologist Jim Wiley. Before sunlight had begun to filter into the landscape, he, another writer and I crept into the forest and hid ourselves in a four-by-six-foot burlap-covered blind set in the branches of a laurel sabino tree within a popular parrot valley known as North Fork. The forest held a ghostly sort of beauty in the still darkness, which contrasted with the lively cacophony of the wakening avian community. We paid little attention to this, however, concentrating instead on the stump of a palo colorado tree. At precisely 6:00 a.m. a small beak poked from an eight-inch hole. This was the female parrot of the nest. She looked around for a moment or two, then hopped onto a perch and began to preen her feathers. We were watching one of the world's rarest birds.

Once her feathers were preened, the North Fork female flew away from her nest, and we didn't see her again. Members of the parrot recovery project have spent thousands of hours sitting in such blinds scattered throughout the parrot habitat, and they can piece together a day in the life of the average Puerto Rican parrot. First, the birds fly a short distance around their roost to reestablish their territory. They then fly a longer distance in search of breakfast. This is when they may be spotted from the restaurant patio. During the midday heat, they take it easy. They again fly a longer distance, perhaps once again over the restaurant patio, this time in search of an early dinner. Finally, they return to their roost and flit from branch to branch before settling into a safe spot amid the thick foliage as night falls. Breakfast and dinner often consist of their favorite food, the small purple fruit of the sierra palm. They pluck the fruit with their bill and hold it in one foot while biting off pieces, eating some 130 fruits at a meal. Seeds, leaves, twigs, bark, flowers and leaf buds also make up part of their repast.

Parrots of the Amazona genus, which encompasses some 26 species living in the rain forests of Mexico, the Caribbean and northern South America, are known for their abilities as mimics. Although biologists have studied the calls of the Puerto Rican parrots during flight — a noisy series of squawks when the birds take off and the loud buglelike calls as they travel — I have neither read nor heard about the parrots' abilities to imitate human chatter. Perhaps the project personnel consider it bad form to try to get the parrots to say "Polly wants a cracker" when they are struggling to edge themselves away from the threat of extinction.

After more than a quarter century of intensive care, Amazona vittata is making a comeback. But if you go to the patio off the old El Yunque Restaurant, don't linger too long looking for them. They may not fly by, and you will have missed an opportunity to search out the two-headed snake, the climbing river shrimp, the hard-working termite, the chanting tree frog, the prolific anole, the ever-hungry tody, and all the other curious creatures of this jungle.

CHAPTER 13
METAMORPHOSES

In the early decades of this century, residents of the rural communities surrounding the Luquillo forests eked out a meager existence, just as their ancesters had done for generations before them. Wood and thatch huts lacked electricity and plumbing. Working on land that often wasn't their own, farmers cultivated subsistence crops to feed their families and earn a few dollars in profits. Children as often as not wore redesigned charcoal sacks and went barefoot. Ironically, it was during the Depression years of the 1930s, when the poverty was most acute and in part because the poverty was so acute, that the forest became the focus of ambitious changes that would protect it, enlarge it, improve it and open it to public recreation.

These were not the first efforts on behalf of the forest. From the early 1500s until 1898, Puerto Rico belonged to Spain, and it was the Spanish colonial government that initiated forestry on the island. Carlos Domínguez Cristóbal of the International Institute of Tropical Forestry has been scouring archives on both sides of the Atlantic for information about forestry in Puerto Rico over the centuries. Forestry regulations in the 1800s, he has discovered, were surprisingly advanced. Of course, the Mother Country could appreciate the importance of lumber; without it, sailors would never have reached the New World. She also recognized the importance of forests in protecting watersheds: as early as 1824 the island's governor (appointed from Spain) urged the planting of fast-growing trees on land around river sources. A board was established to protect the forests and their wildlife, and foresters were sent from Spain to investigate the land belonging to the Crown. In 1876 King Alfonso XII gave new force to the conservation movement by establishing several forest reserves on the island's Crown lands. They included the upper slopes of the Luquillo Mountains, making Luquillo one of the oldest reserves in the Western Hemisphere. A decade later men were hired to guard Luquillo and other island forests.

Crown lands — the words evoke regal gateways, royal hunters, peasants farming for the king. Yet in Puerto Rico Crown lands were more mundane. In the 1800s, Domínguez explained, the Spanish colonial government, eager to increase the island's population and develop agriculture, lured immigrants with the promise of land. Before long, most available land had been distributed. What was left was primarily unfit for agriculture, so the government decided to keep it and establish forest reserves. The island's first silvicultural experiments were carried on in these forests: potential timber species, including trees native to the Philippines, were tested to see how fast they grew, and trees were designated for use as telegraph poles and wind and erosion barriers.

Unfortunately, the enlightened colonial attitude did not necessarily result in thriving forests. In his dissertation on Luquillo forest resources, Frank Wadsworth noted that at one point in the late 1800s the forest service was abolished, apparently for a lack of forests to serve. Also, the men Spain hired to guard the forests formed a skeletal crew at best. One lone guard protected the entire Luquillo Mountains from poachers, woodcutters and land grabbers, a daunting if not impossible task. By the end of the century, the Luquillo Crown land had shrunk to 12,000-plus acres, and it contained the largest tract of virgin forest left on the island.

For several years following the 1898 Spanish-American War, the forest, like much of the island, remained in a legal limbo. The United States was new to the business of maintaining a possession. Under the Treaty of Paris, all Crown lands were turned over to the Federal government. In 1902 Congress gave President Theodore Roosevelt one year to reserve lands necessary for Federal purposes; the rest of the Crown lands would go to Puerto Rico. In 1903, Roosevelt, apparently taking the advice of a Department of Agriculture forester from Florida by the name of John Gifford, set aside lands for public forest reservations. One reason for establishing reserves was to stop the illegal felling of trees, which continued to reduce the island's remaining forests. A large chunk became known as the Luquillo Forest Reserve. The outer boundaries of Luquillo were eventually surveyed, and a guard or two were recommended to keep out charcoal woodcutters. In 1910 someone apparently took a closer look at the Luquillo land and realized that much of it had already lost its

trees. The suggestion was made that, since the forested land was too small to be considered a national forest, the reserve should be turned over to Puerto Rico. The governor at the time (until the 1940s always a stateside American picked by the President) objected. Woodcutters continued to fell trees. In 1916 the boundary of the actual forested land was surveyed. There were 12,433 acres. A year later the U.S. Forest Service was established in Puerto Rico: Luquillo had become a national forest.

There is an expression in Spanish, "no hay mal que por bien no venga", which serves the same purpose as English's optimistic "every cloud has a silver lining." In the decade before World War II Puerto Rico sat under a giant cloud. In 1928 the island was leveled by a hurricane that made records which remain unbroken to this day. In 1929 events occurred on New York's Wall Street that would plunge the United States and its already-poor territory into the Great Depression. In 1932 another major hurricane crossed Puerto Rico. Agriculture, which had caused the destruction of most of the island's forests, was in ruin itself. No forests, no agriculture, poverty settling in around the world — things could not look bleaker, yet out of the tragedy rose Puerto Rico's modern-day forests.

For a start, a good-sized chunk of the subsequent hurricane relief funds was used to buy up and reforest abandoned farmland. The abandoned land was cheap — much of it in the Luquillo area went for three dollars an acre — and tens of thousands of acres across Puerto Rico were set aside for this purpose. Some 8,000 acres were purchased in the Luquillo Mountains. However, the Luquillo purchase was not through hurricane funds, "but through the Weeks Law of 1911, which provided funds for land to be used for timber production in national forests," Wadsworth clarifies when I visit his office to ask him about the forest during the decades prior to World War II.

Once the lands were bought, they became the work sites of hundreds of employees of the Puerto Rican branch of the Civilian Conservation Corps (CCC, known locally as "las tres Cs"), established in 1933 to provide unemployed young men with jobs and job training in conserving and developing the nation's natural resources. Working around the island in stations that resembled U.S. Army camps, the men participated in a carefully prepared program emphasizing road construction, trail building, reforestation and recreational development, and occasionally they pitched in to build concrete homes for the region's poor. Angel Rosa, Manuel Corsino, Manuel Vázquez and many other young men from the Sabana area worked with the CCC. They still speak of those days with pride; not only did they have jobs, but they were also part of a project which would provide lasting benefits to their community. When the CCC was abolished in 1942 due to the war, the island's network of Federal and Commonwealth forests was solidly in place.

Among the island purchases in the decades prior to World War II were some 6,000 acres of land in Toro Negro on the western half of the island, a rugged region sheltering the island's highest peaks and several important watersheds. Luquillo and Toro Negro forests merged into one national forest, and its official name was changed to the Caribbean National Forest, with an eastern and a western unit. Much later, in 1970, the Federal government transferred Toro Negro Forest to the Commonwealth system of forests in exchange for some forested Commonwealth land next to Luquillo, but El Yunque's official name has

remained the same. "Someone from far away apparently thought up the name Caribbean National Forest," Wadsworth comments, "assuming it would cover everything. It isn't really appropriate, but it's that name by law, and it would have to be changed by law, and probably no one really cares."

Wadsworth cares, not so much about the name but certainly about the forest. Fit, white-haired and bespectacled, he is an unpretentious, slightly reticent and gracious man, and he personifies one's idealized version of the veteran forester. Wadsworth is the one person most responsible for making Luquillo (and most island forests and many Caribbean forests for that matter) what it is today. This is an ironic accolade for a man who started out at the other side of the forest world, the Yukon region of Alaska. Son of a wholesale paper seller, Wadsworth explored the timber forests north of his native Chicago at a young age, and by the time he got to the University of Michigan at Ann Arbor, he had decided that forestry would be a good field to study, and the Forest Service a good outfit with which to work. As a student he went with a professor and two other students to Alaska, where he studied forest succession in central Alaska for his Master's thesis, completed in 1937.

After graduation, Wadsworth headed for the dry country of Arizona, where he did silvicultural research on the Ponderosa pine. Silviculture involves the care and cultivation of forest trees for certain objectives, such as watershed protection or timber production. After a brief, uninspiring stint planting trees for farm protection in Nebraska, he returned to Arizona, where he fell in love with the boss's daughter. When he asked for her hand in marriage, his future father-in-law reminded him that nepotism laws would prohibit him from

Old
Caribbean
National
Forest
entrance
sign.

*Tower atop
Mount Britton.*

*Forest visitors
at Baño Grande
pool.*

continuing to work with the Forest Service in Arizona. One of the first new assignments to turn up was with the Caribbean National Forest in Puerto Rico. He and his bride, Peggy, looked at a map and decided to go.

Wadsworth came to Puerto Rico in 1942 as a researcher in silviculture. When the young couple, admitted teetotelers, arrived, they were in for a bit of a social shock. "We found ourselves," Wadsworth reminisces wryly, "in a nest of [expatriate Forest Service] bitchers, alcoholics, social and sexual deviates, people making passes at others' spouses, all-night Friday fiestas." In addition, there was bad blood between the forest administrators and researchers. But there was also a silver lining to the situation. "I was fortunate that I was given two honest people to work with," he tells me. One was his secretary, Ana Vega de Jimenez, the other was fellow forester José Marrero Torrado. Both became close, life-long friends of Wadsworth. Before long, the feuding foresters were shipped out, and Wadsworth and Peggy found they had begun defending the island against unhappy fellow expatriates' criticisms.

They stayed. During the 1940s Wadsworth worked in silviculture and dictated tree practices for the island; at the same time, he completed his doctoral dissertation on forest management in the Luquillo Mountains. In the 1950s he became both Supervisor of the Caribbean National Forest and Director of the Institute of Tropical Forestry, the forest's research branch. He wore these two hats for some 20 years. In 1978 he returned to a position of research forester with the institute, a position he still holds. During this time he has also written more than 90 articles or books, consulted on more than two dozen international tropical forestry projects, directed more

than a dozen short courses on tropical forestry, participated in several United Nations forestry sessions, edited the *Caribbean Forester* magazine, founded the Puerto Rico Natural History Society, advised local environmental groups, and seen his name immortalized in several plant and tree species. He seems far from slowing down. Recently he completed a textbook on tropical forestry; he currently edits a quarterly forestry newsletter; and he still speaks of El Yunque's current challenges and future direction with all the enthusiasm of someone new to the job.

A half century after first setting foot on Puerto Rico, Wadsworth continues to feel the Forest Service is a good outfit with which to work. In most cases "by the time you earn enough money to live on, you're stuck behind a desk," but here he has been able to do sufficient outdoor work to satisfy himself. When I ask if he has any regrets about staying for so many decades in such a small forest, he mentions something about not wasting a place. "If I had gone somewhere like the Amazon, it's so big, I probably wouldn't have done anything. There's also support here, which there wouldn't necessarily be in the Amazon. And there's the human impact." On days when he's feeling a bit low, he lets himself think about what the island's forests and forestry would be like if he hadn't come. There is no question he has made a difference.

❧ Let us picture the Luquillo Mountains in the 1920s, before the Forest Service, with a lot of help from the CCC, began to manage the forest in earnest. It is a region partially untouched and partially abused, impenetrable in some places and bare in others; above all, it is remote and mysterious, veiled under an almost perpetual cloud cover. Along the lower slopes, patches of forest coexist with small farms and pastureland. The paved roads which, like magnets, will draw houses together into small communities have not yet been built. Instead, narrow footpaths lead to isolated homes and to plots that are tended with simple tools. Some plots are abandoned as farmers begin to search for a surer livelihood in the coastal towns and cities. Slightly higher, where the forest seems unbroken, several wide paths are used by woodcutters to retrieve any remaining timber trees. Narrower paths lead to charcoal-smoldering sites.

Higher up, the slopes become steeper, discouraging even the most ambitious farmer or woodcutter. Here the original forests remain. This is the land of tangled trees and dangling plants, of Taino spirits and dwarf forests, the former Crown land, the land the Forest Service has been legislated to maintain. A few modest projects have been undertaken between the time the Forest Service arrived in Puerto Rico and the year of our imaginary journey back in time. A horse trail follows the outer forest boundary, and a road has been built, with the help of prisoners from San Juan, to connect Palmer near the coast with the northern edge of the forest. On the southeastern slopes a penstock taps water from four mountain streams and carries it down to lowland towns below. A narrow gauge railroad ascends a valley along the penstock pipe to the Río Blanco power plant, which will still be serving the community 70 years later. Its small train travels on rails built on ties and pulled by a huge winch in a cable sort of design. It is risky travel; over the decades several crosses appear along the route in memory of those who have died in one accident or another. Farmers using paths along the northwestern slopes of Luquillo in 1931 notice reforestation work taking place on a piece of land known as Harvey's Plantation below the forest boundary.

At this time in the 1920s, the top of the mountains remains scarcely penetrable. A difficult, rarely used footpath winds up the slopes to El Yunque Peak; by the end of the decade the footpath becomes a horse trail. A few intrepid scientists travel the trail, donkey and equipment in tow, for a look at virgin tropical rain forest. Local resident Angel Rosa remembers the path as being for people who want to hike up to the peak and see the panoramic views. His family goes up, but he never does: "Walking so far just to see a view, it doesn't interest me."

Rosa began to work for the CCC in his mid-twenties. "El Yunque was the first site of the CCC on the island," he tells me. "Men came from Barranquitas, Ponce, Aibonito, work was that scarce... The first thing the CCC did was to build a road through the mountains." This became Road 191, which roughly follows the old footpath/horse trail. About 17 miles long, it crosses the Luquillo ridge at 2,530 feet, "opening up the ruggedly beautiful wilderness of the Luquillo Mountains, heretofore little known even to nearby residents," to quote a 1940 booklet about the forest.

Once the road was built, workers started on trails. "First an engineer came in to figure out which way the trail would go," Rosa explains. "Few trees were felled; it wasn't permitted to fell trees. The trails were built with machetes and pickaxes and shovels. It took a year, much more than a year, to complete a trail." Both Rosa and Vázquez worked on El Toro Trail, a long, winding route that links the upper mountains off Road 191 with the western forest near El Verde. Workers lived in a camp nestled on the top of the mountains. "The building was made of sierra palms and zinc," Rosa continues. "We slept in hammocks. I was in a brigade. Each brigade had between 10 and 15 men. We earned around a dollar a day; half of that went for food. At 6:00 a.m. we got up, had coffee, biscuits, perhaps cheese for breakfast. Then we went to work. For lunch we had ñame or yautía [local tubers], rice. One or two of the men would go to the camp to get it. Then we kept working. Around 4:00 we stopped and went back to the camp and bathed in a stream. Dinner was around 4:30. We had rice, perhaps grapefruit, oranges, bread, sometimes meat." When hiking near the source of the Río Icacos, one still comes upon the plant-decked ruins of a concrete oven where bread was baked for the men. "It was cold in the evenings. Some went to bed early, others stayed up and played dominoes. That was about our only entertainment. Alcohol was not permitted. At around 9:00 everyone went to sleep... The men worked five days a week, had weekends off, got paid twice a month. Some stayed at the camp on weekends. I went to stay with my family. Around noon on Sunday I'd start back to the camp. The trip [by foot] took about four hours."

🌿 Now let us picture the Luquillo Mountains in 1940, after the CCC completed most of its work. A young man, let's make him a descendant of our gold miner of the sixteenth century, is driving a chunky black Ford up Road 191. On the seat next to him is a newly published booklet about the Caribbean National Forest of Puerto Rico. He stops at the northern boundary, where a handsome stone gateway fronted by landscaped grounds welcomes visitors. He refers to the booklet. "The road...winds into the depths of the luxuriant tropical forest, passes high cliffs, singing streams, and misty waterfalls, traverses the La Mina recreational area, and passes around the

projecting ridges of the mountains to the divide." Driving past the high cliffs, singing streams and misty waterfalls, the young man enters La Mina Recreational Area and parks his father's car.

La Mina in 1940 is a tropical wonderland. "It includes," the booklet explains, "ample picnic shelters, swimming pools with shallow wading places for children, diving boards, and dressing-room facilities, fireplaces, and a community building with a smooth floor that may be used for dancing." The picnic shelters resemble round thatch bohíos of the sort used by the Taino Indians. The swimming pools, Baño de Oro and Baño Grande, are actually stream-fed swimming holes encircled by concrete or stone walls. The fireplaces provide warmth on dank nights for guests at small stone and concrete overnight cabins near the start of Big Tree Trail. "There are also a number of sites which may be leased at reasonable rates for erection of cottages by private individuals." These sites border the road.

The young man hasn't driven all this way just to sit under a thatch picnic shelter, so he picks up the booklet again. "Hikers and horseback riders will find 25 miles of trails that lead into the most ruggedly beautiful mountain country in Puerto Rico... One trail penetrates the heart of the unique mossy dwarf forest; others pass through stands of virgin trees and lead to waterfalls of great height and beauty." He chooses a footpath that takes him to the dwarf forest of East and West peaks. By the time he returns, drenched from sweat and drizzle, sore of muscle, he regrets that he did not rent a horse and venture up the mountains to Los Picachos, El Yunque and Mt. Britton peaks, each of which is topped by a stone observation tower. "For the use of mountain climbers and hiking parties an overnight shelter has been constructed at the halfway point on the trail leading to the summit of El Yunque. Permission to use this may be obtained from the forest supervisor at Río Piedras." Next time.

Before he leaves, he decides to investigate several intriguing sites shown on the map. One is an Old Spanish Gold Mine. The booklet indirectly refers to it: "Here the Spaniards, centuries ago, penetrated the dense jungle in search of gold. Today shallow pits in the earth tell the story of their disappointment." To his disappointment, he cannot find the mine. He does find a Stone House, a small but solid house built from large blocks of stone. It looks occupied, so he doesn't try to enter. A third site is a Trout Hatchery. According to the booklet, "a most interesting experiment has been undertaken by the Forest Service in cooperation with the Federal Bureau of Fisheries and insular authorities in the introduction of rainbow trout in several of the swift mountain streams in the Federal and insular forests. Although it is still too early to announce the ultimate success of this experiment and to allow the fisherman to get out his rod and fly, indications are that within a few years the national and insular forests will afford good trout fishing." He follows a path to a grouping of breeding ponds that

MOUNT BRITTON TOWER

hold the young trout. At that moment, the drizzle turns into a monsoonlike downpour; holding a large leaf over his head, he slips and slides his way back to the car. The rain lessens, and he decides to get a cup of coffee at the restaurant. The restaurant has been built to resemble a log cabin. With coffee in hand, he sits on the restaurant's patio, where he can look down a valley all the way to the north coast and the ocean beyond.

🌿 To me, the trout hatchery symbolizes the grand scale of the Forest Service work in the Luquillo Mountains, in all its vision, fancy and folly. Those who planned the recreational area undoubtedly wanted to make it a tropical paradise, with romance for everyone — horseback riding through rain forest, bathing in tropical swimming holes, sleeping in the heart of the mountains. Due to their efforts, El Yunque's roads, trails and visitor centers have enticed more than 25 million people into the forest over the decades, ranking it as the most visited and used forest in the Caribbean. Many of those visitors may otherwise never have seen nor come to appreciate a tropical rain forest.

However, not all of the romantic plans for the forest fit its tropical setting. They were instead what temperate foresters deemed desirable in a national forest. The trout hatchery was an idea concocted, no doubt, by a transplanted fly fisherman homesick for the Madison. Paradise, he decided, had to have fly fishing. And so breeding ponds were built beside a stream leading into Río de la Mina, and the young trout were released into the cool mountain water. Though cool, the water proved too warm for spawning; fishermen never did get out their rods and flies, and the program was eventually cancelled. Today the ponds lie in ruins half-hidden under vegetation.

I ask Wadsworth about the trout. He feels the idea may have originated with William Barbour, supervisor of the forest at the time. Later, a trout that is native to the warmer waters of Baja California was found and considered for El Yunque, but Wadsworth does not know what happened to that idea. Barbour, supervisor from 1931 to 1935, was the man behind the creation of the recreational area. Wadsworth remembers him as an aesthete, an outdoorsman, and a man with vision. When the CCC money first came in, the workers continued constructing Road 191 up the mountain. For a time there was a hiatus in the budget, and the men, who were stationed in the area of La Mina, were put to work on smaller projects — pools, trails, towers. Wadsworth imagines Barbour visualizing everywhere he himself wanted to hike, then having the men build the trails.

Referring to the CCC work, Wadsworth notes: "The best thing about the Forest Service at that time was its engineering. They built excellent roads that have held up. The landslide [on Road 191] wasn't the fault of the builders. They also built the pools, the rock bridge, the ranger stations. The network of trails up to El Yunque is complex, yet most of it remains in good condition, it hasn't washed out."

However, not everything accomplished during the time of the CCC has faired so well. Baño Grande is a beautiful spot. A stone wall surrounds the circular pool, and it in turn is rimmed by a bench-lined walkway which is rimmed by another stone wall which holds the forest at bay. Two stone bridges rise over the stream where it enters and leaves the pool. Dark water reflects the green of the trees towering overhead. Interpretive displays explain several aspects of the surrounding nature. Yet only a modest sign explains the solid but deteriorating bathhouse off to one side, and no one is swimming. Nearby, the Baño de Oro pool has a definite look of abandon. Impatiens and other plants grow out of cracks in its bathhouse. Silt and mud fill much of the pool, and bubbles made by underwater creatures periodically rise to the surface. Paint around the edge of the pool is a faded blue, a concrete deck is half-hidden under hibiscus and ferns, and a lifeguard stand has been reduced to a skeletal frame. Both pools were closed in the 1950s. Wadsworth remembers nine people dying in Baño Grande, mostly adults who had drunk too much alcohol or youngsters who came in at night; the pool has no concrete bottom and divers could crack their head on a rock. Baño de Oro had a problem with sediment and was hard to clean.

The weekend cottages the 1940 booklet encouraged private individuals to erect are now hidden by greenery from the view of motorists. As you drive along Road 191 or two short side roads, your eye might be drawn to a locked and rusting gate or a flight of stone steps apparently leading to nowhere. If you follow the steps, you may come upon a small concrete house with holes where there were once windows and a door rusted into a perpetual half-open position. Rust from decaying grillwork seeps down the walls, and large philodendron climb up them. The rooms may still be sparsely furnished — dank, spent mattresses, drawerless chests, lamps without shades. "The summer cabins were set up because people wanted them," Wadsworth tells me. He was against them, but the Forest Service didn't agree for some time. Eventually it realized the concept was a mistake and started removing the cottages from all national forests. It was not easy; some land renters/cottage owners took their complaints to Congress. Several houses in Luquillo remain in use by scientists or official visitors.

I ask Wadsworth about other highlights from the 1940 booklet. The stone house, originally for the forest supervisor, became a retreat for Puerto Rico's governor during a time starting in the mid-1950s when the recreation area was turned over to the island's Sports and Recreation Department as part of a Forest Service policy to minimize investments in recreation. Apparently the governor rarely used it. "It isn't a very hospitable place," Wadsworth admits, "it's wet, always dark, with wide eaves and small windows." During that time, Sports and Recreation officials put their priorities on such things as the cabins and the restaurant at the expense of such things as the trails. Dissatisfied, the Forest Service wrested control of the recreation area back to its own people by the mid-1970s. Today, the stone house is also used by scientists.

Over the years, the restaurant's decor changed from that of a log cabin to that of a mountain lodge, and its original roof survived until shortly before Hurricane Hugo, no small feat in a rain forest. Vegetation closed up the view to the ocean decades ago. Though the restaurant was never a high priority with the Forest Service, Wadsworth encouraged it. He explains that many people who otherwise wouldn't have thought to visit the forest drove up to stop at the restaurant. Even before Hugo, the building itself was beginning to cave in; Hugo damaged it severely, and Wadsworth imagines that, if a forest restaurant opens again, it will be located somewhere on the lower slopes. As for the stone and concrete overnight cabins, "they weren't a good idea to start with. The beds got musty, people got asthma attacks...". The cabins' demise came soon after a certain entrepreneur took over. As the man explained later to Wadsworth, he had to provide jobs for more of his extended family than he had anticipated. So during the week he kept room occupancy high by bringing in young women and running a brothel. Once he was evicted, the walls were knocked out, and the cabins are now very sturdy family-oriented picnic shelters, complete with fireplaces.

Today, many of these buildings are getting the proverbial new lease on life, as historic structures within the forest. There are plans to rehabilitate the restaurant and both pool bathhouses, and the stone house is currently in the process of being restored. Jeff Walker, forest archaeologist and heritage resources manager, would like to see these buildings used — perhaps as small museums or cafés serving light snacks, even as bathrooms. He is especially enthusiastic about an idea to use the old El Yunque Restaurant as a starting point for a series of interconnecting short interpretive trails through this part of the forest.

🌿 Grand as the metamorphosis was in La Mina Recreation Area, it was not the only dramatic change taking place in the forest during the decade of the CCC. Setting aside land for recreational sites is only one aspect of wise forest management, Wadsworth explains. In preparing his 1949 doctoral dissertation, a master plan for managing forest resources in the Luquillo Mountains, he considered the major resources found within the forest in order to provide for the long-term use of each of them. For Wadsworth, selecting areas to be preserved, that is, to be left untouched, held first priority. Apparently heeding his advice, in 1949 the Forest Service officially established the Baño de Oro Research Natural Area, slightly more than 2,000 acres along the Mameyes river valley that is forever set aside as a primitive area where nature cannot be altered in any way and only non-manipulative research can be performed. Next, he looked at the forest's recreational sites, followed by sites for water and electrical power, and, lastly, land for timber production.

Though timber land was the least desirable in the forest, timber production was by no means an insignificant component in Forest Service policy, especially in the decades prior to World War II. It provided the greatest potential for economic benefits, and it could help meet the timber needs of the islanders — for saw timber (trees large enough to produce lumber), posts and charcoal. Thus, in the 1930s, many of the CCC workers became Johnny Appleseeds for future Paul Bunyans.

The recently acquired land along the lower slopes took on a new look. Actually, several new looks. Foresters tried different techniques on different plots. Where there were remnant patches of forest, workers merely rid the plots of their old, damaged or inferior trees and pruned the remaining ones, the way one tends a garden in order to improve it and help it grow faster. Much of the cleared or partially cleared land was left to its own devices, and it followed the natural progression of secondary forests — shrubs and fast-growing pioneer trees followed by the slower growing, more

stately climax trees that characterize a mature forest. In the most ambitious phase of the reforestation project, thousands of additional acres of cleared land were artificially reforested through planting. I ask Wadsworth about the significance of these plantings in the annals of New World tropical silviculture. He thinks for a moment: "Brazil had its eucalyptus plantations by then, and Trinidad and Honduras had plantations, but on a smaller scale." He allows that Puerto Rico's could be considered the first large-scale multi-species plantations in tropical America.

And there was a multitude of species. Beginning in the 1920s, before the CCC work began, hundreds of tree species were tested around the island. They included native island species that were originally found in the region where they were being planted; native island species that were not originally found in the region where they were being planted; exotic (non-native) species from other countries in the tropics; and exotic species from temperate-climate countries.

The results of the 1920s testing were grim; only one species in 50 proved promising. Yet, armed with post-hurricane funds and CCC workers, the foresters pressed onward. In 1947 Wadsworth's friend Marrero looked back on those early years of planting in Luquillo. From 1934 to 1945, he wrote in the *Caribbean Forester* magazine, more than four million seedlings were planted and some 45,000 pounds of seeds were sown onto 54 plantations totalling almost 4,000 acres of land. Twenty-seven tree species were used. The heavyweights included the native moca at almost 25,000 pounds of seeds and two types of exotic mahogany at two million seedlings. Marrero remembers the planting as a laborious process. With machetes in hand, workers cleared the land of tangled shrubs and unwanted saplings; they then planted the seeds and seedlings, by hand, into the ground; and they often returned to the fledgling forests to weed and cut vines. The average cost of planting and five years of maintenance on each acre was $67.56, which seems a large sum for that decade.

Weeding was also carried out by subsistence farmers, who were part of a parcelero system the Forest Service inherited with the new land it had bought. Each farmer — there were some 125 families in the program — was loaned 12 acres of unforested land on which to plant. Ideally, the farmers would grow their subsistence crops — crops used in their everyday diet — between the new trees and aid the Forest Service in maintaining the trees. Although Wadsworth doesn't say so directly, it is apparent he did not consider this the best arrangement. Occasionally there were problems, as when the farmers hoed out young trees along with the weeds or when farmers continued planting their crops after young trees died, causing the soil to deteriorate and the tree planting to become even more difficult. Eventually the farmers left the forest; most moved into sturdy low-income homes built in such nearby communities as Sabana.

The reforestation program involved years of work, dozens of tree species, hundreds of workers, millions of seedlings. From the commercial harvesting point of view, the plantings had not been as successful as foresters had hoped they would be. Marrero attributed some of the problems to nature. In many places, weeds triumphed over trees, and mice made short work of seedlings. Unexpected droughts dried up seeds and seedlings alike. Other problems were man-caused. The Forest Service had too little time to get the work done using the CCC relief funds, and it

forged ahead prematurely. Because the crews were large and for the most part inexperienced, the few experienced foresters were unable to supply the proper supervision, and some of the work was done carelessly.

However, the bulk of the problems seemed to stem from a poor grasp of the ecology involved in tropical planting. The abundant guidelines for planting in temperate zones would not work in the tropics, and parallel studies related to the New World tropics had only just begun. The Luquillo foresters were doing pioneer work, and they learned a lot. They learned that climax species, those accustomed to shady, cluttered mature forests, couldn't take open sites. Species such as teak, they found, didn't adapt well to the humidity. Species such as native tabonuco couldn't survive the shock of being transplanted. Many of the marketable species, such as moca, grew very slowly and were often overpowered by less desirable but faster growers. Artificial regeneration, when foresters put the seeds or seedlings into the ground themselves, proved less successful than natural regeneration; exotic species proved less successful than native ones; and even native ones that were primarily common to other parts of the island couldn't flourish in the high humidity of the Luquillo Mountains. "It is evident now," Marrero wrote, "that in the early days regeneration problems were not being approached ecologically."

Wadsworth agrees with Marrero's conclusions. "It is only fair to say that they [the early foresters] weren't having success." These problems contributed to the bad blood among the personnel Wadsworth encountered when he arrived in 1942. He feels the quality of the land also had something to do with the lack of success: "Remember, that land was the cheapest and some of the worst on the island."

Frustrated though the early foresters must have been at the time, in the long run the reforestation program became an important success. Copious amounts of tropical research came out of the experiments, and foresters found a number of promising species in the process. Among the exotics, the eucalyptus and casuarina, both from Australia, have done well. Among native species, capá prieto (*Cordia alliodora*) has been successful on certain sites, guaraguao has done well in spite of its somewhat slow growth, and maría has proved a good tree even in places where it doesn't grow naturally. In short, from those early plantings foresters learned not only what they could not do but what they could do, and in the ensuing decades they went ahead and did it.

The most spectacular proof of success can be seen today along the lower slopes of the Luquillo Mountains where the foresters replanted. Out of former abused farmland, the CCC workers and their bosses recreated forest. There may be fewer stately marketable trees in this forest than the silviculturists had envisioned, but it is forest nonetheless, forest that rivals the upper virgin slopes in its beauty and lushness. Hundreds of species of understory plants consider it forest, the creatures of the wild consider it forest, and most visitors suppose that it has always been here.

Ironically, in one respect the reforestation program may possibly have proved too successful. Decades later, in the 1980s, foresters prepared to start the Paul Bunyan phase of managing a forest —that of harvesting the trees that have come of age — as they had done previously between 1945 and 1955. However, when the Forest Service publicized its plans to cut trees on the lower slopes of the Luquillo Mountains, environmental groups and many others looked at the mature, complex, flourishing rain forest and said, "now wait a minute...". New plans eventually replaced the old ones, and, as of now, no Timber will be harvested commercially within the forest.

CHAPTER 14
ONE LEG OF THE STOOL

Unlike any other U.S. national forest, El Yunque wears two hats and boasts two official names. One name, the Caribbean National Forest, refers to the forest itself, and the other, the Luquillo Experimental Forest, refers to the research component within the forest. Most national forests have certain areas within the forests which are designated for research purposes, yet Luquillo is the only forest whose research area encompasses the entire area of the national forest itself. Several years ago, Ariel Lugo, project leader of the Institute of Tropical Forestry, the research branch of the U.S. Forest Service in Puerto Rico, explained the system as follows: "The national forest system is like a three-legged stool, with one inordinately large leg. There is the forest itself, which gets 90 percent of the funds; state and private forests, which get four percent; and research, which gets six percent."

Although research is a lesser leg of the stool, budgetwise, El Yunque is nevertheless one of the most important — and most studied — research forests in the world. When Puerto Rico's Center for Energy and Environmental Research compiled a list of publications based on scientific research in the Luquillo Mountains (1989), it unearthed 432 titles, ranging from short articles to long books. An earlier bibliography, prepared for the Forest Service by Menendra Mosquera and JoAnne Feheley on forestry in Puerto Rico, listed 1,357 references to both scientific and technical work that has taken place in El Yunque. Though some of the people behind the titles have done little more than write a lone, forgotten paper, others have contributed extensive work of lasting international importance. Virtually every chapter of this book has been enriched by the results of these research projects.

"For many years now," Lugo offered when we were discussing the slant this book would take, "there has been concern with declining tropical forests. While people bemoan the loss, few are trying to find a solution to the tropical forest problem. At the Luquillo Experimental Forest scientists are working on solutions, have been for some time. A number of the so-called innovations in the forests of Brazil and Costa Rica have been worked on in Luquillo for decades. The forest is a showplace for what can be done."

Let's look at how this showplace came to be.

EARLY EFFORTS

For centuries scientists visited Puerto Rico and examined the interesting flora and fauna that made up this neotropical possession of Spain, amassing collections that exist to this day. One of the earliest records I found was that of a French botanist, August Plée, who traveled through the Lesser Antilles and St. Thomas before gathering a large collection of plants in Puerto Rico between 1822 and 1823.

In the 1880s, a German botanist named Paul Ernest Emile Sintenis reached Puerto Rico and collected extensively around the island. Sentenis worked in Berlin with another German botanist by the name of Urban and was hired in the 1880s by a third German named Krug, the German consul on Puerto Rico's west-coast city of Mayagüez and an avid part-time botanist. Krug had known Urban in Berlin. While on the island, Sentinis collected some 8,000 plants, and he is thought to be the first to have collected specimens atop El Yunque Peak. Many of his specimens remain at the National Herbarium of the National Museum of Natural History in Washington, D.C. A number of island plants have been named after Sentenis, Krug and Urban, and their work is considered the first major, organized study of plant life on the island.

In 1883 a botanist by the name of Baron Eggers spent several months in the Luquillo Mountains. Frank Wadsworth mentioned him in an article on past research in the Luquillo Mountains for the El Verde project. "One of the outstanding collectors of this period," he wrote, "was Eggers, who in 1883 lived on the edge of the primeval forest (apparently on the northwest slopes) for about five weeks at 670 m elevation." The prestigious *Nature* magazine published an article about his work in Luquillo. Intrigued, I tracked down a copy of the article. It turned out to be little more than a letter written to one Sir Joseph Hooker, who in turn sent it on to the magazine, a far cry from what I imagine one must do today to get

published in *Nature*. Eggers lived on an estate on the then-Danish island of St. Thomas, where he avidly tinkered with the productivity of a variety of local trees and plants. He told Hooker that he had "at last accomplished my long-cherished design, partly at least, of exploring the Luguillo [sic] Mountains in Porto Rico, which island I visited during April and May this year. I spent about five weeks there, living for some time in the hut of a 'fibaro' [sic] or native labourer on the Sierra, at an altitude of about 2200', on the edge of the primeval forests that still cover all the higher part of the mountain range." When he wrote to Hooker, he was busily arranging his new collection, which would appear in something titled "Flora Indiae Occidentalis Exsicceata".

Eggers worked his way up the muddy footpaths of Luquillo, past sugar cane and coffee fields, mountain rice and cattle grass, to the jíbaro's wood and thatch hut. He was surprised to find almost no clinging epiphytes — a few bromeliads and a rare orchid or two — and just one species of palm. His visit came less than a decade after two hurricanes passed directly over Luquillo, which may explain the dearth of epiphytes. As for trees, he was quite taken with laurel sabino, "with immense, white, odorous flowers and silvery leaves, which would be very ornamental. The wood is used for timber, and called Sabino." Other flora he noticed included a tree with crimson flowers (icaquillo, *Hirtella rugosa*), an unidentified tree with orangelike foliage and large purple flowers, a large bananalike heliconia, and two species of tree ferns.

After Puerto Rico was transferred to the United States (1898), a new group of scientists, primarily from the States, made their way up the Luquillo slopes. Accessible only by footpaths and ox trails until the 1930s, the Luquillo Mountains remained a no-man's-land to all but the most intrepid. At the same time, it sheltered the largest remaining tract of unspoiled vegetation on the island, a fact that intrigued virtually every botanist and biologist. Wilson, Cook, Collins, Gifford, Britton, Wetmore and Gleason are just a few of the names of early scientists who journeyed to Luquillo to take stock of the forest and its inhabitants.

Several scientists came as part of a major study being sponsored by the New York Academy of Sciences. Looking for uncharted territory to study, the academy settled on the region of Puerto Rico and the U.S. Virgin Islands. The first of a series of articles appeared in 1914. Expected to be completed within several years, the studies continued through the 1940s. Plants, birds, ecology, fungi, bats, reptiles, butterflies, moths, spiders and other members of the insect kingdom came under intense scrutiny. Nathaniel Britton and fellow scientists from the New York Botanical Garden extensively surveyed the Luquillo flora from 1914 to 1930. Along with Percy Wilson (who in 1902 hiked from the Luquillo foothills to El Yunque Peak to collect some 3,000 specimens), Britton compiled the forest's largest collection of spermatophytes (seed-bearing plants) to date. The peak known as Mount Britton is named for Britton and his wife, also a botanist.

Laying the Foundation

The year 1939 proved to be an important one for research in the Luquillo Mountains. In part to find answers for the problems of the reforestation program of that decade, the Forest Service established the Tropical Forest Experiment Station (later the Institute of Tropical Forestry and now the International Institute of Tropical Forestry) within the newly built Forest Service building in Río Piedras, an urban suburb of San Juan. Originally, the building had one floor; a second floor was later added. At the same time, a field station was established within the forest itself, at El Verde on the northwestern slopes.

In 1939 the Forest Service also began to publish a semi-annual technical journal titled *Caribbean Forester*. For almost a quarter century the magazine provided an unusual forum in which both scientists and foresters could contribute; for a time, articles or summaries appeared in three languages — English, Spanish and French. Topics spanned a broad spectrum, from the general ("Forest Policy for the American Tropics") to the specific ("Accidental Introduction of a Beneficial Insect into Puerto Rico"); from the scientific ("Rainfall Interception in a Tropical Forest") to the technical ("Reforestation of Degraded Lands in Puerto Rico") and the commercial ("Timber Sales in the Caribbean Forest Continue to Increase"); from the regional ("Montane Vegetation in the Antilles") to the local ("Angel Montserrate's Forest").

With the addition of the second floor on the Forest Service building, the Institute of Tropical Forestry library came into being. It is a wonderful library. As one brochure states, it "contains virtually all major publications from both hemispheres on tropical forestry, ecology management and utilization. The collection of 6,000 books, 20,000 unbound volumes, 300 maps and 2,000 slides and photos is used worldwide by scientists and the public." To facilitate this worldwide use, librarian Giselle Reyes and her staff handle more than 3,000 mail and telephone inquiries an-

Forestry technician Rafael Corcino measuring tree during species diversity study.

*Scientists
study the forest
from its rocks
and water
to its trees.*

nually. The library is also wonderful because it looks like a library, a real, old-fashioned library, with massive dark wood tables and chairs and dark wood bookcases from which books can be pulled out and perused. Soon the library will be moved to new quarters in a former cafeteria on the far side of the Forest Service parking lot: it remains to be seen if the old-fashioned atmosphere moves with it.

The Phenomenal Sixties

The decade of the 1960s saw a tremendous burst of forest research activity. Among the major projects undertaken during this time were the Arnold Arboretum's dwarf forest study and the Puerto Rican parrot program, both of which have been discussed in previous chapters. Along the northwestern slopes, an important research arboretum was established and a study of irradiation and ecology at El Verde was carried out. When completed, the El Verde irradiation and ecology project became the most monumental research project undertaken within the Caribbean National Forest and the most in-depth study ever made of a piece of tropical rain forest.

❦ One day several years ago, Ariel Lugo, scientist Clyde Asbury and I drive out to the northwestern slopes of the forest. Our first destination is the Luquillo Experimental Forest Arboretum. The arboretum interests me, not only because it showcases a variety of tropical trees but also because, in spite of my years of wandering through the forest, I hadn't even known it existed until several months earlier. An unmarked set of mud steps has been carved into a fern-lined embankment off El Verde Road. It connects with a leaf-strewn trail which leads to a wooden sign, unseen from the road. "El Verde arboreto," the sign

announces, "more than 100 species of lumber trees, native and exotic, planted since 1960." A research arboretum, Lugo explains, is not open to the public, though student groups and educational activities are encouraged to visit. Ahead, trees of all sizes can be seen. Unlike most tropical sites, this one has an uncluttered look; trees were thinned and the understory was recently cut back to keep the plots pure. One of a number of projects that took off under the dynamic forest researcher, Charles Briscoe, the arboretum fell into disrepair after Briscoe left in the mid-1960s, but work started up again when John Francis came to the forest in the mid-1980s to take charge of the plantations. Scents of pine and eucalyptus and unidentifiable smells that conjure up faraway places mingle along the trail, which makes an elongated loop up the mountain between two streams.

Each species, selected for its potential as a timber producer, sits on a 20-meter-square plot (a meter equals slightly more than a yard). Each plot is clearly marked with a small identifying sign giving the name of the species, the country of origin and the date when planted. Red paint bands around the trunks mark the breast diameter height. This is the height of the tree where it reaches a forester's breast; it is used for measuring tree growth. Willowy pines more than 60 feet tall fill the first site. Cones are scattered on the ground. Known as Caribbean pines (*Pinus caribaea*), these trees grow well here and were planted in 1960 as a control species. The Caribbean pines are relatively near their native home of Belize. Other species have come quite a distance. Lugo gives me an arboretum map which lists *Agathis robusta* from Australia, *Araucaria cunninghamii* from New Guinea, *Cedrela toona* from Rhodesia, *Cryptomera japonica* from Taiwan and *Khaya grandifoliola* from Nigeria.

Lugo takes us on a quick tour of the arboretum's upper loop. We pass trees that are flourishing, and a few that are languishing. We come to two of Lugo's favorite species. The first is kadam, *Anthocephalus chinensis*, a fast-growing timber tree with a light wood, originally from southeast Asia. "These trees hightail it up to the light," Lugo explains, "they need light. They were considered the Cecropia of Asia and were called the magic tree, they grew so fast. Foresters felt this tree was going to save the tropics, and they planted it everywhere. Then it got root disease and virtually all the trees were wiped out. Now no one in Central America will touch it." The tree has done well in Puerto Rico, although when Hurricane Hugo passes over the mountains shortly afterwards, its strong winds virtually wipe out a large kadam plantation at the forest entrance. Lugo's other favorite is the Australian *Eucalyptus saligna*, planted in 1962. It is a svelte tree with a shedding bark and a smooth pale beige trunk. Growing up to 120 feet, it is the tallest tree Lugo knows of in the forest.

After visiting the arboretum, we stop at the nearby El Verde Field Station. Nestled within a 100-foot-high ring of unruly forest, including tree ferns, mangoes and royal palms draped in philodendron, it has a damp, weathered feel. The original half-century-old concrete building houses visiting scientists. Three wings form an open-ended rectangle which contains a kitchen and bunk-filled sleeping quarters. Next to the residence a newer L-shaped building of wood and concrete provides a conference/work room, complete with large banquet tables, for the scientists; it also contains a small collection of local flora and fauna, in dried or liquid states, for identification purposes. Alejo Estrada, lifelong resident of the Luquillo region, shows us around. A slight, soft-spoken man, he has managed the station for decades. Though his formal schooling ended with the third grade, he is a well-respected plant taxonomist, and he has researched phenological tree studies that focus on such periodic activities as flowering.

After our brief tour of the station, Lugo takes me to view the place I have long been curious to see — the actual spot where radiation was activated for the El Verde irradiation and ecology project.

On December 7, 1964, a helicopter swooped low over the northwestern slopes of the Luquillo Mountains. As the helicopter hovered, a 1,800 pound cylindrical block of metal known as a pig was carefully lowered onto a concrete slab on the forest floor. Inside the cylinder, three capsules containing 10,000-curie cesium powder were fixed to the underside of a lead plug. On January 19, 1965, through controls at the El Verde Field Station, a magnet raised a lid on the plug, and gamma radiation was released into the forest. Two sets of barbed wire fences encircled the site, 200 warning signs were posted, and a patrol checked the area 24 hours a day to ensure that no one would be harmed by the radiation. In contrast to some of the more nefarious radiation tests, the local public was notified ahead of time through the media. One newspaper called the cylinder a new kind of dosimeter for national defense; a radical student group declared it part of a diabolical plot. After 93 days, the source was retracted back into its shield, at which time the damaging effects of the radiation ceased. A helicopter eventually removed the cylinder. Gamma radiation has no residual effects; once the cesium was removed, the wick of a lantern gave off more radiation than the El Verde site.

The study of irradiation and ecology at El Verde was carried out between 1963 and 1967 by the Puerto Rico Nuclear Center under sponsorship by the U.S. Atomic Energy Commission and in agreement with the Institute of Tropical Forestry. Project director was scientist Howard Odum. Its final published volume is ponderous, three and a half inches thick, weighing nine pounds. One hundred eleven chapters chronicle the forest community before, during and after its exposure to radiation. Some 80 scientists, from such universities as Princeton, the University of Georgia and Odum's University of North Carolina, set up specific research problems, which were then worked on at the irradiated site, a second undisturbed site and/or a control site cut back to resemble the early stages of the irradiated site. State-of-the-art equipment was set up at the Nuclear Center, operated by the University of Puerto Rico in Río Piedras. Studies on post-radiation effects, comprising two-thirds of the book, are organized into botanical, chemical and zoological sections. They focus on such topics as sierra palm gemination, aquatic communities in bromeliad leaf axils, leaf fall and decomposition, and evapotranspiration. Scientists still refer to this volume as the "Bible" of research in the forest.

According to one of the forewords in the El Verde book, the impetus for this project came about in the 1950s, when scientists discovered that pine trees were sensitive to radiation; this contradicted the general belief at the time that plants were radio-resistant. Research, they realized, would have to be done to gauge the effects of nuclear warfare and major reactor accidents on forest as well as human populations. The Atomic Energy Commission began a program of forest radioecology in a variety of climatic zones within the United States. Forests in Puerto Rico were considered especially important to the study because tropical rain forests cover vast areas of the world.

The forewords and preface to the El Verde book have a lofty, even philosophical tone, greatly distanced from matters of politics and the military, in spite of the nature of radiation testing. This tone contrasts, for example, with the terse introduction to a published study carried out quietly during the same decade in several places in Puerto Rico, including El Yunque, that measured the response of trees to the effects of different defoliant herbicides. One of the herbicides was Agent Orange. The tone of the El Verde book seems indicative of the project itself. Compared with other radiation and chemical tests being undertaken at that time, the El Verde study ranks low on the risk scale. The project was well-planned, a non-residual form of radiation was used, the public was informed, ample precautions were taken, and local agencies were asked to participate. Part of reason for the "high road" taken by the project has to do with its director, Howard Odum, a pioneer in early ecological studies. For Odum, Lugo explains when I ask him, an exhaustive study of the ecology (the relationships between organisms and their environment) of a tropical forest was the primary interest; if financial backing was to be obtained by also studying the effects of gamma rays, so be it.

In the preface, Odum himself defined two aims for the project. First was "to learn how a rain forest works as a system and under stress [gamma radiation], including populations, mineral cycles, metabolism, and operations of the complex living structure, by concentrating new and old techniques and many investigators on one small area". Second was "to provide the details for a new wave of effort at El Verde aimed at understanding complex ecosystems and their meaning for man". El Verde was chosen because it was one of few places in the tropical forest world that had both ready access to a center for radio-biological reaseach and an extensive background of long-term rain forest studies, "probably unequalled in tropical forestry," as stated in one foreword of the book.

🌿 The path taking Lugo and me to the former site of the radiation source is slick with mud and sodden leaves and bolstered by rocks. As we walk, a light rain falls intermittently. He points out one of the 100-square-meter plots that have been under study for 50 years. This, he emphasizes, is an example of Luquil-lo's long standing in the forefront of tropical forest studies: "Other places call their five-year-old plots long-term." In temperate climates cold weather stops growth, making definite seasonal marks, but in the tropics, growth continues year-round. A lack of rings makes it harder to age trees, which underscores the importance of sites that have been studied for a long time.

Nearby wire remains from the fence that encircled the source at some 500 yards (500 meters) distance. A swaying steel and cable suspension bridge crosses the Río Sonadora. Built for the project, it was designed by Estrada. Its latticed walkway makes it impervious to torrents; now the river flows ten feet below, but Lugo mentions a photo that shows the water at bridge level. On the other side of the river the trail disappears into numerous

LEAVES IN THE FOREST

imperceptible paths, and we have to retrace our steps several times. Tattered plastic ribbons of different colors mark numerous research sites. Another fence, resembling a giant spider web, stands some 160 yards from the source. We climb a small hill and enter a maze of string that marks off square meter plots, one of periodic studies made to check the long-term effects of the radiation. Lugo asks me to proceed cautiously: "Every step you take is like stepping all over someone's desk."

In the middle of the maze is the site where the radiation was released — a square concrete slab topped by a smaller square slab, three poles tied teepee style and a dangling sling that once held the lead pig encasing the cesium. Standing in front of the site brings back memories for Lugo. Born in Puerto Rico, in the west-coast city of Mayagüez, he originally planned to be a medical doctor. This changed when he came to work with Odum. His first professional job was with the El Verde project, and his first professional activity was carrying concrete blocks, two in the morning and two in the afternoon, from the station into the forest to mark compass directions around the source.

When retracted into the metal pig, the cesium ceased releasing radiation into the forest, and scientists could enter the area. Twice during the three-month experiment the cesium was retracted (only one person had permission to do so) in order to examine the equipment and the site. Lugo remembers the first time it was lifted. Scientists stood at the outer boundary like runners at the start of a race, waiting for the signal to view what they imagined would be death and destruction, shriveled leaves, moribund birds, that sort of thing. Instead, they saw virtually no changes. The same thing happened at the end of the experiment.

From the radiation site, we walk over to a metal tower some 40 yards away which had been constructed for the project. Nearby, two more towers connected with a walkway enable scientists to move around in the forest canopy, "another example of what scientists are calling innovation that has been done here since the 1960s."

Lugo shows me a curious object next to the tower, the rusting remains of a six-foot stand-up fan with motor. This formed part of one of the most controversial studies of the project, "pure Odum" as another scientist put it. Though even today scientists debate its success, Lugo assures me that Odum never cared a hoot about their opinions. Titled "Metabolism and Evapotranspiration of the Lower Forest in a Giant Plastic Cylinder", it was an ambitious attempt to determine the rate of water and carbon being released by the forest community on a global level. Usually scientists calculate such rates on a very small scale, taking, for example, a single leaf and putting it in a chamber to determine its metabolic budget by measuring the leaf's contribution of water and carbon dioxide into the atmosphere with a gas analyzer. Odum went numerous steps further, constructing a huge plastic prism, resembling the sort of curtain that drapes a campsite shower, 67 feet high, 60 feet wide and open at the top, to take in whole trees, soils, micro-organisms, animals, in as near a normal micro-climate as possible.

The effects of the radiation on the forest turned out to be less drastic than anticipated. Lugo shows me a large gnarled palo colorado tree some ten feet from the radiation source. The tree was exposed to 50,000 roentgens of radiation. Five hundred roentgens had proved fatal to man and pine trees, yet, though the side of the tree which had faced the radiation is dead and blackened, the other side still lives and seems to have been scarcely affected. The most obvious effect was defoliation. Shortly after the experiment ended, the ground became bare of plants, and there was a rapid fall of green and yellow leaves from the canopy in a 25-yard radius, which continually widened until 1967. For a time, seedlings germinated only in spots shielded by rocks. More light entering the forest resulted in a seedling explosion, first primarily by shrub plants. One of the heroes of the experiment was *Palicourea riparia*, a plant with bright-green foliage, red-orange stems and small yellow flowers, which grew back in abundance after the radiation zapping. "It must have scrambled eggs for genes," Lugo jokes. A year and a half later such pioneer tree species as Cecropia appeared on the ground, and by 1967 low ground vegetation formed a carpet. Ferns proved unexpectedly resistant to radiation, while sierra palms continued to die on the periphery of the affected area for two years. After six months, tabonuco trunks began dripping sap again, and there was little structural change in the wood, but the trees grew at less than half their normal rate. Vegetation was checked every year until 1977. By that time the forest appeared to be recovering, but in general the growth of the radiated site lagged behind the control site, and trees showed such radiation-induced irregularities as damaged buds and mottled, albino or deformed leaves.

In his preface to the El Verde book, Odum spoke of the future of the Luquillo forest: "Because there is a control of land, electrical power, and close access to a modern city, many instrumental studies were and can be made that are normally restricted to a laboratory. By 1970 over a million dollars will have

been spent by the several supporting groups on the El Verde project, making the site a national resource for further study of tropical forest problems. It is possible now for newcomers to move into intricate, advanced problems at El Verde with few preliminaries because of the base lines laid by the studies described in this volume. We hope the discussions and the many unsettled scientific questions may further stimulate excitement for tropical forest research."

Ironically, for a time the project seemed to stunt rather than stimulate research. Lugo went on to get his doctorate at the University of North Carolina, Chapel Hill, and to teach for a decade at the University of Florida, feeling that everything that could be researched in the Luquillo Mountains had been. Many scientists focused on individual or small-group studies, but there was no major collaboration again until the Bisley Watershed Project, described in a previous chapter, began in the mid-1980s.

LOOKING BACK, LOOKING AHEAD

Every institution that reaches the ripe old age of half a century should take a look back and a glance forward, and that is just what the Institute of Tropical Forestry (ITF) did between May 24 and 26, 1989. Included in its golden anniversary celebrations were a cocktail reception at the Forest Service building in Río Piedras and a two-day symposium at the Condado Beach Hotel in San Juan.

The cocktail reception, a pleasant affair featuring an anniversary cake decorated with hills and a stream (in honor of the Bisley project), took on an air of expectation with the arrival of a frail but dapper gentleman named Leslie Holdridge. An octagenarian, Holdridge is one of those people who live long enough and accrue enough successes to become living legends. An American botanist with a fascination for the tropics, he came to Puerto Rico in the 1930s and was the first scientist at the Luquillo Experimental Station. While here, he began to formulate theories on using simple climatic data to determine flora communities, which he called life zones. Today most countries in the New World tropics have been mapped according to the life zone system created by Holdridge. He eventually settled in Costa Rica, founding the Tropical Science Center in the city of San José and establishing a model farm. Not content to stop with the New World tropics, he has adapted his life zones for worldwide use, and he is now adapting them for the planets and beyond.

"Holdridge was brilliant," Lugo explained to me later, "he revolutionized tropical forestry. He was a philosopher scientist, a 'cosmologist', as he would say. He has now lost most of his sight and is retired. In San José he apparently walks along the streets primarily by memory, going to his center. When he got a medal at the symposium, he had to ask me who the man was giving it to him [it was the Chief of the U.S. Forest Service]. Even though he was there to be honored, he still brought in a paper, on chlorophyll, of all things."

I was also eager to get a glimpse of Howard Odum, of the El Verde project, who was scheduled to talk on the final afternoon of the symposium. His talk was titled "Tropical Forest Systems". Odum is an imposing figure, with white hair, one strand constantly askew, and a prominent nose. He seemed brimming with ideas he wanted to convey to us; as he spoke, with a Southern accent, he was often breathless, and he rarely took the time to finish a sentence. He waved his pointer the way a conductor wields a baton as he pointed out details of diagrams being shown on an overhead projector.

Odum was still a man of the total picture, calling himself a "top downer", and he infused science with economics to create a world overview of tropical forests. "What's important," he stressed, "is looking, not at the parts, but at the large scale." His criticism was diplomatic: he agreed there is a place for scientists who study the tiny aspects of the world, but it is at the overall global stage where policies are made, and scientists should think one step up in order to close the gap between science and policy. His diagrams took on the look of ever more complicated engines; toward the end of the talk, I realized they were probably beyond the grasp of most people in the room, not just me.

The two-day symposium was appropriately titled "A Century of Research at the Institute of Tropical Forestry: Results from the First Half, Themes for the Second". Former ITF director Frank Wadsworth opened the talks with a summary of the first 50 years; Odum and most other speakers focused on present and future research; and Jim Bradley, speaking for Congressman Vento of Minnesota, closed by decrying the present — the Caribbean National Forest, he argued, should be a flagship for the U.S. as its only tropical national forest; instead, it was more like a leaky boat in a backwater — and providing hope for the future with the vision of a new visitor/training center.

Looking back over the span of a half-century, one can get a clearer overview of the general direction in which research has moved within the institute from 1939 to 1989. In brief, that direction has gone from a focus on timber management to a focus on ecology. The year most clearly marking the change can be fixed at 1979.

Although there were a number of important ecological studies during the first four decades, the management of a forest and its timber clearly dominated research. Tree growth studies began in the 1940s, and companion investigations on the utilization of forest products began in the 1950s. Luquillo and other island forests became demonstration models for proper land use and timber management. The *Caribbean Forester* magazine along with conferences and bilingual shortcourses increased the skills of tropical foresters around the world. In cooperation with various Commonwealth and Federal agencies, the institute undertook some 2,500 tests and studies, overwhelmingly of a silvicultural nature. Charles Briscoe worked extensively with pine and other plantations; Martin Chudnoff headed the woods products laboratory for a time and eventually published three volumes on the characteristics of tropical woods; George Englerth developed hot and cold bath treatments to prevent decay of posts and other timber products; Frank Longwood tested the reactions of some 70 Puerto Rican woods to wood-working machinery. Representative of those decades is the institute's bestseller, *Common Trees of Puerto Rico and the Virgin Islands* by Elbert Little and Frank Wadsworth. First published in 1964, it describes, through text and line drawings, 250 tree species; a companion volume, co-authored with Roy Woodbury, covers 500 less common trees.

The emphasis on management is in part due to the philosophy of Frank Wadsworth, consummate research forester, who directed ITF from the mid-1950s until 1979. Lugo had this to say of Wadsworth's term: "When he

came to the island, there was basically no forestry in the region. He did an awful lot of work in other countries and became the Caribbean's spiritual and technical leader. In Puerto Rico he managed the forests, and he did it very well, using state-of-the-art tropical forestry management. An advantage the forest has here is the continuity over many years of one person, a person of his quality. It has paid off." Lugo especially admires Wadsworth's foresight in establishing the long-term plots. "Though he may not admit it, Wadsworth laid the groundwork for today's ecology work."

When he stepped down, Wadsworth later told me, he wanted to find a Puerto Rican successor; it had taken him a long time to acclimate to the island, and he doubted he could find someone from the States who could do as he had. He sent a letter to Lugo, who was working for the University of Florida at the time, asking if he had any interest in the job. There was no answer. Two years later he saw Lugo at a meeting in Washington and asked why he had never answered the letter. Lugo said he never got it; when Wadsworth asked if he were interested in the job, Lugo replied, "You bet I am."

In 1979 Lugo became project leader (the Forest Service term for director) of ITF. Initially, some in the Forest Service looked to Lugo, the consummate scientist, as the enemy. Lugo's studies were in ecology, and an ecologist was a stranger to the Forest Service at that time. In fact, Lugo admitted later, when he finally did apply for the job, he was initially turned down because he was an ecologist and not a research forester. "In the Forest Service," Wadsworth explained, "there are still people interested in lumber, in tree genetics, growing straighter trees and so on. Their whole life has been silviculture, and they are bitter with the move toward studying rather than managing the forest."

Lugo built onto what Wadsworth had done, but he also "shifted the fulcrum toward ecology at a time when that's the way the world was going," Wadsworth admitted. A prolific publisher — he writes as many as 30 papers a year — Lugo is actively involved in the international scientific community. Wadsworth pointed out that Lugo has established one of the biggest research programs in the Forest Service, and he was named distinguished scientist for the entire U.S. Forest Service the first year the award was given. This contrasts greatly with Lugo's early years at the institute as Odum's technician, when he scarcely dared go to the upper floor of the Forest Service building, the floor where the scientists worked.

When I asked Lugo about some of the themes for the second half of the century, he too acknowledged the shift from management to ecology. Times have changed, he commented, needs have changed. Ecologists are now courted by the Forest Service. Today's public questions the cutting of trees for lumber, the planting of exotic (non-native) species. In the future he feels ITF will become more holistic, more global. Scientists will analyze what a tree does to the forest, what certain chemicals in the atmosphere do to the trees, what the forest does to the region. "Research," he added, "helps society make decisions. Because of this, it must be ahead of tomorrow's questions. But no matter what the changes, ITF will be in the thick of things."

There have been several important changes within the institute since the time of its golden anniversary. Recognizing the importance of forestry on an international level and the high quality of the work being done at the institute, the Forest Service has actually added a fourth leg to its three-legged stool, the new leg being an international forestry component. Now officially renamed the International Institute of Tropical Forestry, with Lugo as its director, the institute has expanded its program and its budget to include tropical forests outside Puerto Rico. Currently, it is working closely with the Brazilian government on forestry projects within the Amazon. In addition, the visitor/training center Bradley envisioned is now a reality, its first phase completed and open to the public. And, while the institute still has research foresters, it also has scientists in such fields as atmospheric chemistry and economy. "For the first time," Lugo was happy to report, "they [two new scientists at IITF] are so specialized that even I have a hard time understanding them!"

Lugo seems to have been right. Although research in the Luquillo Mountains has seen many changes over the centuries — from nineteenth-century botanists who first put names to the local trees and plants, to 1930s foresters who analyzed trees for their timber potential, to 1960s scientists who studied the relationships of these trees and plants with the rest of the forest community, to 1990s researchers who look at global influences on the forest —the International Institute of Tropical Forestry is still in the thick of things.

CHAPTER 15
VALLEY OF THE GIANTS

Somewhere in the remote southern section of the upper Luquillo mountains lies the Valley of the Giants. These giants are trees, ancient gnarled palo colorado trees that tower over the rest of the valley's inhabitants. Once upon a time, millenniums ago, they were mere saplings, smaller even than the many plants which today lap at their massive trunks. Protected from fierce hurricane winds by the ridges that surround them, they slowly, inexorably rose above the plants, above the young trees, then above the mature trees within the valley, until at last their upper leaves touched the forest canopy. They continued to grow, expanding their trunks and pushing the canopy even higher. They became giants, not merely a single giant standing alone amid the younger forest, but a group of large, aged trees spaced along the valley floor.

In spite of the monumental aspect of these trees, they have scarcely been seen by humans. Perhaps Indians passed through the valley when the trees were of more modest size, perhaps a prospector or two rested against one of the trunks before continuing in his search for whatever metals the mountain would yield, perhaps lost hikers stumbled into the valley, leaving as quickly as they came and scarcely noticing the oversized trees except as grotesque distortions of their own plight. The same hills — pronounced, closely spaced, disorientingly random — which have spared the trees from the most violent winds have also hidden them to all but those who reach the edge of the valley, and even they might not notice the trees if the fog has come before them.

The Valley of the Giants. The very words conjure up a place of magic and grandeur, a time primeval. The valley has become myth.

Though small in size, the Caribbean National Forest remains a remote, wild and mysterious place. Several years ago, a news brief spoke of three European tourists who were lost in the forest for 19 hours; found by members of the Civil Defense, they were treated for cuts and exhaustion. More recently, another told of a young man from the nearby Naval base who slipped from the rim of a river canyon to his death. These are only two of the occasional reminders that, in spite of the picnic shelters and lookout towers, the forest still has its untamed side.

Its inaccessibility is what makes the forest mythical, Forest Supervisor Pablo Cruz explained to me one day in his spacious office on the first floor of the Forest Service building in Río Piedras. Months earlier, Cruz had told me he was gathering information about the mythical nature of the forest, but it took several attempts for us finally to get together.

He is a boyishly good-looking man, with straight, neatly cut black hair and an earnest attitude about him. Though he half-heartedly complains of the bureaucratic demands, it is obvious Cruz likes his job. Born in the east-coast town of Fajardo, he studied engineering and worked with the Soil Conservation Service before entering the U.S. Forest Service, where he went from the Stanislaus Forest in California to the Washington, D.C. office to the Caribbean National Forest. Here he coordinated work being done after Hurricane Hugo hit. When the forest's district ranger left in 1990, he became the first Puerto Rican hired for the job, which is basically that of an on-site director. When the supervisor left soon afterwards, Cruz became acting supervisor, and in early 1993 he was officially given the top job of forest supervisor.

"Let me use an attic as an analogy," Cruz began when we broached the topic of the forest's mythical nature. "The forest is like a place where one doesn't have access, like an attic. As a kid, you invent all kinds of stories about the attic, because it's inaccessible, it's mysterious." In the same way, he continued, Luquillo has been inaccessible for eons. During the Indians' time, the mountains had no known settlements; the Indians worshipped gods there and had a lot of fear and respect for the place. During the Europeans' time, the lower part of the forest was used for agriculture and some mining, but the rest was still unknown — unknown and probably somewhat feared as a place to which a number of slaves had escaped. The first road through the mountains wasn't built until the 1930s. Settlements never reached the upper mountains: the land was too wet, too hard to live on. "All this created a mystery about the place — a tremendous mysticism and many misconceptions."

Undoubtedly, mystery gave rise to tales. The Indians had their tales of benevolent gods protecting them from the highest peaks, the early colonizers their tales of monstruous Caribs hiding out in the forests, the prospectors their tales of rich gold veins that were found and lost, the settlers their tales of strange creatures in the forest. These tales died with those who told them. Today, most people realize there are no dangerous creatures in the forest — even the snakes are non-poisonous — and the Caribs and slaves are gone. But the forest remains a large uninhabited region on a crowded island, and to many it still is a fearful place.

The forest's mythical tales seem to fall into three broad categories. First are the tales of lost children. These tales have probably been told for centuries. Children go into the forest to picnic, to camp, to hike, to cut lumber, catch river shrimp, search for medicinal plants. They are last seen investigating a strange noise at night, leaving the trail to find a short-cut, huddling under an outcrop in the middle of a storm, standing at the edge of the road in broad daylight. They never come back. Cruz mentioned the case of twins who were said to have disappeared, as if sucked into some fourth dimension. Yet most of the disappearances have mundane resolutions. A newspaper reports a hiker lost; the hiker is found, but the newspaper doesn't find that quite so newsworthy, so people continue to believe the hiker is lost. A girl is abducted from the side of the recreation area road; months later, forest authorities find out she was abducted by one of her parents, who are separated, and whisked to the States.

Most popular are tales of UFO and extra-terrestrial sightings. I recently heard one such tale dating back to the early years of this century. A young boy living in a remote hollow halfway up the mountains went to investigate the frantic bleating of the family goats and came face to face with a small bright-green creature. Contemporary UFO tales are slightly more sophisticated — strange lights hovering over the inky forest on a rainy night; sites where trees grow outward, forming a bowl shape, as if blown backwards by a great force; teenagers leaving their tents to investigate a speck of light in the next valley, never returning.

An impressive number of UFO and extraterrestrial sightings has been reported in the Luquillo Mountains, and Jorge Martin carefully follows them. Martin is currently editor of the magazine *Enigma*, published in San Juan and dedicated to reporting extraterrestrial activities and unidentified flying objects on a local and international level. Martin admits to an interest in such phenomena since childhood. I called him one day to find out more about these reports. Martin has learned of at least a couple dozen sightings in Luquillo, sightings made by people who live in the area, including forest personnel. He explained that there are two common types of extraterrestrials glimpsed in Puerto Rico: small humanoid creatures grayish in color with slender, egg-shaped bodies and big heads with dark eyes; and big-foot sorts of creatures. The latter has not been seen recently in the Luquillo area; the former has. When I asked Martin why so many sightings have been made in Puerto Rico and the Luquillo Mountains, he revealed a theory about some sort of underground center here.

Cruz attends to these reports with the same sort of earnestness he gives to all information brought to him about the forest by the public. One evening he went to the forest with a group of people connected to *Enigma*; he found they were more into the spiritual aspect of the search — sitting with eyes closed, hands held — than the scientific. Nothing out of the ordinary was spotted that night.

In searching for an explanation, Cruz has come up with three possibilities. "But let me make a disclaimer," he told me before he began, "these are my own personal perceptions, in no way a voice of the Forest Service." First, El Yunque has wide open spaces and little human interference, making the sky at night much more apparent and the constellations more spectacular than when glimpsed amid the lights of the city. People who are not used to seeing the firmament in all its glory might mistake a natural phenomenon like a shooting star for something else. Second, the Earth's atmosphere is turning into a bit of a junkyard, with orbiting solar panels and satellites, and some of these objects might pick up a reflection from the sun and seem to be what they are not. Third, Roosevelt Roads Naval Station does a number of joint air maneuvers with friendly nations. Though planes are not supposed to fly over El Yunque because of its designation as an endangered species habitat, some of the pilots might not know this and might take one last spin before landing, hovering over the forest with lights flashing, perhaps trying a hotshot maneuver or two.

As I mulled all this over later, I felt there is a fourth possible explanation, relating to the immediate surroundings of the viewers. If they are watching from mountain peaks and ridges, viewers are surrounded by the ghostly atmosphere of dwarf forest, with its stooped trees, gnarled branches and hanging mosses. At night it is especially otherworldly, and it could create all sorts of fantastic images in the mind's eye.

Aged
palo
colorado.

VALLEY
OF
THE
GIANTS

*Jumbled
terrain along
a tributary
of the Río
Icacos.*

*Clouds
over the forest.*

Tales of lost children, tales of extraterrestrial sightings — the third broad category of tales relates to underground tunnels crisscrossing the mountains. Martin touched on that with his theory of an underground center in the Luquillo Mountains. In another version I heard, the tunnels had been secretly built on orders from Roosevelt Roads Naval Station during World War II. Cruz knows of no manmade tunnels (with the exception of a few short remnants from the mining period); he imagines what people have seen are actually caves, cavities or sinkholes formed by landslides or hydrological conditions. Cruz told me one tunnel tale, which he estimated surfaced in the 1980s. A man stumbled into a tunnellike sinkhole that was hidden by dense undergrowth. Down he fell, landing on the sandy banks of an underground stream. As the man struggled to get out of the sinkhole, his foot unearthed an old bottle, complete with legal seal and wax of the Spanish Crown. Inside the bottle was a treasure map. When the map was lined up with the peaks of Luquillo, its "X" marking the treasure spot pointed to an islet off Fajardo. Unfortunately, the islet, known as Isleta Marina, has been virtually buried under two condominiums and a marina for several decades; whatever treasure might have been there is now well sealed.

El Yunque's wildest terrain sprawls across the southern side of the mountains. Near the ridges, hills are packed close to each other; hiking across them is like clawing one's way up and down the tracks of a rollercoaster. Farther south, the land tilts steeply, forming the sort of precipitous Marquesan terrain Herman Melville described in his travel adventure *Typee*. Road 191 once dissected this region, but an ever-growing landslide at one point has made it impassable, and it is closed to vehi-

cles at the edge of the recreation area. El Toro Trail, a.k.a. the Tradewinds Trail, meanders along upper ridges to El Toro Peak, and a little maintained branch trail descends from the main trail towards the Río Espíritu Santo. The rest of this entire area, which comprises a good third of the forest, remains untouched but for a handful of barely perceptible paths.

In 1977 the Forest Service completed a roadless area review evaluation and recommended that some 10,000 acres in this southwestern part of the forest be officially designated wilderness. In wilderness areas, the natural processes predominate, and human intervention is kept to a minimum. Currently, El Yunque has no wilderness areas, which must be granted by an act of Congress, but the current proposed long-term management plan for the forest recommends the inclusion of these 10,000 acres. Known as the El Toro area, they encompass El Toro Peak, highest in the forest, and neighboring El Cacique Peak to the northeast. In one evaluation of the area, this is what foresters had to say under the subheading of challenging experiences: "The area offers an opportunity to test one's ability and stamina in handling steep, slippery junglelike terrain. Travel by foot off of trails across country is extremely difficult, and disorientation caused by dense screening vegetation is very common."

Although the Valley of the Giants is not in the proposed wilderness area — it lies slightly to the east — it is in the heart of the same sort of disorienting, junglelike terrain.

❦ In 1948 a forester making a tally of trees on the southern slopes of Luquillo came upon a palo colorado with a diameter of 104 inches. Foresters figure the diameter of a tree by measuring it at breast height. Often a few vines and roots stubbornly clinging to the trunk are included in the measurement, inflating it a bit, but even so, this diameter was almost 8 inches larger than the official largest tree in the forest, a palo colorado off Road 186 in northwestern El Verde. Before any decisive action was taken, the forester died. Some 20 years later Frank Wadsworth and others went on a surveying trip into the same part of the forest; while there, they hoped to find the 104-inch-diameter tree. They didn't, but they did find a four-acre valley that contained more than 25 palo colorados they estimated to be between 80 and 90 inches in diameter. The foresters sat down and had lunch in the shade of the trees and measured a few of the trunks to confirm their estimates. Some time later Wadsworth again came upon the valley, again by accident.

Large palo colorados are impressive not merely for their size but for what the size implies about their age. Scientists estimate these trees grow about three inches in diameter a century. Palo colorados do have growth rings but, since there is no cold season in the tropics, the rings are not reliable in determining age. By calculating three inches a century, the official largest tree —the 96-incher in El Verde — should be some 3,200 years old and the elusive larger tree 3,450 years old. Though it is intriguing to imagine these trees as seedlings when ancient Egyptian civilization was at its zenith, the truth is probably less dramatic. Biologist Peter Weaver believes the massive El Verde trunk is actually two neighboring palo colorados which fused together several centuries back. If palo colorados grow that large, he once reasoned to me, then why are there no intermediate-sized specimens in the forest? Weaver estimates the giant palo colorados as 500 to 1,000 years old; Wadsworth believes some could be over a

1,000 years old, but he, too, questions the 3,000-plus estimates.

"What I find amazing," Wadsworth told me, "is that these old ones have probably gone through a hundred hurricanes. Like willow trees, palo colorados break at the top and sprout again, but in the valley almost none looked broken. All the old ones have huge, broken limbs, which make the nest cavities for the Puerto Rican parrots. In the valley there were big holes, holes a person could live in." He remembered the soil in the valley as being fairly stable.

At 9:00 a.m. one April day in 1989, Wadsworth, forester Jerry Bauer, Wadsworth's wife Isabel, hydrologist Fred Scatena, ecologist Vicente Quevedo, a visiting scientist from England and I meet at the Catalina Field Office at the foot of the mountains and pile into a Forest Service van on the first leg of our search for the Valley of the Giants. At the southern boundary of the recreation area a padlocked gate blocks Road 191. Bauer has a key, and we pass through. Beyond the gate, the road's condition changes dramatically. It is pocked with holes and buckles and cracks. Encroaching vegetation has reduced it to a single lane, and dead leaves and branches have settled on top of it. Ferns poke out of embankments along the side of the road, and bamboo and spindly yagrumo branches arch overhead. Two side roads lead up the mountain toward El Yunque Peak; down the mountain, the views extend across tiers of forest to East Peak and down the Icacos Valley toward the south coast. A former summer home or two lie in ruin along the side of the road. A couple of paths, invisible to the uninformed eye, lead to the remains of an old Civilian Conservation Corps camp —half-buried foundations and walls, an occasional pottery shard. Road

191 has the feel of a road to nowhere, gateway to a lost civilization, byway through land that time forgot.

A sturdy, well-engineered little road, 191 was completed in 1937 to bisect the Luquillo Mountains, connecting the small towns of Palmer/Mameyes to the north and Naguabo to the south and opening up the exotic beauty of the rain forest to the motorist. There were no environmental impact statements back then, Francisco José Ferrer reminds readers in a bulletin of the Natural History Society of Puerto Rico. For 33 years, he continues, Road 191 remained open, impervious to numerous storms and resulting landslides. Roadmen (camineros) lived in nearby homes and maintained specific stretches of roads, ridding them of debris and cleaning out their culverts after a storm. During World War II foresters cut trees for charcoal and firewood up to 300 feet on both sides of the road. Coinciding with the transfer of the care of 191 from Federal to local hands in the 1950s, the island's camineros were replaced with brigades of workers from regional offices who tended to provide the best care to roads that handled the most voters. As a result, Road 191 received virtually no care. When several severe storms hit the island in the early 1970s, landslides tumbling down the mountains ripped 191 apart in several places. Each successive storm widened the gaps; the largest is now over 600 feet across.

In spite of its disheveled appearance, 191 has not been forgotten. As we drive, we see sections where the road has been cleared, holes have been patched and embankments have been shored up. There is talk of reopening the road. In the ensuing years, the talk becomes bonafide plans, but environmental groups oppose the plans, citing the effects this reopen-ing would have on the forest, and, as of 1996, the plans remain stalled.

At the umpteenth fern-decked, bamboo-shaded curve along the road, we stop and look out onto the forest. Wadsworth remembers more or less where he entered when he found the Valley of the Giants; he also remembers more or less how many steps he took when he left the valley to get back to the road. By calculating the length of his step, he is able to estimate that we will walk about a mile until we reach an especially jumbled bit of terrain, then we will head to the right and, voilá, enter the valley. Bauer and Quevedo have brought tagging tape to tie around trees along the way and mark the route for posterity. Bauer takes a compass reading and notes a point in the distance. We head for it.

Immediately, the forest plunges down a ravine, forcing us to grab roots and small trunks to keep from sleighing to the bottom. There, sierra palms fill a small hollow. It is the first of numerous hollows tucked between narrow ridges we will encounter. From the hollows, views extend only to the surrounding ridges, ridding us of all sense of direction. From the ridges, which are dense with vegetation, views scarcely reach the neighboring ridges, a distance of rarely more than several hundred feet. Huge mossy boulders resemble the hulls of ships abandoned in the forest; roots and leaves form treacherous mats between the boulders. This is what we must cross to find one small valley of giant trees, and this is why even a seasoned forester like Wadsworth, who never actually went out looking for the valley before today, cannot say where it is with any sort of exactitude. The prospect of success seems less sure from the hollow.

We soon enter the Río Icacos valley. Several small streams with crystal-clear water slip over mossy rocks and funnel into sand-bottom pools as they make their unhurried way down the mountains. Although the terrain has the look of a rollercoaster track, the mountains have scarcely begun their steep southerly descent toward the sea. Scatena mentions this water is clearer than the water found on the northern side of the mountain; it has no organic matter in it. Sierra palms drape over the streams; in the background, trees form dark silhouettes. Sierra palms also cling to the steepest slopes along ridges separating the streams while an open sort of moderately dwarfed vegetation predominates on top. Within the forest such trees as palo colorado, nuez moscada and cupeíllo raise gnarled branches toward the sky. Marcgravia vines snake around trunks, bromeliads nest in branches. Club moss, a far-flung plant with family members in the Arctic, hugs the ground. At one point we step around a small pit and a few tree stumps, remains of World War II charcoal production. It seems a long and tortuous distance to come for wood.

At another point a stream follows a meandering U-shaped route along the valley. The ground here is flat, soggy, with few trees. Periodic floods ensure that all but the most stubborn saplings are washed away. Moisture is heavy, and the very air seems to have a green hue. Wadsworth recalls botonist Nathaniel Britton saying he saw trees cut in the Luquillo forest whose severed branches were still green when he returned three months later. Wad-

sworth considers the statement somewhat hyberbolic, but the moisture is overwhelming. The entire Icacos river valley, exceptionally pristine throughout, is an exquisite example of the tropics as gentle paradise. It parallels 191, passing quite close to the road in several places, which is one reason environmentalists fear reopening the road to vehicular traffic.

On the other side of the Icacos valley, Wadsworth spies a liana dangling from a tree. "Bejuco de agua," he announces — water liana. This plant gives a mini-lesson in the dichotomy between foresters who use the forest and researchers who study it: While the foresters in our group brandish their machetes and slash the liana — twice in the same place — until water drips out and we can sample it, the researchers stand back with a slightly worried look at this assault on the vine.

We cross a dry stream bed filled with large boulders. Wadsworth points out a nearby landslide to Scatena. Beyond, a hollow resembles a sinkhole: it is deep and circular, with rocks and a stream at the bottom. Geological forces seem to have gone berserk around this point. The land rises and falls much more precipitously, boulders increase in size and quantity, and I lose count of the number of meandering stream beds. We slip our way down one virtually vertical precipice, then ascend another, wedging our feet against trees and hoisting ourselves up with roots. Our precipices are chosen at random; there is no

LOS PICACHOS PEAK

way of seeing which will provide the easiest crossing nor knowing what lies on the other side. Bauer doesn't even bother getting his compass out, and he and Quevedo have stopped tagging trees. At this point, we have our first bad encounter with the appropriately-nicknamed razor grass.

At the top of the umpteenth ridge, site of another patch of moderately dwarfed vegetation, we stand around limply. Most of us are spent. A series of blue tags we had been following has disappeared. Orange tags appear but going in the wrong direction; Wadsworth speculates they lead to a landslide being studied. Two more ridges poke up nearby. We head to the right, as per Wadsworth's earlier directions. This route soon has us plunging down to another stream coursing around boulders. Scatena and the visiting Englishman scramble up the other side, which is in the shape of a large amphitheater. They find nothing. It is noon, two and a half hours after we started. We grab a couple of boulders and extricate lunches out of our backpacks. It seems the Valley of the Giants has eluded us.

"There are no miramelinda [impatiens], no pomarrosa here," Wadsworth comments. Both species were introduced into Puerto Rico. There is little doubt that this is virgin forest, unaltered by man. Bromeliads nest in the sierra palms, delicate ferns dangle from the boulders, an anthurium grows atop a nearby rock.

After lunch, we follow the stream downriver, keeping an eye out for our valley. Initially, the terrain is wild. Boulders discourage an easy stroll along the stream bed, and the banks are steep. We opt for getting out of the stream bed, climbing high to reach the top of the bank. On the opposite side a grouping of interconnecting rocks has been smoothed to form a sloping wall. Soon the terrain levels out, and we are able to alternately slosh along the stream and step out onto patches of flat land above its banks. Eventually we leave the stream and, guided by Bauer's compass again, strike out cross-country in the general direction of the road. Patches of highly absorbent sphagnum moss cover the ground in places. Farther along, Quevedo shows Wadsworth an elliptical leaf from a nearby tree. Wadsworth recognizes the leaf immediately. "I've been telling foresters to kill these trees off whenever they see them," he quips. It belongs to the tree *Byrsonima wadsworthii*, so named in honor of Wadsworth. Locally known as almendrillo ("little almond", for its small egg-shaped stone fruits), it is a rare tree, found only in the high mountain regions of Puerto Rico. Soon we spy bamboo, an introduced species, and know we are near the road. We come out south of the van and walk somewhat woodenly up the road, stepping over dead yagrumo leaves and picking native raspberries that grow along the shoulders.

When we reach the van, we take one last look across the mountains. Hidden somewhere beneath that long expanse of forest is the Valley of the Giants. Ever the enthusiast, Bauer talks about making another attempt to find it before he leaves for work in Central America, perhaps fanning out from different areas. Isabel suggests we return again and camp out. We open the van and pile in.

❦ I have seen Wadsworth several times since that trip. He has suggested organizing another attempt to find the valley, but I don't push him. I have a picture of the Valley of the Giants in my mind. It is a grand and mysterious place, representative of all that is wondrous about the Luquillo Mountains. I'm not sure I want to find it.

BIBLIOGRAPHY
GLOSSARY

BIBLIOGRAPHY

The following articles and books were used in the writing of this book. This is not meant as a complete bibliography of forest publications.

Ackerman, J.D. *The Orchids of Puerto Rico and the Virgin Islands*. San Juan: The University of Puerto Rico Press, 1992.

Alexopoulous, Constantine J. "Rain Forest Myxomycetes." From *A Tropical Rain Forest: A Study of Irradiation and Ecology at El Verde, Puerto Rico*. Washington, D.C.: U.S. Atomic Energy Commission, 1970.

Bannister (Cintrón), Barbara A. "Ecological Life Cycle of Euterpe globosa Gaertn." From *A Tropical Rain Forest: A Study of Irradiation and Ecology at El Verde, Puerto Rico*. Washington, D.C.: U.S. Atomic Energy Commission, 1970.

Barbour, William R. "Forest Types of Tropical America." *Caribbean Forester* 3.4 (July, 1942): 137-150.

Basnet, Khadga, Likens, Gene E., Scatena, F.N., Lugo, Ariel E. "Hurricane Hugo: Damage to a Tropical Rain Forest in Puerto Rico."

Bauer, Gerald P. "Reforestation with Mahogany (Swietenia SPP.) in the Caribbean National Forest, Puerto Rico." Presented at Seminario-Taller de Cooperación y Manejo de Bosques Tropicales, Peru, 1987.

Beard, J. S. "Climax Vegetation in Tropical America." *Ecology* 25.2 (April, 1944): 127-158.

Beinroth, Friedrich H. *An Outline of the Geology of Puerto Rico*. Río Piedras: Agricultural Experiment Station, 1969.

Brau, Salvador. *La colonización de Puerto Rico*. San Juan: Instituto de Cultura Puertorriqueña, 1966.

Brown, Sandra, Lugo, Ariel E., Silander, Susan, and Liegel, Leon. *Research History and Opportunities in the Luquillo Experimental Forest*. United States Department of Agriculture, General Technical Report SO-44, September, 1983.

Cardona, Walter A. "El Yunque Mineral Prospects, Eastern Puerto Rico." *Caribbean Journal of Science* 20.1-2 (1984).

Caufield, Catherine. *In the Rainforest*. Chicago: University of Chicago Press, 1984.

Domíguez Cristobal, Carlos. "Situación forestal de Puerto Rico durante el siglo XIX." *Acta Científica* 3.1 (1989): 24-25.

Drewry, George E. "A List of Insects from El Verde, Puerto Rico." From *A Tropical Rain Forest: A Study of Irradiation and Ecology at El Verde, Puerto Rico*. Washington, D.C.: U.S. Atomic Energy Commission, 1970.

Eggers, H. "Porto Rico." *Nature*, December 6, 1883.

Ewel, J.J. and Whitmore, J.L. "The Ecological Life Zones of Puerto Rico and the U.S. Virgin Islands." Forest Service Research Paper ITF-18, December, 1973. Río Piedras: Institute of Tropical Forestry.

Fernández Méndez, Eugenio. *Crónicas de Puerto Rico*. Río Piedras: Editorial de la Universidad de Puerto Rico, 1969.

Figueroa Colón, J., ed. *The Scientific Survey of Puerto Rico and the U.S. Virgin Islands: Eighty years in the Study of the Natural History of the Islands*. New York: Annals of the New York Academy of Sciences, in press.

Forsyth, Adrian and Miyata, Ken. *Tropical Nature*. New York: Charles Scribner's Sons, 1984.

Howard, Richard. "The Ecology of an Elfin Forest in Puerto Rico. 1. Introduction and composition studies." *Journal of the Arnold Arboretum* 50.2 (1968): 225-262.

Iñigo Abbad y Lasierra, Fray Agustín. *Historia geográfica, civil y natural de la Isla de San Juan Bautista de Puerto Rico.* Río Piedras: Editorial de la Universidad de Puerto Rico, 1979 (originally published 1782).

Kepler, Angela Kay. *Common Ferns of Luquillo Forest, Puerto Rico.* San Juan: Inter-American University Press, 1975.

Kepler, Cameron B. and Parkes, Kenneth C. "A New Species of Warbler (Parulidae) from Puerto Rico." *The Auk* 89.1 (January 17, 1972): 1-18.

Kitchens, Robert. "Damage Assessment for Caribbean National Forest due to Hurricane Hugo." Atlanta: U.S. Department of Agriculture, 1989.

Lamb, F. Bruce. *Mahogany of Tropical America: Its Ecology and Management.* Ann Arbor: The University of Michigan Press, 1966.

Leopold, Aldo. A *Sand County Almanac.* San Francisco: Sierra Club/Ballantine, 1970.

Little, Elbert L., Jr. and Wadsworth, Frank H. *Common Trees of Puerto Rico and the Virgin Islands.* Washington, D.C.: United States Department of Agriculture, Forest Service, 1964.

Little, Elbert L., Jr. and Wadsworth, Frank H. *Trees of Puerto Rico and the Virgin Islands.* Second Volume. Washington, D.C.: United States Department of Agriculture, Forest Service, 1974.

Little, Elbert L., Jr. and Woodbury, Roy O. "Trees of the Caribbean National Forest." (Forest Service Research Paper ITF-20) Río Piedras, Puerto Rico: Institute of Tropical Forestry, (U.S. Forest Service) September, 1976.

Lugo, Ariel E. "Biosphere Reserves in the Tropics: An Opportunity for Integrating Wise Use and Preservation of Biotic Resources." Paper at the Fourth World Wilderness Congress, Symposium on Biosphere Reserves, Estes Park, Colorado, 1987. Washington, D.C.: National Park Service.

Lugo, Ariel E. "Water and the Ecosystems of the Luquillo Experimental Forest." United States Department of Agriculture, General Technical Report SO-63, August, 1986.

Lugo, A.E., and Lowe, C., eds. *Tropical Forest: Management and Ecology.* New York: Springer Verlag, 1995.

Marrero, José. "Forest Planting in the Caribbean National Forest: Past Experience as a Guide to the Future." *Caribbean Forester,* 9:85-213.

McMahan, Elizabeth A. "Radiation and the Termites at El Verde." From *A Tropical Rain Forest: A Study of Irradiation and Ecology at El Verde, Puerto Rico.* Washington, D.C.: U.S. Atomic Energy Commission, 1970.

McMahan, Elizabeth A., and Sollins, Nancy F. "Diversity of Microarthropods After Irradiation." From *A Tropical Rain Forest: A Study of Irradiation and Ecology at El Verde, Puerto Rico.* Washington, D.C.: U.S. Atomic Energy Commission, 1970.

Melgarejo, Jhoan. "Memoria sometida por el Capitan Jhoan Melgarejo, Gobernador de Puerto Rico, 1582." From *Crónicas de Puerto Rico* (edited by Eugenio Fernandez Méndez). Río Piedras: Editorial de la Universidad de Puerto Rico, 1969.

Meyerhoff, Howard A. *Geology of Puerto Rico.* Río Piedras: The University of Puerto Rico, 1933.

Mitchell, Raoul C. *A Survey of the Geology of Puerto Rico.* Río Piedras: Agricultural Experiment Station, 1954.

Morales Carrión, Arturo. *Puerto Rico, A Political and Cultural History.* New York: W.W. Norton and Company, Inc., 1983.

Mosquera, Menandra and Feheley, JoAnne. *Bibliography of Forestry in Puerto Rico.* New Orleans: Southern Forest Experiment Station, U.S. Department of Agriculture, 1984.

Navarro Haydon, Rosa. *Cómo se formó Puerto Rico.* San Juan: Instituto de Cultura Puertorriqueña, 1968.

Odum, Howard T., ed. *A Tropical Rain Forest: A Study of Irradiation and Ecology at El Verde, Puerto Rico.* Washington, D.C.: U.S. Atomic Energy Commission, 1970.

Ogle, Carol June. "Pollen Analysis of Selected Sphagnum-Bog Sites in Puerto Rico". From *A Tropical Rain Forest: A Study of Irradiation and Ecology at El Verde, Puerto Rico.* Washington, D.C.: U.S. Atomic Energy Commission, 1970.

O'Hanlon, Redmond. *In Trouble Again: A Journey between the Orinoco and the Amazon*. New York: The Atlantic Monthly Press, 1988.

Olsen, Fred. *On the Trail of the Arawaks*. Norman: University of Oklahoma Press, 1974.

Pané, Fray Ramón. "Relación de Fray Ramón Pané acerca de las antigüedades de los Indios, 1505." From *Crónicas de Puerto Rico* (edited by Eugenio Fernandez Méndez). Río Piedras: Editorial de la Universidad de Puerto Rico, 1969.

Perry, Donald. *Life above the Jungle Floor*. New York: Fireside Book (Simon & Schuster), 1986.

Pinchot, Gifford. *Breaking New Ground*. New York: Harcourt, Brace and Company, 1947.

Pool, Raymond J. *Basic Course in Botany*. Boston: The Athenaeum Press, Ginn and Company, 1940.

Press, Frank and Seiver, Raymond. *Earth*. New York: W.H. Freeman and Company, 1986.

Proctor, George R. *Ferns of Puerto Rico and the Virgin Islands*. New York: Memoirs of the New York Botanical Garden, 52:1-389, 1989.

Raffaele, Herbert A. *A Guide to the Birds of Puerto Rico and the Virgin Islands*. San Juan: Fondo Educativo Interamericano, 1983.

Reagan, Douglas P. "Ecology of the Puerto Rican Boa (Epicrates inornatus) in the Luquillo Mountains of Puerto Rico." *Caribbean Journal of Science* 20 (1984):3-4.

Reagan, Douglas P. and Waide, Robert B., eds. *Food Web of a Tropical Rain Forest*. Chicago: University of Chicago Press, in press (1996).

Recher, Harry and Judy. "Birds of El Verde." From *A Tropical Rain Forest: A Study of Irradiation and Ecology at El Verde, Puerto Rico*. Washington, D.C.: U.S. Atomic Energy Commission, 1970.

Rivero, Juan A. *The Amphibians and Reptiles of Puerto Rico*. San Juan: Editorial de la Universidad de Puerto Rico, 1978.

Roberts, R.C. *Soil Survey of Puerto Rico*. Washington, D.C.: United States Department of Agriculture, Bureau of Plant Industry, 1942.

Salivia, Luis A., M.D. *Historia de los temporales de Puerto Rico y las Antillas*. San Juan: Editorial Edil, Inc., 1972.

Santiago-Valentín, Eugenio. "*Callicarpa ampla, Ilex sintenissi, Styrax portoricensis, Ternstroemia luquillensis, and Ternstroemia subsessilis* Recovery Plan." Atlanta: U.S. Fish and Wildlife Service, 1993.

Scatena, Frederick N., Lugo, Ariel E., Asbury, Clyde. "Study Plan: Hydrology, Sediment and Nutrient Budgets in Three Humid Forest Watersheds in Puerto Rico." F-SO-2518.

Schwartz, Marvin W. *Huellas*. Text by Robert Friedman. San Juan: Institute of Puerto Rican Culture, 1976.

Seiders, Victor M. "Cretaceous and Lower Tertiary Stratigraphy of the Gurabo and El Yunque Quadrangles, Puerto Rico." *Geological Survey Bulletin* 1294-F. Washington, D.C.: U.S. Government Printing Office, 1971.

Seiders, Victor M. "Geologic Map of the El Yunque Quadrangle, Puerto Rico." U.S. Geological Survey, Washington, D.C., 1971.

Snyder, Noel F. R., Wiley, James W., Kepler, Cameron B. *The Parrots of Luquillo: Natural History and Conservation of the Puerto Rican Parrot*. Los Angeles: Western Foundation of Vertebrate Zoology, 1987.

Stearn, Colin W., Carroll, Robert L. and Clark, Thomas. *Geological Evolution of North America*. New York: John Wiley & Sons, 1979.

Steen, Harold K. *The U.S. Forest Service: A History*. Seattle: University of Washington Press, 1976.

Tamsitt, J.R. and Valdivieso, Darío. "Observations of Bats and Their Ectoparasites." From *A Tropical Rain Forest: A Study of Irradiation and Ecology at El Verde, Puerto Rico*. Washington, D.C.: U.S. Atomic Energy Commission, 1970.

Tannehill, Ivan Ray. *Hurricanes: Their Nature and History*. Princeton: Princeton University Press, 1945.

Townsend, Daniel S., Stewart, Margaret M., Pough, F. Harvey, Brussard, Peter F. "Internal Fertilization in an Oviparous Frog." *Science* 212 (24 April 1981): 469-471.

Turner, Frederick B. and Gist, Clayton S. "Observations of Lizards and Tree Frogs in an Irradiated Puerto Rican Forest." From *A Tropical Rain Forest: A Study of Irradiation and Ecology at El Verde, Puerto Rico*. Washington, D.C.: U.S. Atomic Energy Commission, 1970.

Tschirley, Fred H. "Response of Tropical and Subtropical Woody Plants to Chemical Treatments." U.S. Department of Agriculture and Department of Defense.

Vilella, Francisco J. and Arnizaut, Ana B. "Making the Best of Mother Nature: Managing the Puerto Rican Parrot after Hurricane Hugo." *Endangered Species Technical Bulletin* XIX.2 (1994).

Wadsworth, Frank H. *The Development of the Forest Land Resources of the Luquillo Mountains, Puerto Rico.* Ann Arbor: University of Michigan, 1949.

Wadsworth, Frank H. "Forest Management in the Luquillo Mountains." *Caribbean Forester*, July, 1951.

Wadsworth, Frank H. "Review of Past Research in the Luquillo Mountains of Puerto Rico." From *A Tropical Rain Forest: A Study of Irradiation and Ecology at El Verde, Puerto Rico.* Washington, D.C.: U.S. Atomic Energy Commission, 1970.

Wadsworth, Frank H. "The Climate of the Luquillo Mountains and its Significance to the People of Puerto Rico." *Caribbean Forester* 9-10 (1948-49): 321-335.

Waide, Robert B. "The Fauna of Caribbean Island Ecosystems: Community Structure and Conservation." *Acta Científica* 1.2-3: 64-71.

Walker, Lawrence R., Brokaw, Nicholas V.L., Lodge, D. Jean, and Waide, Robert B. *Biotropica Special Issue: Ecosystem, Plant, and Animal Responses to Hurricanes in the Caribbean.* The Association for Tropical Biology, Inc. 23.4, Part A. (December, 1991).

Weaver, Peter L. "Hurricane Damage and Recovery in the Montane Forests of the Luquillo Mountains of Puerto Rico." *Caribbean Journal of Science* 22.1-2 (1986): 53-70.

Weigert, R. G. "Energetics of the Nest-Building Termite, Nasutitermes costalis (Holmgren), in a Puerto Rican Forest." From *A Tropical Rain Forest: A Study of Irradiation and Ecology at El Verde, Puerto Rico.* Washington, D.C.: U.S. Atomic Energy Commission, 1970.

Weinbren, M.P. and Weinbren, B.M. "Observations on the Mosquito Population in the Irradiated Forest at El Verde." From *A Tropical Rain Forest: A Study of Irradiation and Ecology at El Verde, Puerto Rico.* Washington, D.C.: U.S. Atomic Energy Commission, 1970.

FEDERAL PUBLICATIONS:

Caribbean National Forest of Puerto Rico. Washington, D.C.: U.S. Department of Agriculture, Forest Service, Southern Region, 1940.

Caribbean National Forest General Report to the Public 1991. Río Piedras: USDA Forest Service, 1992.

"Endangered and Threatened Wildlife and Plants." U.S. Fish andWildlife Service, U.S. Department of the Interior. August 20, 1994.

Final Land and Resource Management Plan for the Caribbean National Forest and Luquillo Experimental Forest. Río Piedras: U.S. Department of Agriculture, Forest Service Southern Region and Southern Forest Experiment Station.

"Hurricane, The Greatest Storm on Earth." National Oceanic and Atmospheric Administration, U.S. Department of Commerce.

"Publications from the Luquillo Experimental Forest." Río Piedras: Center for Energy and Environment Research.

"Puerto Rican Parrots Transferred from Luquillo Aviary to Río Abajo Aviary." News Release, Department of the Interior, U.S. Fish and Wildlife Service, 1993.

"Rare and Endangered Animal Species of Puerto Rico." U.S. Department of Agriculture Soil Conservation Service, 1973.

"Rare and Endangered Plants of Puerto Rico." U.S. Department of Agriculture Soil Conservation Service and Puerto Rico Department of Natural Resources, 1975.

"A Summary of the Draft Environmental Impact Statement, Caribbean National Forest/Luquillo Experimental Forest, Puerto Rico." Río Piedras: U.S. Department of Agriculture, Forest Service Southern Region, 1994.

GLOSSARY

The following glossary includes terms used in this book whose definitions are not readily found in dictionaries.

BIOSPHERE RESERVE — established by UNESCO; nuclei of virgin forest surrounded by re-established forest which demonstrate preservation, research, tourism, rehabilitation and traditional uses of land.

COMMERCIAL TIMBER HARVESTING — felling trees for profit.

DEPARTMENT OF NATURAL AND ENVIRONMENTAL RESOURCES — Puerto Rican agency in charge of the island's natural resources, formerly the Department of Natural Resources.

ENDANGERED SPECIES — U.S. Fish and Wildlife term for species (both plant and animal) that are in immediate danger of extinction, unlikely to survive without special care and protection.

ENDEMIC SPECIES — species that are native (natural) to a region and grow only in that particular region.

EXOTIC (INTRODUCED) SPECIES — species transported from one region to another region where they did not exist in the past.

INTERNATIONAL INSTITURE OF TROPICAL FORESTRY— the research branch of the U.S. Forest Service in Puerto Rico, formerly known as the Institute of Tropical Forestry.

NATIVE SPECIES — species that have grown naturally in a certain region as far back as humans can determine.

NATIONAL FOREST — under the U.S. Department of Agriculture Forest Service system, forests in which the primary goal is that of management, of using the various aspects of the forest wisely.

NATIONAL PARK — under the U.S. Department of the Interior, parks in which the primary goals are that of preservation and recreation.

NATURALIZED SPECIES — species introduced to a region that eventually are able to regenerate on their own in that region.

PIONEER (SUCCESSIONAL) SPECIES — species which are quick to move into open clearings; first species to return to damaged land.

PRIMARY (OLD-GROWTH)FOREST — forest that has not been touched by humans for at least 80 years.

RARE SPECIES — uncommon species, species found in small numbers, often in limited or specialized habitats.

SECONDARY FOREST — forest that has grown back or been replanted on land that was deforested at one time.

SELECTIVE LUMBERING — in which only selected, mature trees are felled, leaving the rest of the forest untouched.

SENSITIVE SPECIES — term used by the U.S. Forest Service to refer to species which need to be watched.

SPECIES — a biological classification that comprises related organisms that share common characteristics and are capable of interbreeding.

SUSTAINABILITY — the ability of the forest to maintain itself while at the same time producing marketable timber.

THREATENED SPECIES — U.S. Fish and Wildlife term for uncommon species that are likely to find their existence in jeopardy in the foreseeable future.

TROPICAL FOREST — forest (wet or dry) found between the Tropic of Cancer and the Tropic of Capricorn; the northernmost and southernmost regions are sometimes (not in this book) referred to as sub-tropical.

TROPICAL RAIN FOREST — the tallest, most luxuriant, most complex type of vegetation in the American tropics, primarily found below 2,000 feet, where annual rainfall exceeds 90 inches, temperatures average 73 degrees F., and soil is relatively well drained.

VIRGIN (ORIGINAL) FOREST — forest that has never been touched by humans.

INDEX

This index has been prepared to help readers find information about the forest more easily. It is not meant to be all-inclusive.

HIKES.
The following hikes are described in the book. Refer to the index for page numbers.

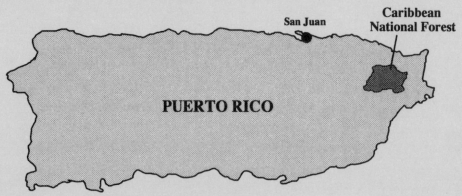

Atlantic Ocean

San Juan

Caribbean
National Forest

PUERTO RICO

Caribbean Sea

Río Grande

El Toro Trail

El T
(352

road

trail

river

▲ peak

● tower/lookout